WILLIAM J. KOCH

University of North Carolina
Chapel Hill

Plants in the laboratory

a manual and text for studies of
the culture, development, reproduction, cytology,
genetics, collection, and identification
of the major plant groups

The Macmillan Company   NEW YORK

Collier-Macmillan Limited, London

DEDICATION

*To all who love to learn
and love to facilitate the learning of others—
especially to* DOT

The Macmillan Company
866 Third Avenue, New York, New York 10022

Collier-Macmillan Canada, Ltd.
Toronto, Ontario

Library of Congress catalog card number: 78–180295

Printing: 1 2 3 4 5 6 7 8   Year: 3 4 5 6 7 8 9

Preface

Plants in the Laboratory is written for use in courses that include studies of broad ranges of plants. It has developed mainly from the author's experience in teaching courses called "Plant Diversity," "Plant Kingdom," "Plant Morphology," and "Evolutionary Survey of Plants." The heart of such courses is the laboratory.

This book is designed not only to help students learn about the major kinds and groups of plants but also to learn basic techniques for working with and analyzing different kinds of plants. Insight into plants is offered through several approaches: field observations and collecting; identification and classification; culture; cytology; genetics; anatomy and histology; studies of the structure, development, and reproduction of type plants in the major groups; and textual material. Emphasis is placed on studying living plants and on growing plants and watching their development.

I feel that it is to the advantage of both the teacher and the student to have available a large number of projects using various approaches. It allows for flexibility in programming a student's laboratory work. The teacher can pick out the things that he wants his students to do, and the student has good directions for doing projects on his own.

Parts Three and Four are both text and manual. The projects in Part Four are the heart of the laboratory work in most introductory plant kingdom courses or courses treating a portion of the plant kingdom. The instructor may wish to have his students do portions of Part Four in combination with portions of Parts One to Three. If they are supplemented with portions of Part Four, projects in Parts One to Three can serve as the student's guide for laboratory work in a plant kingdom course or a course dealing with a portion of the plant kingdom. These projects are designed to help bridge the gap between more traditional elementary laboratory work and botanical research. They help lead a student into elementary plant research.

To my students and colleagues and the many botanists whose efforts are reflected in this work I extend my gratitude. Marion Seiler, artist in the Botany Department of the University of North Carolina at Chapel Hill, made the final drawings.

Thanks are gratefully extended also to J. Edison Adams, Russ Aiuto, Carol Aregood, Sandra Bowden, John N. Couch, John Fenton, Victor A. Greulach, Bob Hardwick, Peggy Holland, Max H. Hommersand, P. Barry Hounshell, Bruno Kowalczyk, Rick Leonard, Bill Lindemann, Rand McNitt, Chet Michalski, Sabina Mueller, Lytton J. Musselman, Martha Powell, Albert E. Radford, Bal Rao, Tom Register, Bill Sherwood, Paul Szaniszlo, H. Roland Totten, Reggie Twyman, and Don Windler for their help at the University of North Carolina.

Special thanks are due to the following experts, my colleagues, for reviewing the textual portions of the projects in Part Four as follows: fungi, Lindsay S. Olive; algae, R. Malcolm Brown, Jr.; bryophytes, Norton G. Miller; and vascular plants, William C. Dickison.

I am also grateful to those who gave ideas for the revision of the whole manuscript: Dr. H. Weston Blaser, University of Washington; Dr. Herbert M. Clarke, University of Wisconsin; Dr. John D. Dodd, Iowa State University; Dr. Robert A. Paterson, Virginia Polytechnic Institute; Dr. George W. Burns, Ohio Wesleyan University; and William R. Bowen, Ripon College.

Any errors that remain are, of course, mine.

W. J. K.

Contents

Contents

Part Four
Survey of the
major groups
of plants

Part One
Methods in identification, isolation, culture, and plant development

The purpose of this part is to help you to learn some basic techniques for working with plants and to help you to learn about the collecting, identifying, culturing, and growth and development of representative plants by employing these techniques.

Project 1   Collection and identification

Contents

Introduction

If you wish to gain an elementary knowledge of where plants grow and how they may be identified, as well as how they are classified or related to each other, you should personally collect, identify with one of the manuals, and preserve or draw about 52 plants—more if time permits. An approximate number of the major kinds of plants needed for gaining this insight is indicated in the Project.

Through this field and laboratory work it is hoped that you will gain more taxonomic prowess or methodology and ecological insight than you now have. Instead of trying to preserve your algal and fungal collections, you can keep a record by making drawings sufficiently good for identification. These identification drawings are a good substitute for preserved specimens.

References for the collection and identification of plants are listed by plant group. The list for vascular plants is long, primarily because many of the books treat plants of restricted geographical areas. Introductory chapters in many of the reference books give you the special directions you need to have for collecting, identifying, and preserving this diverse group of organisms. In addition, some special techniques needed for collecting (isolating) molds or microscopic fungi are given in Project 3 (III and VI, pp. 24 and 29). Directions for the isolation and enrichment culture of algae from soil are given in Project 4, p. 33, but most algae, like other green plants and fleshy fungi, can be collected directly in nature.

Project

I. Scanning the reference books

Look through the available reference books to get some idea of how each can be of use to you.

II. Collect and identify

A. Ten genera of fungi (true fungi, slime molds, bacteria)
B. Ten genera of algae
C. Two genera of lichens
D. Five genera of bryophytes (mosses and liverworts)
E. Five species of pteridophytes (ferns and their "allies")
F. Twenty species of trees, shrubs, or other seed plants

References

These references are listed under the following plant groups: *bacteria, slime molds, true fungi, algae, lichens, bryophytes,* and *vascular plants,* which are listed in three subgroups *(regional and state floras, trees and shrubs,* and *general).*

Bacteria

BREED, R. S., et al. 1957. *Bergey's Manual of Determinative Bacteriology,* 7th ed. Williams & Wilkins, Baltimore.

Slime molds

BONNER, J. T. 1967. *The Cellular Slime Molds,* 2nd ed. Princeton University Press, Princeton, N.J.
MARTIN, G. W., and C. J. ALEXOPOULOS. 1969. *The Myxomycetes.* University of Iowa Press, Iowa City, Iowa.

True fungi

BARNETT, H. L. 1972. *Illustrated Genera of Imperfect Fungi,* 3rd ed. Burgess, Minneapolis.
CHRISTENSEN, C. M. 1965. *Common Fleshy Fungi,* 3rd ed. Burgess, Minneapolis.
COOKE, W. B. 1963. *A Laboratory Guide to Fungi in Polluted Waters, Sewage, and Sewage Treatment Systems.* U.S. Public Health Service Publication 999-WP-1, Cincinnati.
DENNIS, R. W. C. 1968. *British Ascamycetes,* 2nd ed. Bernard Quaritch Ltd., London.

EDMONDSON, W. T., ed. 1959. *Fresh-Water Biology,* 2nd ed. Wiley, New York. (Sparrow's illustrated key to aquatic Phycomycetes, pp. 50–89.)

FERGUS, C. L. 1960. *Wood Decay Fungi*. Burgess, Minneapolis.

FITZPATRICK, H. M. 1930. *The Lower Fungi—Phycomycetes*. McGraw-Hill, New York.

FUNDER, S. 1968. *Practical Mycology, Manual for Identification of Fungi*. Hafner, New York.

LANGE, M., and F. B. HORA. 1963. *A Guide to Mushrooms and Toadstools*. Dutton, New York.

SMITH, A. H. 1949. *Mushrooms in Their Natural Habitats,* 2 vols. Sawyer, Inc., Portland, Ore.

SPARROW, F. K. 1960. *Aquatic Phycomycetes,* 2nd ed. University of Michigan Press, Ann Arbor, Mich.

Algae

DAWSON, E. Y. 1956. *How To Know the Seaweeds*. William C. Brown, Dubuque, Iowa.

EDMONDSON, W. T., ed. 1959. *Fresh-Water Biology,* 2nd ed. Wiley, New York.

LEEDALE, G. F. 1969. *Euglenoid Flagellates*. Prentice-Hall, Englewood Cliffs, N.J.

PALMER, C. M. 1959. *Algae in Water Supplies*. U.S. Public Health Service, Publication 657, Cincinnati.

PATRICK, R. C., and C. W. REIMER. 1966. *The Diatoms of the United States*. Academy of Natural Sciences, Philadelphia.

PRESCOTT, G. W. 1962. *Algae of the Western Great Lakes Area,* 2nd ed. William C. Brown, Dubuque, Iowa.

———. 1970. *How to Know the Fresh-water Algae,* 3rd ed. William C. Brown, Dubuque, Iowa.

SMITH, G. M. 1950. *The fresh-water Algae of the United States*. McGraw-Hill, New York.

TAYLOR, W. R. 1957. *Marine Algae of the Northeastern Coast of North America,* rev. ed. University of Michigan Press, Ann Arbor, Mich.

———. 1960. *Marine Algae of the Eastern Tropical and Subtropical Coasts of the Americas*. University of Michigan Press, Ann Arbor, Mich.

WHITFORD, L. A., and G. J. SCHUMACHER. 1969. *A Manual of the Fresh-Water Algae in North Carolina*. N.C. Agricultural Experiment Station, Tech. Bull. 188, Raleigh, N.C.

Lichens

FINK, B. 1935. *The Lichen Flora of the United States*. University of Michigan Press, Ann Arbor, Mich.

HALE, M. E. 1961. *Lichen Handbook*. Smithsonian Institution, Washington, D.C.

———. 1969. *How to Know the Lichens*. William C. Brown, Dubuque, Iowa.

NEARING, C. C. 1947. *The Lichen Book*. Published by the author, Eidgeway, N.J.

SHUTTLEWORTH, F. S., and H. S. ZIM. 1967. *Non-Flowering Plants*. New York, Golden Press.

Bryophytes

BODENBERG, E. T. 1954. *Mosses: A New Approach to the Identification of Common Species*. Burgess, Minneapolis.

CONARD, H. S. 1956. *How to Know the Mosses*. William C. Brown, Dubuque, Iowa.

DIXON, H. N., and H. G. JAMESON. 1954. *Students Handbook of British Mosses,* 3rd ed. Eastbourne, Sumfield & Day, London. Sold by Wheldon & Wesley.

GROUT, A. S. 1947. *Mosses with a Handlens,* 4th ed. Published by author, Newfane, V.
———. 1928–1940. *Moss Flora of North America.* Published by the editor, New York.

MACVICAR, S. M. 1926. *Student's Handbook of British Hepatics,* 2nd ed. Eastbourne, Sumfield. Wheldon & Wesley, London.

SCHUSTER, R. M. 1966–1969. *The Hepaticae and Anthocerotae of North America East of the Hundredth Meridian,* Vols. 1, 2. Columbia University Press, New York.

WELCH, W. H. 1957. *Mosses of Indiana.* Indiana Department of Conservation, Indianapolis.

Vascular plants

Regional and state floras

ABRAMS, LEROY. 1923–1960. *An Illustrated Flora of the Pacific States.* Stanford University Press, Stanford, Calif. (Vol. IV by R. S. Ferris)

DAVIS, R. A. 1952. *Flora of Idaho.* William C. Brown, Dubuque, Iowa.

DEAN, C. C. 1940. *Flora of Indiana.* William B. Burford, Indianapolis.

FASSETT, N. C. 1957. *Spring Flora of Wisconsin,* 3rd ed. University of Wisconsin Press, Madison, Wis.

FERNALD, M. L. 1950. Gray's *Manual of Botany,* 8th ed. American Book, New York.

GLEASON, H. A. 1962. *The New Britton and Brown Illustrated Flora of the Northeastern United States and Adjacent Canada,* 3rd printing, slightly revised. Published for the New York Botanical Garden by Hafner, New York. (3 Vols.)
——— and ARTHUR CRONQUIST. 1963. *Manual of Vascular Plants of Northeastern United States and Adjacent Canada.* Van Nostrand Reinhold, New York.

HARRINGTON, H. D. 1954. *Manual of the Plants of Colorado.* Authorized by the Colorado State Board of Agriculture and prepared with the cooperation of Colorado A & M College. Sage Books, Denver.

JONES, G. N. 1963. *Flora of Illinois, Containing Keys for Identification of Flowering Plants and Ferns,* 3rd ed. University of Notre Dame Press, Notre Dame, Ind.

KEARNEY, T. H., and R. H. PEEBLES. 1960. *Arizona Flora,* 2nd ed., with supplement by J. T. Howell, Elizabeth McClintock, et al. University of California Press, Berkeley, Calif.

MUNZ, P. A., in collaboration with D. D. KECK. 1959. *A California Flora.* Published for the Rancho Santa Ana Botanic Garden by University of California Press, Berkeley, Calif.

PECK, M. E. 1961. *A Manual of the Higher Plants of Oregon,* 2nd ed. Binfords & Mort, Portland, Ore.

RADFORD, A. E., H. E. AHLES, and C. R. BELL. 1968. *Manual of the Flora of the Carolinas.* University of North Carolina Press, Chapel Hill, N.C.

RYDBERG, P. A. 1922. *Flora of the Rocky Mountains and Adjacent Plains,* 2nd ed. Published by the author, New York.

SHREVE, FOREST, and I. L. WIGGINS. 1964. *Vegetation and Flora of the Sonoran Desert.* Stanford University Press, Stanford, Calif. (2 vols.)

STEMEN, T. R., and W. S. MYERS. 1937. *Oklahoma Flora.* Harlow Publishing, Oklahoma City, Okla.

STEYERMARK, J. A. 1963. *Flora of Missouri.* Iowa State University Press, Ames, Iowa.

STRAUSBAUGH, P. D., and E. L. CORE. 1952–1964. *Flora of West Virginia.* West

Virginia University Bulletin, ser. 52, no. 12–2, ser. 53, no. 12–1. West Virginia University. Herbarium Contribution, pp. 95–96. (4 vols.)

TIDESTROM, IVAR. 1925. *Flora of Utah and Nevada.* U.S. Government Printing Office, Washington, D.C. U.S. National Museum, contributions from the U.S. National Herbarium, 25.

Trees and shrubs

BAERG, H. J. 1955. *How To Know the Western Trees.* William C. Brown, Dubuque, Iowa.

BARRETT, M. F. 1956. *Common Exotic Trees of South Florida (Dicotyledons).* University of Florida Press, Gainesville, Fla.

BENSON, LYMAN, and R. A. DARROW. 1954. *Trees and Shrubs of the Southwestern Deserts,* 2d ed. University of Arizona Press, Tucson, Ariz.

COKER, W. C., and H. R. TOTTEN. 1945. *Trees of the Southeastern States.* University of North Carolina Press, Chapel Hill, N.C.

COLLINGWOOD, G. H., and W. D. BRUSH. 1964. *Knowing Your Trees.* The American Forestry Association, Washington, D.C.

CORE, E. I., and N. P. AMMONS. 1958. *Woody Plants in Winter; A Manual of Common Trees and Shrubs in Winter in the Northeastern United States and Southeastern Canada.* Boxwood Press, Pittsburgh.

CURTIS, C. C., and S. C. BAUSOR. 1943. *The Complete Guide to North American Trees.* New Home Library, New York.

CURTIS, C. C., and S. C. BAUSOR. 1943. *The Complete Guide to North American Trees.* New Home Library, New York.

DALLIMORE, WILLIAM, and A. B. JACKSON. 1948. *Handbook of Coniferae Including Ginkgoaceae,* with drawings by G. Lister, 3rd ed. Edward Arnold, London.

DEAN, B. E. 1961. *Trees and Shrubs in the Heart of Dixie, Including Some Cultivated Plants and Common Vines.* Coxe Publishing Co., Birmingham, Ala.

GILKEY, H. M., and P. L. PACKARD. 1962. *Winter Twigs; A Wintertime Key to Deciduous Trees and Shrubs of Northwestern Oregon and Western Washington.* Oregon State Monographs, Botany 12.

GRANT, J. A., and C. L. GRANT. 1967. *Trees and Shrubs for Pacific Northwest Gardens.* Frank McCaffrey, Seattle.

GRAVES, A. H. 1956. *Illustrated Guide to Trees and Shrubs,* 3rd ed. Harper & Row, New York.

GREEN, C. H. 1939. *Trees of the South.* University of North Carolina Press, Chapel Hill, N.C.

GRIMM, W. C. 1957. *The Book of Shrubs.* Stackpole, Harrisburg, Pa.

————. 1962. *The Book of Trees,* 2nd ed. Stackpole, Harrisburg, Pa.

GROOM, P. 1907. *Trees and Their Life Histories.* Cassel & Co., London.

HARGREAVES, DOROTHY, and ROBERT HARGREAVES. 1964. *Tropical Trees of Hawaii.* Hargreaves Industrial, Portland, Ore.

HARLOW, W. H. 1957. *Trees of the Eastern and Central U.S. and Canada,* 2nd ed. Dover, New York.

————. 1959. *Fruit Key and Twig Key to Trees and Shrubs.* Dover, New York.

HARRAR, E. S., and J. G. HARRAR. 1962. *Guide to Southern Trees,* 2nd ed. Dover, New York.

HOUGH, R. B. 1947. *Handbook of the Trees of the Northeastern States and Canada East of the Rocky Mountains.* Macmillan, New York. (reprint of 1907 ed.)

JAQUES, H. E. 1946. *How to Know the Trees,* 2nd ed. William C. Brown, Dubuque, Iowa.

MCKEAN, W. T., ed. 1956. *Winter Guide to Native Shrubs of the Central Rocky Mountains with Summer Key.* Colorado Dept. of Game and Fish, Denver, Colo.

MENNINGER, E. A. 1962. *Flowering Trees of the World for Tropics and Warm Climates.* Hearthside Press, New York.

PETRIDES, G. A. 1958. *A Field Guide to Trees and Shrubs.* Houghton Mifflin, Boston.

PRESTON, R. J., JR. 1961. *North American Trees (Exclusive of Mexico and Tropical United States),* 2nd ed. Iowa State University Press, Ames, Iowa.

REHDER, A. 1940. *Manual of Cultivated Trees and Shrubs.* Macmillan, New York.

ROSENDAHL, C. O. 1955. *Trees and Shrubs of the Upper Midwest.* University of Minnesota Press, Minneapolis.

SYMONDS, G. W. D. 1958. *The Tree Identification Book.* M. Barrows, New York.

————. 1963. *The Shrub Identification Book.* M. Barrows, New York.

VINES, R. A. 1960. *Trees, Shrubs, and Woody Vines of the Southwest,* with drawings by S. K. Arendole. University of Texas Press, Austin, Texas.

WATKINS, J. V. 1961. *Your Guide to Florida Landscape Plants; Palms, Trees, Shrubs, Vines.* University of Florida Press, Gainesville, Fla.

WYMAN, DONALD. 1959. *Trees for American Gardens.* Macmillan, New York.

General

BAILEY, L. H. 1949. *Manual of Cultivated Plants,* Rev. ed. Macmillan, New York.

BLOOMQUIST, H. L. 1934. *Ferns of North Carolina.* Duke University Press, Durham, N.C.

CAMPBELL, C. C. 1962. *Great Smoky Mountains Wildflowers.* University of Tennessee Press, Knoxville, Tenn.

CUTHBERT, MABEL (JAQUES). 1948. *How To Know the Fall Flowers.* William C. Brown, Dubuque, Iowa.

————. 1949. *How to Know the Spring Flowers,* rev. ed. William C. Brown, Dubuque, Iowa.

DeWITT, H. C. D. 1964. *Aquarium Plants.* Blanford Press, London.

EVERETT, T. H., ed. 1960. *New Illustrated Encyclopedia of Gardening.* Greystone Press, New York. (6 vols.)

FASSETT, N. C. 1960. *A Manual of Aquatic Plants,* 2nd ed. University of Wisconsin Press, Madison, Wis.

GREENE, W. F., and H. L. BLOOMQUIST. 1953. *Flowers of the South, Native and Exotic.* University of North Carolina Press, Chapel Hill, N.C.

HARRINGTON, H. D. 1957. *How To Identify Plants.* Sage Books, Denver, Colo.

KUCK, L. E., and R. C. TONGG. 1958. *Hawaiian Flowers & Flowering Trees: A Guide to Tropical & Semitropical Flora.* Tuttle, Rutland, Vt. (reprinted 1960)

PRESCOTT, G. W. 1969. *How To Know the Aquatic Plants.* William C. Brown, Dubuque, Iowa.

RICKETT, H. W. 1963. *The New Field Book of American Wild Flowers.* Putnam, New York.

————. 1966. *Wild Flowers of the United States.* McGraw Hill, New York.

TRYON, R. M., N. C. FASSETT, D. W. DUNLOP, and M. E. DIEMER. 1953. *The Ferns and Fern Allies of Wisconsin,* 2nd ed. University of Wisconsin Press, Madison, Wis.

WHERRY, E. T. 1964. *The Southern Fern Guide.* Doubleday, Garden City, N.Y.

Project 2   General cultural techniques

Contents

Introduction

In many of the exercises in this book you will grow plants in laboratory culture. The following general directions will be of use to you.

In I and II you will become acquainted with sterile techniques, the preparation of culture implements and media, and the inoculation or transfer of cultures. In III you will learn about culture media for fungi and in IV about culture media for growing algae, bryophytes, fern gametophytes, and pollen tubes. Some general references for culturing are listed at the end.

At the outset, study the figures. Make the special implements listed in the Project. Learn how to make culture media, how to sterilize culture media, glassware, and implements, how to pour culture plates (petri dishes) with agar media, how to make agar slants, and how to inoculate or transfer a culture.

Project

I. Preparation of implements

A. *Micropipettes* (Pasteur or capillary pipettes). Commercially available in some sizes. Make two micropipettes, one larger than the other (Fig. 2-1), as follows:
1. Heat to softness by rotating in the wide flame of a small fishtail bunsen burner a 6-in. length of glass tubing with an internal diameter of about 4–5 mm.
2. When the heated portion becomes "floppy," pull the two ends apart. If pulled apart immediately after heating, a very narrow thin-walled pipette is obtained. However, if a few seconds elapse before pulling, a wider capillary is formed, which has thicker walls. With practice, pipettes can be made that have different capillary sizes and wall thicknesses.
3. Break at the narrow region. Break one pipette to have a larger aperture than the other.
4. Affix a rubber suction bulb to each micropipette.
5. (Optional) With a heated dissection needle burn a hole through the apex of the rubber suction bulb. (When sucking up material, your index finger covers this hole. After the material is sucked into the micropipette you take your index finger off the hole. This allows you to move the pipette around without fear of inadvertently expelling the contents in an unwanted place. To expel the material, cover the hole with your finger and press the bulb.)

B. *Needles.* Needles of two sizes are needed:
1. *Macroneedle.* Use an ordinary dissecting needle or put a sewing needle in a needle holder.
2. *Microneedle* (Fig. 2-2). Fix the end of the finest available insect-sticking needle (Minuten) in a needle holder, or attach the Minuten needle to glass tubing or a pipette using the flame of a fishtail bunsen burner. (Note: If you need to flame sterilize a Minuten needle, use the cooler flame of an alcohol lamp rather than the flame of a bunsen burner.)

C. *Wire loop* (for streaking agar plates, etc.) (Fig. 2-3). Cut off a 2- to 3-in.-long

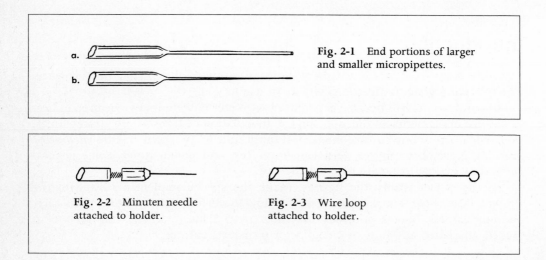

a.

b.

Fig. 2-1   End portions of larger and smaller micropipettes.

Fig. 2-2   Minuten needle attached to holder.

Fig. 2-3   Wire loop attached to holder.

Fig. 2-4 Making a microspatula: (a) Chromel wire in holder. (b) Wire pounded flat with a hammer. Dashed lines on the flattened part indicate where the two scissor cuts will go. (c) Finished spatula after cutting with scissors.

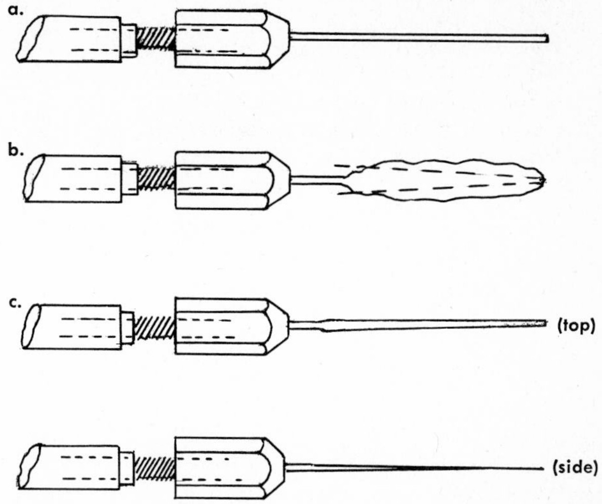

piece of thin Chromel or Nichrome (chromium–nickel) wire (Nos. 24 or 26 gauge). Put one end in a needle or loop holder. Bend the free end into a loop about 5 mm in diameter (use the tapered end of a sharpened pencil).

D. *Microspatulas* (for cutting out small chunks of agar, etc.) (Fig. 2-4)

    1. Large. With the cutting edges of pliers cut off a 2-in. length of thick (No. 20 gauge) Chromel or Nichrome wire. Fix one end in a needle holder (Fig. 2-4a). Flatten the free end by pounding it with a hammer against a hardened steel object (e.g., the side of another hammer head) (Fig. 2-4b). With scissors cut the flattened end to the desired shape (Fig. 2-4b and c). Flatten again and recut if you need to make the spatula thinner.

    2. Small. Follow the same directions, only use thin (No. 24 or 26 gauge) Chromel wire. After the first hammering and cutting, it is necessary to hammer again and then cut to the final shape.

II. Sterilization, preparation of media, and transfer of cultures

A. *Sterilization*

    1. Dry-heat sterilization of glassware, implements, etc., is done in an oven at 170–190°C for 2–5 hours. At temperatures over 175°C, cotton and paper begin to char.

    2. Steam-under-pressure sterilization of liquids (water, culture media, etc.) is done in an autoclave or pressure cooker at 15 lb of pressure for 15 minutes. Cover cotton plugs with paper or foil to keep them dry. (Glassware, implements, etc., can be steam sterilized if they are wrapped with paper or foil to keep them dry.)

    3. Flame sterilization of wire loops, spatulas, etc., is done in the flame of a bunsen burner or alcohol lamp:

        a. (Optional) Dip the portion of the implement that will come in contact with sterile media, cultures, etc., in 70 per cent alcohol.

11

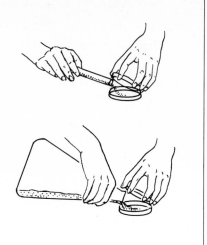

Figs. 2-5 and 2-6   Pouring sterile, melted agar into a sterile culture plate (petri dish). One edge of the lid is raised only high enough to allow placement of the mouth of the tube (2-5) or flask (2-6) of agar.

   b. Put the appropriate portion of the implement (e.g., wire loop) in the flame until it is visibly hot (e.g., red hot) (see Fig. 2-9a).
   c. Let the implement cool before using it, making sure not to touch the flame-sterilized part of the implements to any surface that is not sterile.
B. *Preparation of culture media*
   1. Making media
      a. Ingredients of culture media are given in parts III and IV of this project.
      b. Ordinarily, 1-liter quantities are prepared and the ingredients of a culture medium, after measuring or weighing, are put in $1\frac{1}{2}$-case or 2-liter Pyrex erlenmeyer flasks plugged with nonwettable cotton or other material and then steam sterilized (autoclaved).
   2. Pouring agar plates (Figs. 2-5, 2-6).
      a. Culture dishes (petri dishes). Sterile, disposable culture dishes cost very little. If you use glass petri dishes, either dry sterilize them in an oven (175–190°C for 2–5 hours) or wrap them with paper or foil and autoclave or pressure cook (15 lb of pressure for 15 minutes).
      b. If you are to pour many agar plates using medium that has been sterilized in an erlenmeyer flask, let the flask of medium cool to about 45°C (which is not too hot to touch). Ordinarily, 25–30 plates can be poured from 1 liter of medium. If you are pouring one or a few plates from agar medium that has been put in tubes (see Fig. 2-7) and stored, stand the tubes of agar in boiling water until they melt.
      c. Sterilize the table or bench top by wiping it with a sponge or cloth soaked with 70 per cent alcohol or 5 per cent Lysol.
      d. Put the sterile petri dishes on the cleaned table or bench top.
      e. Light a bunsen burner and work close to it.
      f. If you are pouring from tubes of melted agar medium, remove one from the water bath, lift off the cotton plug, and bring the mouth of the tube across the bunsen flame to eliminate any contaminants around the mouth of the tube. Open the petri dish slightly and quickly pour the contents of one tube (20–30 ml) into the dish (10 cm in diameter)

(Fig. 2-5). Quickly cover the dish. Essentially the same procedure is followed when you are pouring plates from medium in an erlenmeyer flask (Fig. 2-6).

3. Making agar slants (Figs. 2-7, 2-8).
   a. After the agar medium has been melted and the ingredients thoroughly mixed (this may be done in an autoclave or water bath), it must be poured into culture tubes in such a way that it does not streak the sides of the tubes (Fig. 2-7).
   b. The medium must be poured quickly so that the agar does not have time to solidify.
   c. Fill culture tubes about one third full (Fig. 2-8a).
   d. Plug the tubes and sterilize (autoclave).
   e. Prop the sterilized culture tubes on a table or bench top at an appropriate angle (Fig. 2-8b), and let them cool and the agar gel.

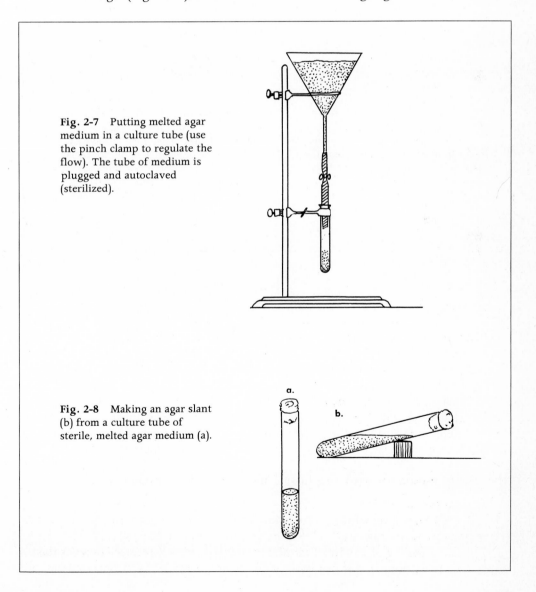

Fig. 2-7 Putting melted agar medium in a culture tube (use the pinch clamp to regulate the flow). The tube of medium is plugged and autoclaved (sterilized).

Fig. 2-8 Making an agar slant (b) from a culture tube of sterile, melted agar medium (a).

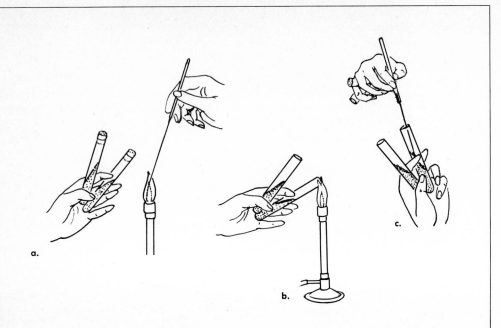

Fig. 2-9 Inoculation or transfer of an agar-slant culture: (a) Flame sterilize the transfer spatula or loop. (b) Remove plugs from the tubes by grasping them between the fingers of the hand holding the transfer implement and pass the mouths of the tubes through the flame of the burner to eliminate any potential contamination. (c) The transfer implement is inserted into the tube containing the inoculum (culture) and then introduced into the tube of medium to be inoculated. After this the mouths of the tubes are again flamed, the stoppers replaced, and the transfer implement is flame sterilized.

    C. *Inoculation or transfer of a culture* (Figs. 2-9, 2-10).
      1. Flame sterilize the transfer spatula or loop (Fig. 2-9a).
      2. Remove plugs from the tubes by grasping them between the fingers of the
         hand holding the transfer implement and pass the mouths of the tubes
         through the flame of the burner to eliminate any potential contamination
         (Fig. 2-9b).
      3. The transfer implement is inserted into the tube containing the inoculum
         (culture) and then introduced into the tube of medium to be inoculated
         (Fig. 2-9c). After this, the mouths of the tubes are again flamed, the
         stoppers replaced, and the transfer implement is flame sterilized.

III. Culture media for growing fungi, slime molds, and bacteria

    A. *Isolation media*
      1. (HI) Hay infusion agar, for slime molds, mucors, imperfects, and other
    nonaquatic molds.
        a. Infuse 5 g of hay in 1 liter of distilled H_2O (in a 2-liter erlenmeyer flask)
        for $\frac{1}{2}$ hour in a water bath or for 15 minutes at 15 lb of pressure.

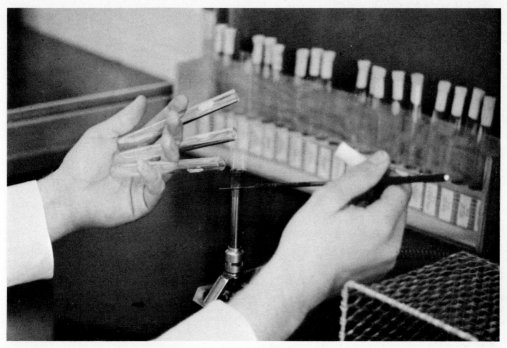

Fig. 2-10 Inoculation or transfer of an agar-slant culture.
(Courtesy Carolina Biological Supply Company.)

   b. Filter this hay infusion through cheesecloth, a cloth towel, or Kimwipes. Restore to volume (to 1 liter).
   c. Add 0.6 g of $K_2HPO_4 \cdot 3H_2O$ and test for a pH of 7.0.
   d. Add 15 g of agar and autoclave at 15 lb of pressure for 20 minutes. Note: If the materials for making this agar are not available, cornmeal agar (CMA) is a fairly good substitute.
2. (AIM-1) Antibiotic isolation medium for most freshwater phycomycetes.

Glass distilled water	1,000.	ml
Difco brand: agar	30.	g
glucose	0.05	g
peptone	0.05	g
yeast extract	0.05	g
NBCo streptomycin sulfate (USP)	0.5	g
NBCo penicillin "G" sodium (USP)	0.5	g

   Notes: (1) Add antibiotics after autoclaving and after cooling (just before pouring agar plates). Swirl the plugged flask about 30 seconds to completely dissolve and mix the antibiotics. (2) Penicillin has 1,625 units per milligram. Streptomycin has 740 units per milligram. (3) Media with higher nutrient concentrations produce rapid overgrowth of the agar surface by filamentous fungi. This medium was developed especially for isolating from water propagules concentrated by membrane filtration or continuous flow centrifugation.
3. (AIM-2) Antibiotic isolation medium for most freshwater phycomycetes. Make up CMDY or CMDP enrichment media with the addition of antibiotics, according to the directions for AIM-1.

15

4. (AIMM) Antibiotic isolation medium for marine fungi.
   Autoclave together

Agar	12.	g
Glucose	1.	g
Gelatin hydrolysate (NBCo)	1.	g
Liver extract (NBCo, 1:20)	0.01	g
Yeast extract	0.1	g
Seawater	1,000.	ml

   After sterilization (see Note 1 for AIM-1) add

Streptomycin sulfate USP (NBCo)	0.5 g
Penicillin "G" sodium USP (NBCo)	0.5 g

5. (AW) Antibiotic water for growing aquatic fungi on baits in water.
   0.05 per cent streptomycin sulfate USP (NBCo) and 0.05 per cent penicillin "G" sodium USP (NBCo) dissolved in water.

B. *Enrichment media*

1. (CMDP) Cornmeal–dextrose–peptone agar, an excellent general culture medium for a wide variety of fungi.

Difco cornmeal agar	17 g
Dextrose	10 g
Peptone	2 g
Distilled water	1 liter

   Check and record pH (optional)

2. (CMDY) Cornmeal–dextrose–yeast extract agar, especially for water molds and many other molds.

Difco cornmeal agar	17 g
Dextrose	2 g
Yeast extract	1 g
Distilled water	1 liter

3. (CMA) Cornmeal agar, especially for water molds and many other molds.
   Use Difco brand cornmeal agar and follow directions on the bottle.
   Ingredients:

Infusion from cornmeal	50 g
Bacto-agar	15 g
Distilled water	1 liter

4. (MPW) Weak maltose–peptone agar

Maltose	1.5 g
Peptone	50.0 mg (milligrams)
Agar	15.0 g
Distilled water	1 liter

   Check and record pH. (optional)

5. ($\frac{1}{2}$PDA) Potato-dextrose agar, half-strength, for various fungi. (This freshly made PDA is better than that supplied in dry form by Difco. Difco's is often unsatisfactory for aquatic fungi, but it is excellent for some fungi, e.g., *Schizophyllum*.)

   a. Boil 300 g of diced (about 1 cm square) potatoes (including skin) in 1 liter of water (in a 2-liter flask) for 1 hour in a steamer or for 30 minutes in an autoclave at 10 lb of pressure.
   b. Strain twice through a cloth towel and restore volume (to 1 liter).
   c. Mix: Potato extract 500 ml
       Distilled water 500 ml

Dextrose	10 g
Peptone	1 g
Agar	15 g

Note: Quarter-strength PDA is excellent for aquatic fungi and is similar to CMDP in growth of aquatic fungi.

6. (NB) Nutrient broth, especially for bacteria and detecting bacterial contamination.

a.
Peptone	10 g
Dextrose	40 g
Tap water	1 liter

Check and record pH. (optional)

or

b.
Beef extract	3 g
Peptone	3 g
Distilled water	1 liter

7. (YPSS) Yeast extract–phosphate–sulfate–starch agar, especially for *Allomyces* and similar water molds.

Use Difco brand "Emerson YpSs Agar" and follow directions on bottle.

Ingredients:

Bacto-yeast extract	4.0 g
Soluble starch, Difco	15.0 g
Dipotassium phosphate	1.0 g
Magnesium sulfate	0.5 g
Bacto-agar	20.0 g
Distilled water	1 liter

C. *Water*

1. Pure water (either glass-distilled water or water run through a cation and anion resin exchange column).

a. Have sterile distilled water in 1- to 2-liter erlenmeyer flasks available for use when needed.

b. Put sterile distilled water in sterile glass or plastic washing bottles (for washing water molds growing on hemp seed and other baits).

2. DS (dilute salt) solution

0.00005 M $MgCl_2$

0.0005 M K_2HPO_4

0.0005 M KH_2PO_4

0.0005 M $(NH_4)_2HPO_4$

0.00005 M $CaCl_2$

pH is automatically 7.0

3. Natural water

a. Freshly filtered lake or pond water.

b. Sterile lake or pond water.

Note: The water is used full strength or diluted one or two times with pure water to induce sporangial germination.

4. Soil water

a. Stock solution. (See directions for making soil-water stock solution in part IV of this project.)

b. For use, dilute 1 part soil-water stock solution with 19 parts of sterile distilled water.

5. Artificial seawater

Use Rila Marine Salt Mixture obtained from Rila Products, Teaneck, N.J. or Instant Ocean, Synthetic Sea Salt, obtained from Aquarium Systems, Inc., Wickliffe, Ohio. Dissolve 40 g of Rila Marine Salt Mixture in 1 liter of distilled water.

IV. **Culture media for growing algae, bryophytes, fern gametophytes, and pollen tubes**

A. *(B) Bristol's solution for growing algae, bryophytes, and fern prothalli*

Six stock solutions, 400 ml in volume, are employed. Each contains one of the following salts in the amounts listed:

$NaNO_3$	10.0 g
$CaCl_2$	1.0 g
$MgSO_4 \cdot 7H_2O$	3.0 g
K_2HPO_4	3.0 g
KH_2PO_4	7.0 g
NaCl	1.0 g

Ten ml of each stock solution is added to 940 ml of glass-distilled water. To this is added a drop of 1.0 per cent $FeCl_3$ solution.

Solidify with 15 g of agar per liter, if desired.

B. *(PGM) Modified Pringsheim's salt agar for growing algae, bryophytes, and fern prothalli*

KNO_3	0.2 g
$(NH_4)_2HPO_4$	0.02 g
$MgSO_4 \cdot H_2O$	0.01 g
$CaCl_2 \cdot 6H_2O$	0.0005 g
$FeCl_3$	0.0005 g
Agar	30.0 g

Soil water (10 per cent stock solution) or substitute spring, lake, distilled, or even tap water 2.0 liters.

C. *(SW) Soil solution for growing algae and other autotrophs*

Soil solution no.:	(1)	(2)
Distilled water	94 ml	84 ml
Stock soil solution	5 ml	15 ml
5 per cent aqueous KNO_3	1 ml	1 ml

D. *Soil-water stock solution*

1. Put 500 g of sandy loam (e.g., garden soil) in a $1\frac{1}{2}$- to 2-liter erlenmeyer flask. (Select soil with only medium humus content.)
2. Add 1 liter of distilled water and plug flask.
3. Autoclave for 1 hour at 10 lb of pressure.
4. Filter first through a towel and then through filter paper.
5. Restore to volume (1 liter).
6. Sterilize in autoclave for 20 minutes at 15 lb of pressure.

E. *Artificial sea water*

Use Rila Marine Salt Mixture obtained from Rila Products, Teaneck, N.J. (Their Technical Bulletin 342 lists the 23 ingredients and their quantities.) Dissolve 40 g in 1 liter of water or 1 lb (453.95 g) in 3 gallons (11.3559 liters) of water.

F. *(M) Moore's solution for bryophytes and fern prothalli*

NH_4NO_3	0.5 g
KH_2PO_4	0.2 g
$MgSO_4 \cdot 7H_2O$	0.2 g
$CaCl_2 \cdot 2H_2O$	0.1 g
Distilled water	1.0 liter

For use: Dilute 1:1 with distilled water and add 1 ml of trace solution per liter of diluted medium just before autoclaving.

G. *Trace solution*

$MnCl_2 \cdot 4H_2O$	0.04	g/liter
Boric acid	0.06	g/liter
$ZnCl_2$	0.06	g/liter
$CuCl_2$	0.03	g/liter
MoO_3	0.015	g/liter
*$FeCl_3$	0.25	g/liter
KI	0.001	g/liter
$CaCl_2 \cdot 6H_2O$	0.04	g/liter
$NaSO_4 \cdot 6H_2O$	0.045	g/liter

*Do not add the ferric cloride to the stock solution of trace elements; add it to the medium containing the other trace elements just before autoclaving.

H. *(FM) Fern medium for prothalli*

$Ca(NO_3)_2 \cdot 4H_2O$	1.0	g
KH_2PO_4	0.25	g
$MgSO_4 \cdot 7H_2O$	0.25	g
$(NH_4)_2SO_4$	0.50	g
$FePO_4 \cdot 4H_2O$	0.025	g
Agar	15.0	g
H_2O	1.0	liter
Trace solution	1.0	ml

I. *(PT) Pollen tube growth medium*

Lactose (or sucrose)	12.0 g
Agar	1.5 g
Distilled water	100. ml

References

AARONSON, S. 1970. *Experimental Microbial Ecology.* Academic Press, New York.

COLLINS, C. H. 1967. *Microbiological Methods,* 2nd ed. Butterworth, London. 404 pp., illus. Incubators, water baths, etc., thermostatic control, pp. 53–64; sterilization, pp. 65–75; glassware, etc., choice, preparation, and cleaning, pp. 76–83; preparation of culture media, pp. 89–124; cultural methods, pp. 30–38, 125–133.

KLEIN, R. M., and D. T. KLEIN. 1970. *Research Methods in Plant Science.* Doubleday (Natural History Press), Garden City, N.Y.

PURVIS, M. J., D. C. COLLIER, and D. WALLS. 1966. *Laboratory Techniques in Botany,* 2nd ed. Butterworth, London. 439 pp., illus. Aquaria, pp. 190–208; culture, pp. 219–286.

STANIER, R. Y., M. DUODOROFF, and E. A. ADELBERG. 1963. *General Microbiology*. Macmillan, New York. Chap. 2, The Principles and Practices of Pure Culture.

Project 3   Isolation and culture of fungi

Contents

Introduction

This project will acquaint you with cultural techniques that you may use for studying fungi. In I and II we deal with cellular and plasmodial slime molds. In III and IV we treat isolation, enrichment culture, and axenic or pure culture techniques for aquatic fungi, and in V the culture of water molds for their reproductive stages is discussed. In VI and VII isolation and culture techniques for terrestrial fungi are given. VIII deals with growing mushrooms. Some references are listed at the end.

Ingredients and instructions for making culture media used for growing fungi, slime molds, and bacteria are given in Project 2, III, p. 14.

Project

I. Cellular slime molds *(Acrasiales)*

The best cellular slime mold for study is *Dictyostelium discoideum*. Cultures and culture kits are available from biological supply companies.

A. *Using an actively growing plate culture of Dictyostelium discoideum and its food source, Escherichia coli:*
   1. Place a sterile loop down on the agar plate culture and rub it around, picking up either bacteria and amoebae or bacteria and spores, or all three.
   2. Streak this inoculum along a single, broad line on a diameter of a fresh agar plate (H.I. agar, Turtox lactose, or other common culture medium).
B. *Using separate stock cultures:*
   1. With a sterile loop inoculate an H.I. or other agar plate with *E. coli* along a single, broad line. (*E. coli* may be supplied instead in the form of a broth suspension.)
   2. With a sterile loop inoculate the line of bacterial inoculum with spores of *D. discoideum*.
   3. After the myxamoebae have appeared, the culture can be maintained in the feeding stage by additions of the food organism.
C. *Study* (refer to Project 21, p. 161).
D. *Preparing stock cultures.* Transfer the food organism (*E. coli*) to Four agar slants and add the spores of *D. discoideum* to two of them. When the stock cultures have developed mature sorocarps, stopper them together with a separate culture of *E. coli* and store under refrigeration.
E. *Isolation from nature.* Follow the directions in part VI of this project. For additional details on the isolation of cellular slime molds, see Raper, 1951.

II. Plasmodial slime molds *(Myxomycetes)*

Physarum polycephalum is the best known myxomycete. Living plasmodia and dry, living sclerotia are available from biological supply companies.

A. *Paper-culture technique for starting plasmodial growth from dried sclerotia*
   1. Into a petri dish or other culture bowl that can be covered, place 12–24 strips of filter paper about 1 in. wide.
   2. On top of these strips place a piece of filter paper about the size of the culture dish.
   3. Saturate the paper with sterile distilled water (or soil water or natural water; refer to Project 2: III.C).
   4. Invert dish to allow the excess water to drain off.
   5. Place a piece of sclerotium in the center of the filter paper, cover, and allow several hours to overnight for the sclerotium to become active (start germinating into a plasmodium).
   6. Place a grain of rolled oats (Quaker Oats) on top of the activated sclerotium.
   7. After from several hours to a day, the yellow plasmodium will probably have covered the rolled oat and turned it yellow. Soon the plasmodium will grow away from this rolled oat.

8. Add new grains of rolled oats at the rim or rims of the progressing plasmodium. Add new grains daily as the plasmodium continues to gain in size.

B. *Paper-culture cultivation starting with plasmodium in agar culture.*
   Steps 1–4: same as in A.
   5. Scatter a few grains of rolled oats (Quaker Oats) on the filter paper.
   6. With an inoculating spatula or needle, transfer a bit of plasmodium from an agar culture to the dish, placing each bit next to one of the grains.
   Steps 7 and 8: same as in A.

C. *Obtaining sporangia from plasmodia and obtaining good material for studying plasmodia*
   1. Continue to feed a rolled-oat paper culture (above) for a week or more.
   2. At any time, remove a yellow rolled oat (covered with plasmodium) and place it on the surface of a common agar medium (e.g., HI, CMA, or CMDP) in a petri dish. The plasmodium will creep off the oat and fan out on the agar. (This fanned-out plasmodium is excellent for the microscopic study of plasmodial movement.)
   3. Feed the plasmodium by adding whole or powered rolled oats.
   4. A well-fed culture, either on agar or on paper, will form sporangia within 1 or 2 weeks if the cultures have not been grown in total darkness.

D. *Producing sclerotia from plasmodia*
   1. Following previous directions, obtain a mature, well-fed plasmodium on filter paper.
   2. Place the filter paper with the well-fed plasmodium in a clean petri dish.
   3. Leave the lid ajar and allow the plasmodium to dry slowly (over a 1- to 2-day period). With such treatment a mature plasmodium usually will form viable sclerotia and not sporangia.

E. *Germinating spores*
   1. Remove the cover from a petri-dish culture (see C) to allow sporangia to dry completely. This will take up to several days, depending on the relative humidity. (The spores of *Stemonitis* collected in nature usually germinate well.)
   2. Make a circle of silicone gum (available from Ward's) or petroleum jelly on a glass slide. In the center of the circle place a drop of sterile water.
   3. Using sterile forceps, transfer the dry sporangia to the drop of water, taking care to wet them thoroughly.
   4. Either put the slide in a slide humidity chamber (VI.C.2.a) or put a cover slip on the circle of petroleum jelly.
   5. Flagellated gametes may emerge earlier (3–7 hours) but you can expect them after 18 hours if all goes well.

F. *Study* (refer to Project 22, p. 169).

G. *Isolation from nature.* Follow the directions in part VI of this project. Initial isolation can simply involve placing organic debris or bark from tree trunks in a moist chamber on wet, absorbent paper, such as filter paper. For details of Myxomycete isolation and cultivation, refer to Gray and Alexopoulos, 1968, Chapter 11.

III. Isolation and enrichment culture of some aquatic fungi

Aquatic phycomycetes are abundant in natural bodies of water and in soil, but they must be "baited" for. Most of the water molds you collect will be members of the family Saprolegniaceae, but *Pythium* (order Peronosporales) is also very common, and you may collect *Allomyces* (Blastocladiales) as well. Most of the small, monocentric species that you collect will be chytrids (Chytridiales).

A. *Field work.* In small, wide-mouth, screw-cap jars or Whirl-Pak plastic bags, make ten to thirty fresh collections of a variety of soils and on pond and stream water with algae, sticks, sand, leaves, or other debris (not from stagnant areas). Give each collection a number, for future reference, and record the date and the specific location of each collection.

B. *Baiting*

   1. In the laboratory place *each water collection* in a sterile petri dish to a depth of about 5 mm. Place 1 teaspoon of each soil collection in one side of a sterile petri dish and add sterile distilled water to a total depth of about 5 mm. Bait each dish by submerging two split hemp seeds (cut seeds in half in a sterile petri dish with a single-edge razor blade) and by sprinkling pollen on the water surface. (Pollen of *Liquidambar styraciflua,* the sweet gum tree, and *Pinus,* pine, are excellent.) Other baits that will usually bring out different aquatic species are thinly sliced cow horn and human hair that has been treated with ether to remove oils (these substrata are rich in keratin); insect exuviae and purified shrimp exoskeleton (chitin); cellophane, dialyzing membrane, and filter paper (cellulose); boiled, young Paspalum grass (or other grass); leaf segments; and dead insects, such as termites and flies. Suitable seeds other than hemp are cucumber, pumpkin, squash, sunflower, and radish. With a glass-marking pencil, put collection number and date baited on each culture dish lid.

   2. An experiment you can do relates to finding out if adding antibiotics to water enhances the isolation and enrichment of aquatic fungi from water and soil collections. Set up such a controlled experiment using antibiotic water (refer to Project 2: III.A.5, p. 16).

C. *Hemp-seed cultures.* In from 2 days to 1 week, water molds growing out from the hemp seed will appear. These molds usually can be subcultured (i.e., further enriched or multiplied successfully) by transferring one of the seed halves to sterile lake water in another sterile dish and then adding two new halved hemp seeds. (If necessary, sterile distilled water can be used for subculturing.) Add two new hemp-seed halves to the original culture dish. A few aquatic fungi appear on the bait only after 2 or more weeks of incubation.

   It is likely that more than one species will come out on the original bait. The simplest way to make unifungal cultures from a mixed culture usually is to place the bait with its fungi on a sterile agar plate. Using the highest power of a dissecting microscope cut off a single hypha or, better still, about ten single hyphae-bearing sporangia, and use these for your subcultures.

D. *Pollen cultures.* In from 2 days to 1 week monocentric chytrids should appear on the pollen grains. To look for them, lower the surface of a clean, square cover slip to the surface of the pollen-sprinkled water (cover slip touch method). When you raise the cover slip, pollen grains and a little water will adhere to the cover slip. Put the cover slip down on a microscope slide and examine.

An enrichment culture or subculture often can be made by picking up the pollen by the cover slip touch method and putting the cover slip, pollen grain side up, in a sterile petri dish. Add sterile lake or distilled water and sprinkle the surface with pollen. Add a little more pollen to the original isolation culture.

IV. Axenic or pure culture techniques for aquatic fungi

The following methods are used for getting different kinds of aquatic fungi into uniorganismal culture (axenic or pure culture) from crude or gross culture (mixed culture). The addition of antibiotics to the agar medium aids in getting rid of contaminating bacteria (see Project 2: III.A, p. 14).

A. *Hyphal growth method*. Obtain a gross culture of *Saprolegnia* or other water mold on a half of a hemp seed. Wash off contaminating bacteria and protozoa using a jet of sterile water (use wash bottle). With forceps, pick up the seed and gently press the mycelial mat on an absorbent, smooth-surfaced (lint-free) cloth (e.g., long-sleeved shirt) long enough to blot off free water. Gently place this blot-dry mycelium immediately on a sterile culture plate of agar medium. Use AIM or CMA, either with or without antibiotics, for *Saprolegnia* and most other water molds; use YPSS, either with or without antibiotics, for *Allomyces* (see Project 2: III, p. 14).

After 1 day or 2, examine for purity at the tips of hyphae using low-power and high-dry-power objectives. (Look carefully at hyphae growing directly on the agar surface. They are most likely to have motile bacteria swimming in a thin film of water next to the hyphae. Avoid these hyphae!)

With a flamed (sterile) microspatula, cut out blocks of agar containing hyphal tips free of bacteria and place these on fresh agar plates. This subculture may be free of bacteria.

After 1 to several days, check the purity (bacteria freeness) of your water mold culture by cutting out a 3-mm-square block containing hyphal tips and putting it in a test tube of sterile nutrient broth. Do this in duplicate. If this broth becomes cloudy after several days, your subculture is not bacteria free.

If you want to keep a stock culture of your fungus, use a sterile technique to transfer a small agar block containing hyphae free of contaminating organisms to each of two agar slants (see Project 2: II.B.3 and C, p. 13).

B. *Push Method*. Use monocentric chytrid sporangia (e.g., *Chytriomyces*). With a fine spatula or a fine needle pick up pollen grains bearing monocentric chytrid sporangia with cleaved but undischarged planospores. Place these immediately about 1 cm from the edge and on the surface of a culture plate with a suitable agar medium. Dislodge the pollen grains by pushing the fine spatula or needle into the agar, leaving the pollen grains on the surface. First, use low power of the compound microscope to identify pollen grains bearing large, mature chytrid sporangia. Then, using a very high power of the dissecting microscope and using your

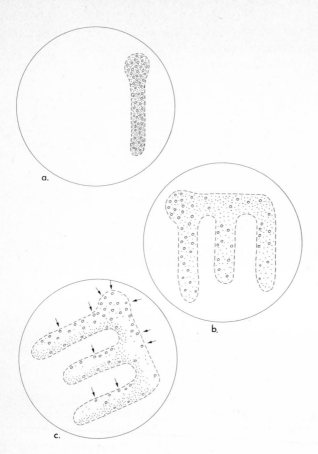

Fig. 3-1 Drop-streak method for axenic culture. Dashed lines represent the borders of streaked drops of water. Tiny circles represent fungal planospores. Dots represent bacteria. Arrows point to spores that will germinate and be free of bacterial colonies. (a) Agar culture plate with a line-like film of water containing fungal planospores and bacteria after the plate has been tilted to streak the suspension. (b) Culture plate with a comb-shaped film of water after having been tilted at right angles to the line-like film. (c) Culture plate propped for drying in a nearly vertical position and at 45° to the comb-shaped film. See text for further explanation.

finest needle (Minuten) in a holder, dislodge a large sporangium and push it along the surface of the agar to about the middle of the dish. Repeat for nine other sporangia, making sure that they are finally spaced about 1 cm apart. Observe with low power of the ordinary compound microscope after about 1 or 2 days to check for viability and the absence of bacteria (and other microbial contaminants). Sporangia that have produced new thalli and are free from bacteria should be transferred to one or more fresh agar plates.

C. *Zoospore drop-streak method.* With a pipette pick up several drops of water containing many motile fungus planospores and as few bacteria as possible. Add 1 or 2 drops to the surface of a culture plate, with suitable agar medium, about 1 cm from the edge. Tilt the petri dish so as to cause the drop to run out, forming a line of spore suspension across the plate (Fig. 3-1a). A few drops of sterile distilled water are added to this line at the position of the original drop and the petri dish is again tilted, but this time at right angles to the line of suspended spores (Fig. 3-1b). The result is that the spores are dispersed in a comb-shaped film of water on the agar surface. Next, the petri dish is propped in a nearly vertical position and at 45° to the streaked drops (Fig. 3-1c). The surface of the agar is then allowed to dry for about 5 minutes, and the petri dish is then covered and set aside for incubation. After the bacterial colonies have become large enough to detect under high power of a dissecting microscope, individual germlings of monocentric species, free of bacteria and other contaminating organisms, are removed with a very small spatula (cut from flattened Chromel wire) and transferred to a fresh agar plate. If contamination is not too great a problem, it is desirable to wait until the thalli have matured, ensuring the transfer of viable thalli. (For additional details see Koch, 1957.)

V. Seed-in-water culture of water molds for their reproductive stages

Beautiful and abundant material for studying the development of zoo-sporangia and gametangia and for watching the liberation of flagellated motile cells can be prepared by the method that follows. It involves putting split hemp seeds on an agar plate culture of a water mold, removing the seed halves after the mycelium has grown throughout them, placing the mycelium-filled seed halves in water, and leaving them undisturbed for an appropriate period of time. Seed-in-water cultures prepared in this way develop repro-ductive structures fairly synchronously, and they are clean or relatively free from contaminating microbes.

A. *General instructions*
1. From the stock agar culture transfer a small block of mycelium to a petri plate of the proper agar medium, placing the block slightly off center to allow more distance for growth (which may be desirable in rapidly growing species).
2. Incubate the inoculated plate at room temperature until the mycelium has grown out about 2 cm or more, but not all the way to the edge of the plate.
3. Place halved hemp seeds, split either crosswise or lengthwise with a single-edge razor blade (and discard any that have dark cotyledons), with the cut surface down just at the edge of the mycelial front.
Notes: (1) Allow one halved hemp seed for each student. (2) If sterile conditions are desired, the hemp seeds may be autoclaved after they are halved. Discard broken seed halves and those with dark cotyledons. Place the halves in a 50-ml erlenmeyer flask with 1 drop of water, plug the flask, and autoclave or pressure cook at 15 lb of pressure for 15 minutes.
4. Allow growth of the mycelium into the hemp seeds to take place for 12–48 hours. The hemp-seed halves should not stay on too long, primarily because they become difficult to remove.
    With sterile forceps remove the hemp seeds from the agar by tugging horizontally across the surface and then lifting. There is no need to include any agar with the hemp seed since the seed should be well penetrated with hyphae, but if some agar is pulled off, the resulting culture is satisfactory.
5. Place 3–5 of these hemp-seed halves into one sterile petri plate partly filled with sterile water so that the seeds are just covered. The kind of water used is significant:
    a. Most satisfactory overall is an unpolluted natural water, such as lake, stream, or spring water. Soil water is a good approximation of this.
    b. Dilute salt solution usually is satisfactory.

      c. Distilled water can be used, but it often prevents or retards normal growth.

      d. Tap water usually is not successful because of its additives.

  6. Allow the plates to remain undisturbed, with the hemp-seed halves evenly spread, until the fungus is mature. Movement may cause premature discharge of sporangia or gametangia, especially in the Saprolegniaceae.

B. *Timetables for Saprolegnia, Achlya, and Allomyces* (timing will vary according to the genotype of the culture and such environmental conditions as temperature and water quality).

  1. For zoospore discharge in *Saprolegnia*:

      5 days before study: Inoculate CMA plates with stock of *Saprolegnia* culture.

      3 days before study: Put sterile hemp-seed halves, cut surface down, on the edge of the colony. (Allow 6 hours with a minimum of 4 hours, maximum 12 hours or overnight, for penetration.)

      2 days before study: Lift hemp-seed halves from colony and place no more than three halves in 10–20 ml of sterile lake water in a 10-cm petri dish. (If necessary distilled water can be substituted for lake water.) Set aside and avoid disturbing.

      Note: Actually, an early-formed set of sporangia may be discharging their spores within 4–12 hours after putting the seeds in water!

      Day of study (see Project 23, p. 183): For demonstrating zoospore discharge the culture may be studied as is in the petri dish under the desired magnification, or a portion may be lifted into a drop of water on a slide as follows: Remove the lid from the seed-in-water culture and hold a clean microscope slide in the water at a 45° angle. Dip forceps in the water and, by the mycelium, pull the hemp seed up the slide with the cut surface down. Dry the underside of the slide and with low power examine the mycelium on the "downstream" side of the seed. Sporangia will be seen in various stages of development.

  2. For sexual stages in *Achlya* or *Saprolegnia*:

      6–8 days before study: Inoculate CMA plate with stock *Achlya* or *Saprolegnia* culture.

      4 days before study: Put sterile hemp-seed halves, cut surface down, on the edge of the colony. (Allow 6 hours with a minimum of 4 hours, maximum 12 hours or overnight for penetration.)

      3 days before study: Lift hemp-seed halves from colony and place no more than three halves in about 20 ml of sterile lake water in a 10 cm petri dish. (If necessary, distilled water can be substituted for lake water.) Set aside and avoid disturbing.

      Day of study (see Project 23, p. 184): For demonstrating the stages in the development of sex organs, the culture may be studied as is in the petri dish under the desired magnification, or a portion may be lifted into a drop of water on the slide, as described for B.1.

  3. For *Allomyces* gametophyte and sporophyte:

      14 days before study: Inoculate YPSS agar plates with stock *Allomyces* cultures (both *n* and 2*n*).

      7–12 days before study: Put sterile hemp-seed halves, cut surface down, on edges of both *n* and *2n* cultures. (Allow at least $1-1\frac{1}{2}$ days for penetration.)

    5 days before study: Lift hemp seeds from the cultures and place no more than five halves in 10–20 ml of sterile lake water (distilled water, if necessary) in a 10-cm petri dish. Set aside and avoid disturbing.

    Day of study (see Project 23, p. 181): Cultures may be studied as in *Achlya* and *Saprolegnia*.

    Note: Refer to Project 15, p. 83, for fuller instructions.

  C. *Saprolegnia reproduction kit.*

    A kit containing all the necessary materials for the study of asexual and sexual reproduction in *Saprolegnia* is sold by the Carolina Biological Supply Co.

VI. Isolation and enrichment culture of some terrestrial fungi

Nonaquatic or terrestrial saprobic fungi are common in soil and on decaying organic matter. You can collect, using the isolating culture technique below, cellular and plasmodial slime molds and many mucors (phycomycetes) and imperfect fungi (ascomycetes).

  A. *Starting methods.* On agar plates containing dilute food and salts (HI), add bits of rich loam, dung, pieces of decaying wood, leaves, and similar debris. In some cases you may wish to push this inoculum along the surface of some of the agar. At 2- 3-day intervals for 2 weeks study the entire agar surface with high power of a dissecting microscope and with low power of the compound microscope (put the entire petri dish on the microscope stage).

    For additional details on the isolation of cellular slime molds, see Raper, 1951. For details of Myxomycete isolation and cultivation, refer to Gray and Alexopoulos, 1968, Chapter 11.

  B. *Isolation and cultivation.* Individual molds can be isolated by the spore touch method (VII.4) and grown on new agar plates of an appropriate agar medium (e.g., CMDP). Separate two molds growing in the same dish using this method.

  C. *Slide culture techniques for studying sporulation.* Three common molds are *Rhizopus* (Phycomycetes), and *Penicillium* and *Aspergillus* (Ascomycetes). Directions for studying their structure and development are given on pp. 184 and 193.

    1. Try to isolate these fungi from air-contaminated agar culture plates by the spore touch method.

    2. Grow and study these isolates (or ones supplied by the instructor) using slide culture techniques as follows:

      a. Slide humidity chamber. A V-shaped piece of glass tubing is put in the bottom of a petri dish. An ordinary glass microscope slide is placed on the V-shaped tubing. The top is put on the petri dish and the assembled chamber is autoclaved.

      b. Agar-block slide culture technique. Ten milliliters of agar medium is poured into a 10-cm petri dish, allowed to harden, and divided into approximately 1-cm squares with a flame-sterilized scalpel or spatula. (The 1-cm squares are about 1 mm thick. Actually, agar squares of any thickness can be used.)

The cover of the slide humidity chamber is removed, and one square of the agar is added to the center of the slide with a flame-sterilized spatula. The agar is inoculated with spores by drawing an L-shaped needle or a small loop with its load of spores around the four sides and the top of the agar block.

A clean, sterile, cover glass is placed over the agar block. To the bottom of the petri dish is added about 10 ml of sterile distilled water. (The V tube will prevent flooding of the slide and the water will prevent drying out of the culture.)

To observe growth and satisfactory sporulation, the top of the petri dish may be removed at times and the culture observed directly under the low-power and high-dry-power objectives of the microscope. The culture can be mounted when it has grown to the point at which good sporulation is taking place.

To mount the preparation, the cover slip is removed from the agar block (mycelium, conidiophores, and conidia will cling to the underside of the cover glass). A drop of water (or Amann's lactophenol if a semipermanent slide is desired) is placed on a clean glass slide, and the cover slip is placed on the drop. If too many air bubbles develop, a drop of 70 per cent alcohol may be placed on the culture that has grown on the cover slip. This may be drained off before placing the cover slip on the drop of water or Amann's solution. To mount the slide on which the culture was growing, the block of agar is removed without disturbing the growth on the slide and discarded. A drop of 70 per cent alcohol is added, which is allowed to evaporate or drain off; a drop of water or Amman's solution is added to the center of the colony, and a clean cover slip is placed over the whole. (Note: A good substance for sealing the cover slip to the slide with a wet mount is Zut Slide-Ringing Compound, Bennetts, Salt Lake City).

c. Agar-drop slide culture technique. Put a tube of sterile agar medium and a pipette in a beaker of water. Heat to boiling. When the agar melts, remove the heat source.

Add 1 drop or 2 of the melted agar to a sterile glass microslide and let it cool until it gels. This can be hastened by placing the slide in a sterile petri dish in a refrigerator. As directed above, inoculate with spores, add a cover slip, incubate in a humidity chamber, and study.

The main advantage of this technique (agar-drop) over the agar-block slide culture technique is that the agar is on the slide in a thin layer, and this enhances good microscopic observations of germination and further growth.

d. Shoemaker slide culture technique. The success of this method depends on the fact that agar, although it takes a temperature of over 80°C to liquify, once melted will remain liquid until it cools to 35–40°C. It can thus be "seeded" with fungal spores at a temperature of 45°C, which is not enough to kill them.

Put tubes of sterile agar medium in a beaker of water and heat until boiling and the agar melts. Take the beaker off and allow to cool, with a thermometer in the water. While the agar is cooling, sterilize pipettes by standing them in the beaker of boiling water for several minutes.

When the temperature falls to 45°C, inoculate (or "seed") the liquid agar in the tubes by stirring in a few loopfuls of spores from culture slants or plates or a natural source. Twirl a seeded tube between the hands to get an even suspension.

Flame sterilize shoemaker slides and cover the depression of each slide with a flamed cover slip. With a warm, sterile pipette, take some agar suspension (spore-seeded agar) from a tube and run it in at one side of the depression, so that it runs under the cover slip. Do not fill the depression completely. The edge of the agar film should come halfway.

After 2–3 days conidiophores and conidia will be developed at the edge of the agar film.

VII. Axenic or pure culture techniques for terrestrial fungi

A. *Spore touch method.* Obtain an agar plate containing a mixture of sporulating molds. From a sterile CMDP, PDA, or other suitable agar plate cut out a tiny chunk of sterile agar with your fine spatula or needle. Fix the chunk of agar to the tip of the spatula or needle by jabbing the agar chunk with the tip of the tool. With the aid of a dissecting microscope touch the spores of one species of mold in the mixed culture with the chunk of agar and transfer this chunk with adhered spores to a fresh agar plate. Repeat this procedure for each of the sporulating species present.

B. *Push method.* Get an ascomycete in pure culture by pushing ascospores or asci on an agar surface to free from bacteria. Cut out small chunks of agar with the pushed asci or ascospores using a microspatula and transfer to a suitable medium.

C. *Balistospore method.* Fix to the center of the inside of a lid of a sterile PDA or CMDP agar plate (adhere with Vaseline, Canada balsam, mucilage, or similar substance) a piece including the hymenial (spore-producing) surface of a suitable basidiocarp or ascocarp (e.g., *Coprinus, Schizophyllum, Panus, Ascobolus,* or any other freshly collected specimen that is producing spores). After several minutes or longer (during which time spores are being discharged onto the agar surface), remove the fungus tissue from the lid. After 12–48 hours examine with low power to observe germination of the spores. With a microspatula, cut out single germlings on a block of agar and transfer to a fresh plate. (For details with *Schizophyllum,* see Project 17, p. 114.)

VIII. Growing mushrooms

A. *Agaricus campestris, the common field or lawn mushroom.* Grow basidiocarps ("mushrooms") from commercially supplied spawn (secondary or dikaryotic mycelium growing in rich humus) according to the directions supplied with the spawn. (Directions for studying mushroom structure and development are in Project 25 p. 203.)

B. *Schizophyllum commune, one of the wood decay mushrooms.*
   1. Collect a basidiocarp from an outdoor woodpile or from fallen trees or tree limbs. (Basidiocarps can be purchased.)
   2. Start an agar culture by the balistospore method above.
   3. Basidiocarps develop in the agar culture plate in about 2 weeks.

Note: See Project 17, p. 114, for detailed directions.

References

ALEXOPOULOS, C. J. 1960. Morphology and laboratory cultivation of *Echinostelium minutum. Am. J. Botany 47:* 37–43.

COOKE, W. B. 1963. *A Laboratory Guide to Fungi in Polluted Waters, Sewage, and Sewage Treatment Systems, Their Identification and Culture.* Public Health Service Publication 999-WP-1, Cincinnati, Ohio. 132 pp., illus.

COUCH, J. N. 1939. Technique for collection, isolation, and culture of chytrids. *J. Elisha Mitchell Sci. Soc. 55:* 208–214.

GOLDIE-SMITH, E. K. 1950. Note on a method of inducing sporangium formation in *Pythium undulatum* Petersen, and in species of *Saprolegnia. Trans. Brit. Myc. Soc. 33:* 92–93.

GRAY, W. D., and C. J. ALEXOPOULOS. 1968. *Biology of the Myxomycetes.* Ronald, New York.

KOCH, W. J. 1957. The new chytrids in pure culture . . . . *J. Elisha Mitchell Sci. Soc. 73:* 108–122.

RAPER, K. B. 1951. The isolation, cultivation and conservation of simple slime molds. *Quart. Rev. Biol. 26:* 169–190.

SPARROW, F. K. 1960. *Aquatic Phycomycetes,* 2nd ed., University of Michigan Press, Ann Arbor, Mich.

Project 4 Isolation and culture of algae

Contents

Introduction

This project will acquaint you with cultural techniques that you may use for studying algae. I deals with collecting and maintaining mixed populations of algae; in II and III isolation and enrichment culture techniques and methods for obtaining unialgal cultures are given; and IV deals with the culture of algae for their sexual stages. References are listed at the end.

Ingredients and instructions for making culture media used for algae are given in Project 2: IV, p. 18.

Project

I. Collecting and maintaining mixed populations of algae

In small, wide-mouth jars make collections of algae and the water they are growing in from ponds, streams, ditches, and other aquatic habitats. Use a plankton net for collecting smaller algae in large bodies of water such as lakes. Also collect algae growing on moist soil.

After returning to the laboratory, place culture plates (petri dishes) on white paper. Put portions of the aquatic algal collections into the bottoms of petri dishes, filling a dish to a depth of about 5–7 mm. Do not overcrowd; that is, put only a small amount of the filamentous algae in the water they were collected with. Put terrestrial algal collections into petri dishes and add, if necessary, a slight amount of water to make sure that the soil stays moist. Put the lids on. Keep in constant light by either leaving the room lights on or directing lamp light toward the culture dishes. Most algae maintain themselves well for several weeks or longer.

If need be, one can purchase living marine and freshwater algae from biological supply companies. Carolina Biological Supply Co. keeps a large number of freshwater and marine algae in culture.

II. Growing algae

A. *Enrichment culture of various algae*
1. Put clean test tubes (culture tubes) in a rack. (Note: Large culture containers can be used by adding proportionately larger amounts of materials.)
2. Add a pinch of calcium carbonate ($CaCO_3$) to the bottom of half of the tubes.
3. Add $\frac{1}{2}$ in. of moist garden soil to each tube. Choose a loam that is not too rich in organic matter or clay.
4. Fill each tube to three-quarters full by running distilled water down the side of the tube.
5. Stopper loosely with cotton.
6. Steam the prepared culture tubes for 1 hour at $100°C$ on each of 2 successive days.
7. Store in refrigerator for 1 day or until the water has cleared.
8. Add what appears to be a single kind of alga to two culture tubes, one with and one without $CaCO_3$.
9. Incubate at room temperature in constant light.

B. *Enrichment culture of Euglena*
1. Add 1 liter of spring, well, or lake water to a deep culture vessel.
2. To the water add 40 wheat grains, 35 rice grains, and 5 g of dry skim milk or 50 ml of liquid skim milk.
3. Boil for 5 minutes and let cool.
4. Inoculate, using a culture of *Euglena*.

C. *Isolation and enrichment culture of some terrestrial algae*
Method 1: Using fresh soil
a. Add a "pinch" from each of several freshly collected soils to a 125-ml flask containing about 50 ml of an algal culture solution (e.g., PGM). Stopper the flasks loosely with cotton.
b. Place these inoculated culture flasks on white paper to increase the amount of light they receive.
c. Observe at weekly intervals for a month. Keep in mind that different algae may be cultivated from the same soil in the different culture media. Look for different algae to come out in the flasks with different soils.
Method 2: Using dry soil
a. Samples of mud from the edge of a lake or pond can be air dried and stored even for year, to preserve certain algae in the dried but living condition.

b. A pinch of this soil added to a deep petri dish and flooded with sterile water gives a rich flora. By putting the pinch of soil to one side of the dish, a large clear area is left that can easily be observed with a dissecting microscope. Certain organisms that are very rare under these conditions (e.g., *Astrephomene* and *Volvulina*) will often appear in abundance if a boiled garden pea is added.

c. Algae can be isolated directly from the dish using a micropipette.

III. Methods for obtaining unialgal cultures

A. *Pipette method*

1. Pick up single cells or colonies using a micropipette pulled so that the bore diameter is just slightly larger than the cell.
2. Transfer single cells through a series of washes (in spot plates) using sterile medium or water.
3. After the tenth wash, deposit the alga in a fresh tube of medium.

Note: A good technique for testing your ability to isolate unialgal cultures is to start with a mixture of several algae that includes a very small one such as *Chlamydomonas*. Attempt to isolate one of the larger algae. *Chlamydomonas* contamination in your tubes indicates failure.

B. *Push method.* By unilateral light, concentrate a mixed culture of a "colonial" alga like *Volvox* or *Gonium*. With a pipette place a drop containing the alga on a PGM agar plate. With the dissecting microscope and a flamed fine needle (be sure it is cool!) push out single plants away from other algae, and using a flamed microspatula cut out agar block with its "clean" plant on it. Then quickly transfer the block to sterile algal culture solution in a 125-ml flask. Make several of these unialgal cultures.

C. *Streak method*

1. Using a PGM and a CMDP agar plate, "streak" a loopfull of a mixed culture or collection of *Chlamydomonas*, bacteria, and other unicells. From this streaked plate obtain *Chlamydomonas* in pure (bacteria-free) culture on PGM and a *bacterium* in pure culture on CMDP agar. Ultimately, the alga must be tested for purity or freeness from bacteria by inoculating nutrient broth with a separated *Chlamydomonas* colony on the streaked plate. (To determine if the bacterial culture was derived from a single cell, you must restreak from your "presumed" pure culture to find out if all the colonies of the new culture are the same.)
2. If you have a filamentous alga, such as *Stigeoclonium* or *Oedogonium*, that is liberating *zoospores*, the streak method is excellent for getting the filamentous alga into unialgal culture. Streak a loopful of water containing zoospores on a plate of algal agar medium and incubate. After several days, cut out single germlings (free of contaminants) and transfer them to fresh tubes or flasks of medium.

IV. Culture of algae for their sexual stages

The strain numbers referred to in the directions that follow are among those which have proved to be more reliable than others for demonstrating the sexual process in algae. The directions are adapted from Starr, 1964, and are based on experiences with the cultures at the Indiana Collection (now handled by the

Carolina Biological Supply Co.). One must expect some variation in reaction time when cultures are used in other laboratories, where differences in light intensity, media, temperature, etc., may be encountered.

A. *Chlamydomonas:* *C. eugametos* (Nos. 9 and 10)
                           C. moewusii (Nos. 96 and 97)
                           C. reinhardtii (Nos. 89 and 90)

1. Grow these heterothallic strains separately on Bristol's agar (p. 18) in petri dishes for about 1 week at 350 ft-c illumination (never in direct sunlight).
2. The afternoon before you wish to observe sexual fusions, wash from the agar plate culture the cells of each strain, using approximately 50 ml of sterile glass-distilled water. Each cellular suspension should be placed in a separate flask.
3. Illuminate the flasks for several hours and then remove them to the dark.
4. About 2 hours before you are to make your observations, again illuminate the flasks.
5. After the flasks with the conditioned cultures have been in the light for about 2 hours, mix on a clean glass slide a drop from each culture. For example, if you are working with *Chlamydomonas reinhardtii*, mix a drop from the flask containing strain 89 with a drop from the flask containing strain 90.

   Sexual reproduction is evidenced by the immediate clumping of the flagellated gametes. In *C. reinhardtii*, pairing and fusion of the gametes occur within a few minutes. In *C. moewusii* and *C. eugametos*, the clumping is excellent and pairs can be observed within a few minutes after mixing. The pairs swim about, joined at their anterior ends; fusion (plasmogamy) does not occur in these two species until 6–8 hours later.
6. See Project 28, p. 216, for study directions.

B. *Vaucheria sessilis* (No. 761)
1. Grow this alga in a soil-and-water medium containing $CaCO_3$ (p. 34).
2. To induce sexual stages, place a tuft of the alga in a petri dish containing 15–20 ml of the liquid part of fresh soil-and-water medium.
3. Put the dishes under illumination of 250–350 ft-c intensity at a temperature of 20°C.

   If placed under alternating 16-hour-light and 8-hour-dark periods, oogonia and antheridia will usually appear within 10 days. If placed under constant light, sex organs will appear within 4–5 days and will continue to be formed as the *Vaucheria* grows.
4. See Project 31, p. 238, for study directions.

C. *Oedogonium, Cosmarium,* and *Chlamydomonas mating kits.* Mating kits for these algae are sold by the Carolina Biological Supply Co. The mating sets contain all of the necessary materials for the study of sexual reproduction in these algae.

References

BOLD, H. C. 1942. The cultivation of algae. *Botan. Rev. 8:* 69–138.

FOGG, G. E. 1965. *Algal Cultures and Phytoplankton Ecology.* University of Wisconsin Press, Madison, Wis.

JAMES, D. E. 1969a. Unialgal cultures. *Carolina Tips 32:* 33–36.

———. 1969b. Maintenance and media for marine algae. *Carolina Tips 32:* 45–46.

LEWIN, R. A. 1959. The isolation of algae. *Rev. Algol. 5:* 181–197.

PRINGSHEIM, E. G. 1946. *Pure Culture of Algae.* Cambridge University Press, New York. 199 pp.

———. 1950. The soil-water culture technique for growing algae, *The Culturing of Algae, a Symposium.* The Charles F. Kettering Foundation, Yellow Springs, Ohio.

———. 1951. Methods for the cultivation of algae, in *Manual of Phycology,* ed. by G. M. Smith. Chronica Botanica Co., Waltham, Mass. Appendix A, p. 347.

PROVASOLI, L., J. J. A. MCLAUGHLIN, and M. R. DROOP. 1957. The development of artificial media for marine algae. *Arch. Mikrobiol. 25:* 392–428.

STARR, R. C. 1964. The culture collection of algae at Indiana University. *Am. J. Botany 51:* 1013–1044.

THE CHARLES F. KETTERING FOUNDATION. 1950. *The Culturing of Algae, a Symposium.* Yellow Springs, Ohio. 114 pp.

Project 5   Culture of moss protonemata and gametophores

Contents

Introduction

This project is designed to acquaint you with how the gametophytic phases of mosses grow and to allow you to study their development.

Project

I. Culture media

A. Ingredients and instructions for making moss culture media are given in Project 2: II, p. 11, and IV, p. 18.
B. *Mineral nutrient solution*
   1. Moore's (M) solution is recommended, but you can use Bristol's (B) solution or modified Pringsheim's (PGM) or fern medium (FM) with the agar omitted.
   2. Put 100 ml of a nutrient solution in each 250-ml erlenmeyer flask or 50 ml of solution in each 125-ml flask. Plug the flasks and sterilize in an autoclave or pressure cooker. Prepare an extra flask of medium to be used in washing capsules (unless you have a vial of viable spores to start with.)
C. *Mineral nutrient agar*
   1. Solidify any of the above nutrient solutions with 1.5 per cent agar (Difco

Bacto-agar is excellent); that is, add 15 g of agar to 1 liter of solution before sterilizing.

2. Pour the sterilized nutrient agar into sterile culture dishes (petri dishes).

II. Inculum (spores)

A. Either collect moss capsules containing viable spores or purchase moss capsules or vials of moss spores from a biological supply company.

B. *Getting spores out of capsules.* If a transfer (culture) chamber is available, follow these procedures in it:
   1. Arrange four sterile petri dishes containing the following solutions in this order:
      a. A dish containing a few milliliters of absolute alcohol.
      b. A dish containing a few milliliters of Chlorox.
      c. A dish containing a few milliliters of sterile nutrient solution.
      d. Another dish containing about 5 ml of sterile nutrient solution.
   2. Place a ripe, *unopened* moss capsule in dish 1 for approximately 1 minute; with forceps transfer the capsule to dish 2 and immerse the capsule in the Chlorox for approximately 1 minute; flame the forceps and transfer the capsule to the first dish of sterile nutrient solution to wash it; then transfer the capsule with sterile forceps to the second dish of nutrient solution and break open the capsule with flamed dissecting needles to release the spores into the medium.

III. Inoculation

A. *Inoculating flasks of nutrient solution*
   1. Starting with spores taken out of capsules (II.B). Inoculate each flask (I.B) with a sterile wire loopfull of spores.
   2. Starting with a vial of viable spores. Pass the bristles of a camel's-hair brush through a mass of spores. Then gently tap the brush to remove the excessive masses of spores that may be clinging to the bristles. Now sow the spores on the solution in a flask (I.B) by gently tapping the brush handle.

B. *Inoculating plates of nutrient agar.*
   1. Starting with spores taken out of capsules (II.B). Inoculate each agar plate (I.C) with one or two sterile wire loopfuls of spores. Streak the suspension of spores back and forth in several directions across the plate to spread out the spores as much as possible.
   2. Starting with a vial of viable spores. Pass the bristles of a camel's-hair brush through a mass of spores. Then gently tap the brush to remove the excessive masses of spores that may be clinging to the bristles. Now sow the spores on an agar plate (I.C) by gently tapping the brush handle. The surface of the agar plate should be evenly covered with spores rather than spotted with large masses.
   3. Preventing drying of the agar. To keep the agar plate cultures from drying and depleting the nutrient supply during the several-week period of growth, cut out and remove completely a section of the agar (about one fifth of the agar). Add distilled water to this pond. If nutrients become depleted—if the plants become chlorotic—add nutrient solution to the

pond. (Note: Drying out of agar plate cultures also can be alleviated by wrapping them in Saran wrap.)

IV. Incubation

Place the inoculated flasks and agar plates in a place as near 24°C as possible under continuous illumination from 40-watt cool white fluorescent lamps (1–3 ft from lamps). Light intensity of 200 to 300 ft-c is sufficient.

V. Examination of cultures or observations (refer to Project 37)

A. *Agar plate cultures* are very good for easily following the progress of development. Remove the lid of the dish and put the culture plate on the microscope stage. Study from low power and high dry. Also follow the directions in (B).

B. The directions that follow are based on nutrient solution (M) cultures incubated as stated above. With certain obvious alterations you can follow these directions for agar plate cultures.

1. Procedure. Beginning on the third day after inoculation of the cultures, remove samples every 2 or 3 days to study germination and protonemal growth. Remove samples from the surface of the liquid medium under a transfer cabinet with a sterile wire loop and place the material in a drop of water on a slide. Replace the cotton stopper and place the flasks back under the lights. If you are careful in preparing the cultures and in removing samples for study, the cultures will not become contaminated and can be kept and studied for several weeks. After the first few days, samples need not be taken but about once a week.

2. Things to look for. When a sample is taken on the third and fourth days after inoculation of the cultures, look for the formation of a germination papilla on the spores. Notice the large chloroplasts in the spores and in the cells of the protonema as it grows. Protonemata exhibit heterotrichous growth. After a protonema has become several cells long, notice how some of the branches of the filament grow upward, but the main part of the filament is prostrate. The upright branches are positively phototropic and are called aerial filaments by some people. The main filament is called the prostrate filament. Notice that the prostrate filament has oblique cross walls, elliptical chloroplasts, and rather long cells. The aerial branches have vertical cross walls, large round chloroplasts, and the cells generally are not as long as those of the prostrate filaments. The protone- mata will continue to grow by division of the tip cells, and if you look carefully you may be able to see some of the cells in the process of dividing. Branches on the filaments begin as small protuberances on the sides of cells. The protuberance is eventually cut off by the formation of a wall, and it will continue to grow and may form branches itself. Buds, from which gametophores develop, also begin as protuberances. Look for them between the seventeenth and twentieth days after inoculation of the cultures. As the buds develop, you should be able to see the apical cell; the formation of thin, almost colorless rhizoids at the base of the bud; the development to leaves; and the growth of the leaves. At the end of 4 weeks, if all goes well, you should have some gametophores in your cultures that are about 4 mm in height.

Project 6   Culture of fern gametophytes and young sporophytes

Contents

Introduction

This project is designed to acquaint you with how the gametophytic (prothallial) and early sporophytic phases grow and to allow you to study their development.

Project

I. Culture media

Ingredients and instructions for making the following media for growing ferns are given in Project 2: II, p. 11, and IV, p. 18.

  A. *Nutrient solution.* Use either Bristol's (B) or Moore's (M) solution or use modified Pringsheim's (PGM) or fern medium (FM) with the agar omitted.

  B. *Nutrient agar.* Solidify the mineral nutrient solution with 1.5 per cent agar (Difco Bacto-agar is excellent); that is, add 15 g of agar to 1 liter of solution before sterilizing.

  C. *Soil water* (decoction). Use soil solution (SW) No. 1 (distilled water, 94 ml; stock soil solution, 5 ml; 5 per cent aqueous KNO_3, 1 ml).

II. Inoculum (spores)

Either collect fresh fern spores or purchase viable spores from a biological supply company such as CCM: General Biological or Carolina Biological Supply Co. Freshly collected fronds (leaves) with mature sporangia may be placed on white paper in a covered box in a dry room. Mature sporangia will readily shed spores on the paper in a few hours.

III. Substrata

With the spores of one or more species of fern, inoculate (see IV) one or more of the Four substrata listed (D is the best for easily observing all developmental events):
A. Moist, sandy loam in a finger bowl or other kind of terrarium covered with glass or clear plastic.
B. Cinder block or brick standing (partly submerged) in a mineral nutrient solution or soil water (decoction) in a covered finger bowl, aquarium, terrarium, or similar container.
C. Sterile mineral nutrient solution in small, covered finger bowls or in erlenmeyer flasks. (Put 100 ml of a nutrient solution in a 250-ml flask or 50 ml of solution in a 125-ml flask.)
D. *Nutrient agar plates*. Sterile mineral nutrient agar in culture (petri) dishes.

IV. Inoculation

Inoculate by passing the bristles of a camel's-hair brush through a mass of spores, which are on paper or in a vial. Then gently tap the brush handle to remove the excessive masses of spores that may be clinging to the bristles. Now sow the spores on the substratum by gently tapping the brush handle. The surface of the cultural substratum should be evenly covered with spores rather than spotted with large masses.

V. Incubation

A. *Temperature and light*. Keep cultures at room temperature, as close to 24°C as possible, avoiding extremes of heat or cold. Do not grow the cultures in direct sunlight. Light intensity of 50–300 ft-c is sufficient. Cultures may be grown under continuous illumination from cool white fluorescent lamps.
B. *Preventing drying of agar plate cultures*. To keep agar plate cultures (III.D) from drying and depleting the nutrient supply during the several-week period of growth, cut out and remove completely a section of the agar (about one fifth of the agar). Add distilled water to this "pond." If nutrients become depleted—if the plants become chlorotic—add nutrient solution to the pond. (Note: Drying out of agar plate cultures also can be alleviated by wrapping them in Saran wrap.)

VI. Observations (refer to Project 40)

A. Agar plate cultures are very good for easily following the progress of development. Remove the lid of the dish and put the culture plate on the microscope stage. Study from low and high dry.
B. Observe cultures after about 3 days, and weekly thereafter. (Mount

germlings and young prothallia and study from high dry.) Is the first cell to emerge from the germinating spore the initial rhizoid? Does the rhizoid contain chloroplasts?

C. Identify the spore wall, initial rhizoid, secondary rhizoids, chloroplasts, nucleus, apical cell, apical notch, and marginal gland cells.

D. As the prothallia mature, sex organs will form. Usually the antheridia develop first and then archegonia, along with other antheridia. Archegonia can be recognized after fertilization of the egg by their brownish color. If you remove a mature gametophyte from an agar culture dish and place it ventral side up in a drop of water on a glass slide, you should be able to see the antheridia discharge their sperms and the archegonium neck open. When you see many sperms swirling in the mount, put on a cover slip and with high dry optics look for sperms swimming down the neck of an archegonium. (You may also be provided with a prepared slide of a prothallium fixed at this stage.) Stain and observe sperms, looking especially for the spiral nucleus and the numerous flagella of the whiplash type (refer to Project 11, p. 62).

E. Several-week-old cultures have embryos and young sporophytic plants, each with its first leaf and first root easily observable. The foot is embedded in the gametophytic prothallus.

VII. Fern culture kit

A fern culture kit is sold by the Carolina Biological Supply Co.

Project 7   Culture of seed plant microgametophytes (pollen tubes)

Contents

Introduction

This project is designed to acquaint you with how the pollen tubes or micro-gametophytes of seed plants grow from pollen grains and to allow you to study their development.

Project

I. Collection and handling of pollen

A. Collect pollen from freshly opened flowers by plucking anthers from the flowers with clean forceps. (*Tradescantia* and many others are excellent.)
B. Place the anthers in a petri or similar dish and shake to separate the pollen.
C. It is important to keep the pollen dry from the time of collection to the time of culture. Dry in a desiccator if the pollen is not used when it is collected; that is, store in a desiccator if necessary.

II. Preparations

A. Refer to Project 2 for general cultural techniques.

44

B. *Culture medium and materials*

Lactose (or sucrose)	60.0 g
Agar	7.5 g
Distilled water	500.0 ml
(Optional—see 6 following):	
1.0 per cent colchicine stock solution (refrigerated)	5.0 ml

1. Put the ingredients without colchicine in a 1-liter erlenmeyer flask and plug the flask.
2. Cover a 500-, 800-, or 1,000-ml beaker with foil or paper.
3. Sterilize the flask of medium and the covered beaker in an autoclave.
4. Sterilize as many slides or cover slips as you will want to use for making culture slides.
5. After sterilization let the agar medium cool to 70–60°C.
6. Colchicine may be added as the agar medium cools (about 70–60°C).
7. Keep the agar medium liquid at about 60°C until ready to use.
8. Carefully lift the cover on the beaker, pour the agar into the beaker, and replace the cover. Now make your culture slides (see C following).

Note: *Caution!* Colchicine is poison and must be used with care. It is optional in the pollen growth medium. Colchicine is necessary only when you wish to study metaphase figures in some detail. It tends to shorten chromosomes and makes their enumeration and morphology simpler to study.

C. *Preparing the culture slides.* Spread the medium on clean glass slides or on cover slips. You may do this by dipping the slide into liquid medium, allowing the excess to drip from a corner, and wiping off the underside of the slide. Keep these prepared slides in a horizontal position in a moist chamber until used!

D. *Sowing the pollen.* With a clean, dry camel's-hair brush, quickly dust a bit of pollen on a moist agar-coated slide. A thin, even film of pollen will produce the best growth. Do not allow sown slide or agar-coated slide to dry out. Quickly place sown slides in slide humidity chambers (see Project 3: VI.C.2.a, p. 29).

III. Growing the pollen

A. Keep sown pollen slides in your moist chamber. Growth is best at 20–22°C, although room temperature is satisfactory. (Growth is poor above 25°C and pollen is killed by temperature greater than 30–32°C.)

B. Optimum growing time for a maximum number of nuclei in metaphase will vary with temperature, species, and other factors. With *Tradescantia* (spiderwort), a few metaphase nuclei can be found as early as 9 hours, increasing with longer periods. Best growth may be found at about 20 hours (18–22) when grown at 20°C.

IV. Fixation and staining

Slides may be stained with the simple acetocarmine technique. Feulgen is far superior, but carmine is adequate for ordinary observations. (Refer to Project 14, p. 73.)

V. Observations

Record the results of your studies with each of the pollens tried.

VI. Notes

A. These directions are adapted from Conger, A. D., Stain Technology, *28:* 289, 1953.

B. Pollen of *Impatiens* (touch-me-not) germinates well on 10 per cent sucrose solution. (Refer to Project 45: III, p. 392.) *Lilium* pollen germinates well on 8 per cent sucrose solution, giving good pollen tubes in 24–36 hours.

Project 8

Growth of angiosperms with short life cycles

Contents

Introduction

In this project you will learn about one of the best flowering plants for total life-cycle studies, *Arabidopsis thaliana,* mouse-ear cress, of the family Cruciferae. It can be grown in soil or in axenic culture, and it will go through as many as 12 generations in 1 year, making it easy for you during an academic quarter or semester to study its complete development or total life cycle. Because it is easy to grow and produces flowers and seeds in a short time, this angiosperm is an excellent "tool" for developmental, physiological, and genetic studies.

Seed require a 2°C cold treatment before they will germinate, and they have a 2- to 4-day germination time. Plants grow well at 800–1,200 ft-c light intensity and a 10–30°C night temperature. This is a long-day plant, requiring about a 16-hour-light period for flowering. Plants flower 14–20 days after planting seed. Flowers produce seed after 10–15 days.

If time and facilities are available, you should obtain some seeds of this flowering plant and design experiments relating to questions of structure, development, physiology, and genetics that you are curious about.

Project

I. Seeds

A. *Sources.* Seeds of *Arabidopsis thaliana* should be available from biological supply companies. Also, the following investigators have offered to supply seeds: Dr. G. P. Redei, 117 Curtis Hall, Department of Field Crops, University of Missouri, Columbia, Missouri, 65202; Prof. J. H. M. Brown, Biology Department, University of Notre Dame, Notre Dame, Indiana, 46556.

B. *Care and germinability*. Keep freshly harvested seed in a well-ventilated place. Good seeds generally germinate within 3–4 days at 20–25°C, except in the first days after harvesting. Germinating ability remains unchanged for 2 years.

II. Growing in soil

Plant seeds on the surface of soil that has sufficient drainage. Once started, protect the seeds from drying. Spray as often as necessary with a fine mist, or irrigate from underneath by placing the pots in 1-in.-deep distilled water.

III. Growing in aseptic (axenic) culture

Mineral culture medium: NH_4NO_3, 200 mg/liter distilled H_2O; $MgSO_4 \cdot 7H_2O$, 100; $CaH_4(PO_4)_2 \cdot H_2O$, 100; KH_2PO_4, 100; K_2HPO_4, 50; $FeC_6H_5O_7 \cdot 3H_2O$ (ferricitrate), 2.5.

The plants grow well in shaken liquid culture. The medium may be solidified with 0.8–1.2 per cent agar. Addition of 2 per cent dextrose or sucrose ensures better growth. Do not submerge the seed in the agar. The surface disinfection of the seed is necessary. Calcium hypochlorite (5 per cent) treatment for 8 minutes followed by rinsing 4–6 times with sterile water is recommended. Follow the general rules of aseptic plant cultures to avoid contamination.

IV. General culture conditions

Arabidopsis is sensitive to prolonged high temperature (above 25–28°C) especially when cultured under low light intensity. To ensure rapid development, keep it under continuous illumination. Under shorter daily illumination, its growth is more vigorous and yields more seed. Direct high-intensity sunlight often causes burns. Good slow-growing cultures can be established in cold rooms (about 15°C) even under 200-ft-c light intensity. Protect the plants from aphids.

Part Two
Microtechnical methods and studies

The purpose of this part is to help you to learn some basic microtechniques used for studying plants. The projects deal with light microscopy, cytochemical tests and special structures, flagellated cells, slide making, making replicas of leaf surfaces, and squash techniques for studying chromosomes. Some reference books that treat various kinds of microscopy, photography, and microtechnique are listed at the end of Project 9.

Project 9   Using a light microscope

Contents

Introduction

The purpose of this project is to help you to use more effectively your light microscope, especially when you are using the oil-immersion objective. Some reference books that treat not only microscopy but also photography and microtechnique are listed under References.

Project

I. Cleaning and setting up

    A. Clean the microscope lenses by first dusting lightly with lens paper and then wiping clean with new, doubled lens paper. The paper or the lens surface may be moistened by breathing heavily on it. Pay special attention to the back of the lower lens of each ocular.

51

B. If your microscope does not have a built-in light source, take the lamp apart and with lens paper clean (1) the reflector and (2) the lens. Now clean the microscope mirror.

C. If your microscope lamp is separate, place the back of the base of your microscope on the edge of the desk in the place where you wish to use it throughout this course. Put the microscope lamp in line with the front of the lens housing about 4 in. from the stage of the microscope.

Arrange for permanent placement of your lamp and microscope. A special board that will fix the positions of the microscope and lamp could be constructed and would serve best, but masking tape carefully outlining the positions of the microscope and lamp on the table will be adequate.

D. If it is possible to do so, focus the light source in the lamp on the iris diaphragm of the condenser, taking the following steps:
1. Take out from the lamp the daylight and diffusion (ground-glass) filters.
2. Close the lamp iris diaphragm to almost minimal size.
3. Adjust the light source so that its image is in the center of the plane mirror. The concave mirror is not used. (The condenser does a better job of what the concave mirror does without a condenser—condensing light—but parallel light rays, reflected from the plane mirror, should be used with a condenser.)
4. Focus the lamp filament on the closed iris diaphragm of the microscope condenser. Observe this focusing by looking at the image of the diaphragm reflected in the plane mirror. (A bit of neck contortion is required!)

II. Focusing the condenser

Focus the condenser as follows:

A. Open the lamp diaphragm all the way; leave the condenser diaphragm nearly closed.
B. Rack down the condenser.
C. Rotate the mirror to center the light, as observed on lens paper placed taut on a microscope slide.
D. Rack up the condenser until the light is in focus on the lens paper, which is the position in which objects for study will be. The image of the light source now will be focused on the mounted objects for microscopic examination.
E. Replace the daylight and density filters.

III. Determining diaphragm settings

Looking at a mount of any chosen material, determine the proper settings of the condenser diaphragm and lamp diaphragm for each of the objective lenses, starting with low power, as follows:

A. Open the condenser and lamp diaphragms fully.
B. As you look through the microscope, slowly close the condenser diaphragm until the light begins to fade. Light from the condenser now just fills the back lens of the objective.
C. Slowly close the lamp diaphragm until the light begins to fade. Light from the lamp now just fills the aperture made by the diaphragm in the condenser.
D. Repeat the above for the other objective lenses.

These settings can be checked visually, after removing any ground-glass diffusion filter from the system, by removing an ocular lens and looking at the images of the diaphragms in the tube (the position of the condenser may have to be adjusted slightly by racking up or down).

IV. Getting better resolution and image quality

A. Prepare a thick mount of an alga (e.g., *Spirogyra*). Looking at the finest granules or other markings, or perhaps granular debris elsewhere in the mount, observe different resolving powers (Numerical Aperture or N.A.) of the dry objectives (× 10 and × 40).

B. Use the oil-immersion lens first without and then with the condenser immersed. Notice the difference.

C. While still under oil, make the mount thin by blotting with filter paper. Note the difference in the resolving power and the general image quality. Note that the material directly under the cover slip gives better image quality than that farther down in the mount. This is an important consideration when looking for very fine detail.

V. Improvising a darkfield

A. Improvise a darkfield with your microscope by (1) using your finger to partially obstruct the light path between the mirror and bottom of the condenser and by (2) making and using a cardboard disc (picture-framing cardboard serves well) to fit in the filter frame of the condenser assembly. An eccentric hole about 5 mm in diameter (a paper hole puncher will do this) should be cut in the cardboard. Some adjusting of the mirror and rotating of the cardboard usually are required to achieve a darkfield. Take out all filters. Open fully the condenser and lamp diaphragms.

B. Observe swimming cells in your improvised darkfield. Remove all light filters and open all iris diaphragms fully (maximum light intensity is essential). Mount a drop, spread fairly thin, and do not cover with a cover slip. Put immersion oil on the microscope condenser. Make contact with the oil and the slide under the drop. Observe swimming cells with low power. Magnification can be increased by using high-power oculars.

VI. Drawing

A. Attach a camera lucida (C.L.) and adjust. Direct light on drawing paper. For ease in the making of C.L. drawings, balance the light on your drawing paper with the light through the microscope. This is the best way to attain the proper light balance. If there are density filters or filter discs in the camera lucida, set them to 100 per cent transmission—with no filters in the optical paths.

B. Using any material, practice drawing at different magnifications. Keep your pencil lead very sharp by using an abrasive surface such as sandpaper.

Microtechnical References

General

DeROBERTIS, E. D. P., W. W. NOWINSKI, and F. A. SAETZ. 1970. *Cell Biology,* 5th ed. Saunders, Philadelphia. 555 pp., illus. Refer to Part Three, Methods for the Study of the Cell, Chap. 6, Instrumental Analysis of Biological Structures, in which all kinds of microscope equipment and techniques are discussed (pp. 87–102), and Chap. 7, Methods for Cytologic and Cytochemical Analysis (pp. 103–133).

FREY-WYSSLING, A., and K. MÜHLETHALER. 1965. *Ultrastructural Plant Cytology.* American Elsevier, New York.

KLEIN, R. M., and D. T. KLEIN. 1970. *Research Methods in Plant Science.* Doubleday (Natural History Press), Garden City, N.Y.

O'BRIEN, T. P., and M. E. MCCULLY. 1969. *Plant Structure and Development.* Macmillan, New York. 114 pp., illus.

PURVIS, M. J., D. C. COLLIER, and D. WALLS. 1966. *Laboratory Techniques in Botany,* 2nd ed. Butterworth, London. 439 pp., illus. (Chaps. 1–6 deal with cytological apparatus and techniques.)

Microscopy

Light microscopy

BARRON, A. L. 1965. *Using the Microscope,* 3rd ed. Chapman Hall, London. 257 pp. illus.

BELLING, J. 1930. *The Use of the Microscope.* McGraw-Hill, New York. 315 pp. illus.

COLLINS, C. H. 1967. *Microbiological Methods,* 2nd ed. Butterworth, London. (see pp. 47–52).

Phase microscopy

WREN, L. 1963. *Understanding and Using the Phase Microscope.* Unitron Instrument Co., Newton Highlands, Mass. 64 pp., illus.

Polarization microscopy

HALLIMOND, A. F. 1953. *Manual of the Polarizing Microscope.* Cooke, Troughton & Simms, Ltd., York, England.

Interference microscopy

HALE, A. J. 1958. *The Interference Microscope in Biological Research.* E. and S. Livingstone Ltd., Edinburgh.

Electron microscopy

KAY, D., ed. 1965. *Techniques for Electron Microscopy,* 2nd ed. F. A. Davis, Philadelphia. 560 pp., illus.

PEASE, D. C. 1960. *Histological Techniques for Electron Microscopy.* Academic Press, New York.

WISCHNITZER, SAUL. 1962. *Introduction to Electron Microscopy.* Pergamon, Elmsford, N.Y. 132 pp., illus.

Photography

BLAKER, A. A. 1965. *Photography for Scientific Publication, a Handbook*. W. H. Freeman, San Francisco. 158 pp., illus. (Macrophotography)

SCHENK, R. 1962. *Photomicrography* (translated by F. Bradley). Chapman & Hall, London. 132 pp., illus.

Microtechnique (slide making, cytochemistry, staining, etc.)

CONN, H. J. 1961. *Biological Stains*. 7th ed. Williams & Wilkins, Baltimore. (Description of stains and uses. Also general nature of dyes, classification, and mechanism of staining.)

DARLINGTON, C. D., and L. F. LaCOUR. 1960. *The Handling of Chromosomes*. Macmillan, New York.

EMIG, W. H. 1959. *Microtechnique: Text and Laboratory Exercises*. Published by the author. (Contains essential information on techniques and processes; also instructions and laboratory procedure for different techniques and various materials.)

GRAY, PETER. 1952. *Handbook of Basic Microtechnique*. Constable & Co., London.

JENSEN, W. A. 1962. *Botanical Histochemistry*. W. H. Freeman, San Francisco. (Contains some formulas not found in the others, in addition to histochemical techniques.)

JOHANSEN, D. A. 1940. *Plant Microtechnique*. McGraw-Hill, New York. (The standard reference book; good on stain identification and synonomy.)

SASS, J. E. 1958. *Botanical Microtechnique*, 3rd ed. Iowa State University Press, Ames, Iowa. (Easier to find formulas than in Johansen; some formulas appear easier to follow.)

Stain Technology. (A monthly periodical publishing new cytochemical and histochemical techniques.)

WILLEY, R. L. 1971. *Microtechniques—A Laboratory Guide*. Macmillan, New York.

Project **10**
Cytochemical tests and special structures

Contents

Introduction

Project

Introduction

In this project you will learn some special microchemical tests and look at some special structures of both nonvascular and vascular plants.

Project

I. Nonvascular plants

  A. *Special tests*
    1. Starch (I_2KI test)
      a. Make a thin section of the thallus of *Anthoceros*. Place on a slide and add 2 or 3 drops of iodine solution. Add a cover slip. Examine. Note the many dark blue to black starch grains around the pyrenoid of the single chloroplast in each cell. Make a whole mount of *Spirogyra* or another green alga. Stain and examine as above.
      b. How to make solution: Dissolve 2 g of KI in 100 ml of water, and then dissolve 0.2 g of iodine in the KI solution. Pour into brown dropping bottles. This solution also is referred to as IKI solution.

2. Cellulose (chloroiodide of zinc test)
   a. Mount several filaments of a water mold (e.g., *Achlya*), a green alga (*Spirogyra*), and cotton fibers in 2 or 3 drops of chloroiodide of zinc. Wait 30 seconds. Cover and observe, looking for blue to purple cellulosic walls.
   b. Mount *Oscillatoria* as above. After adding a cover slip, blot the mount and then observe under oil immersion. Inner wall should be colored.
   c. How to make solution: Dissolve 50 g of zinc chloride and 16 g of KI in 17 ml of water. Add an excess of iodine and allow to stand for several days. Pour the supernatant into brown dropping bottles. (This solution also is referred to as zinc-chlor-iodide solution.) (A slightly different formula for chloroiodide of zinc follows: 30 g of $ZnCl_2$, 5 g of KI, 0.89 g of I_2, and 14 ml of distilled water.)
3. Chitin (stained chitosan test)
   a. Autoclave the mycelium of a nonaquatic fungus at 15 lb of pressure and 121°C in 23 M KOH for 15 minutes. The chitin will be converted to chitosan at this stage.
   b. Wash the mycelium and place it on a slide with a few drops of IKI in 1 per cent H_2SO_4.
   c. Chitosan will stain voilet. Brown is considered a negative reaction. Treat a control with 2 per cent acetic acid before applying the IKI–1 per cent H_2SO_4. The chitosan is soluble in the acetic acid (cellulose is not).
4. DNA (Feulgen reaction). Refer to Project 14, p. 75.
5. H-piece wall structure (chromic acid test). Mount several dozen filaments of *Tribonema* or *Microspora* in 2 or 3 drops of 40 per cent chromic acid. Add a cover glass and observe with high dry. (Take care not to get chromic acid on the lenses.)
6. Leucosin (neutral red stain)
   Make a thin mount of actively growing yeast. Add 1 drop of 1 per cent neutral red to one edge of the cover slip and observe with the oil-immersion lens the "diffusion front." Vitally stained cells with leucosin granules will show bright red.
7. Mucilerous glands of *Euglena* (neutral red stain). Technique as in No. 4.
8. Chromosomes (acetocarmine smear technique)
   Dissect out ten young to very young globules (male structures) of *Chara*. Place in several drops of acetocarmine reagent on a glass slide. Add a cover slip and press firmly. "Blot." Heat the slide gently over an alcohol flame. Observe spermatogenous cells, looking especially for division stages showing chromosomes and for spiral nuclei in the sperm cells themselves. Note: Additional details on this technique, including how to make the reagent, are given in Project 14, p. 73.

B. *Special structures*
   1. Mitochondria: Hyphal tips of *Allomyces* (see Project 15, p. 93)
   2. Coenocytic thallus: *Saprolegnia* and *Vaucheria*
   3. a. Plasmodial thallus: *Physarum*
      b. Amoeboid thallus: *Dictyostelium* and *Physarum*
   4. Wall:
      a. H-piece construction (see previous directions No. 5 under Special Tests)
      b. Ring markings: *Oedogonium*

   c. Punctations: diatoms and placoderm desmids
   d. Pseudosepta: *Allomyces*
   e. Pores: dead leaf cells of *Sphagnum*
   f. Clamp connections: secondary mycelium of a mushroom (see Project 17)
   g. Lorica: *Dinobryon* or *Trachelomonas*
   5. Chloroplasts:
   a. Disc: *Chara*
   b. Spiral: *Spirogyra*
   c. Medial band: *Mougeotia*
   d. Parietal band: *Draparnaldia* and *Ulothrix*
   e. Star: *Zygnema*
   f. Cup: *Chlamydomonas*
   g. Reticulate: *Oedogonium*
   6. Eye spot:
   a. Solid: *Chlamydomonas*
   b. Granular: *Euglena*
   7. Pyrenoid and starch grains: *Closterium, Spirogyra*
   8. Salt vacuole: *Closterium*
   9. Contractile vacuole: *Chlamydomonas*
   10. Paramylum granules: *Euglena*
   11. Flagella: Observe the number and the position of attachment of the flagella in *Euglena, Chlamydomonas* (or other volvocales), *Allomyces,* and *Saprolegnia.*
   a. I_2KI kills, fixes, and weakly stains flagella. Add a drop of iodine solution to one edge of the cover slip and let it diffuse under.
   b. Osmic acid (OsO_4) fixation and crystal violet staining
   (1) Put a drop with motile cells on a microscope slide (do not add a cover slip).
   (2) Invert the slide for 30 seconds to 1 minute over several drops of 1–2 per cent osmic acid in a small dish within a closed petri dish. (Caution: Use a fume hood if it is available. Osmic acid fumes are injurious to human tissue, they can fix the eyeball!)
   (3) Remove the slide, add a small drop of a 1 per cent solution of crystal violet stain, add a cover slip, and study with high dry and oil-immersion lenses.
   c. Note: For additional directions, see Project 11, p. 61.

II. Vascular plants

   A. *Tests for specific substances.* In the following tests for specific substances present in the stem, use extreme care in placing slides on the microscope stage. Do not get the solutions on the instrument.
   1. Starch: In some species starch is stored in certain tissues of the stem. I_2KI solution turns starch grains dark blue or purple. Mount a fresh section of stem in iodine solution and observe with the microscope. (Name the tissues in which starch is stored.)
   2. Cellulose:
   a. Methylene blue stains cellulose blue. Mount a fresh section of a stem in methylene blue for 5 minutes or longer. (Sycamore, *Platanus,* has a good stem for this test.) Observe which tissues stain deepest blue and which

stain greenish blue. The depth of the blue stain indicates the purity of the cellulose in the walls. Remove the excess blue by adding water and drawing off with blotting paper. (Do all the cells have cellulose in their walls?)

   b. For chloroiodide of zinc test for cellulose; see I. A. 2, p. 57.

3. Lignin: Phloroglucin solution and hydrochloric acid turn lignin reddish. Mount the section of sycamore from which the excess methylene blue has been removed and add several drops of phloroglucin solution. Observe the section as it clears and until the solution begins to crystallize around the edge of the drop. Watch for changes in the cellulose stain. Add 2 drops of HCl. Watch for development of a greenish color, where cellulose is present, and for red stain indicating lignin. The brighter the red, the more completely the tissue is lignified. (Name the cell types in which lignin, if found, is found. Is lignin found only in secondary walls?)

4. Cutin and suberin: The Sudan III and the chlorophyll tests for suberized and cutinized walls are as follows:

B. *Color reactions of wall substances to reagents*

Reagent	*Stain*	*Wall*
1. Toluidine blue 0 (0.05% aqueous solution) an excellent polychrome stain.	Pinkish purple	Carboxylated polysaccharides (e.g., pectic acids)
Wash sections 1 min in H_2O; then put them in toluidine blue for 10 sec to 1 min; wash in H_2O for 1 min; mount in water	Green, greenish blue or bright blue	Polyphenolic compounds (e.g., lignin and tannins)
2. Phloroglucin Soak sections 5 min in a 1% solution of phloroglucin in water or in alcohol; soak 2 min in 50% HCl; mount in glycerin.	Red	Lignified (suberized will show some red. In nature there is always some lignin with the suberin)
3. Chloroiodide of Zinc Dissolve 30 g of chloride of zinc, 5 g of KI, and 0.89 g of iodine in 14 g of dist. HOH (Keep solution in the dark). Mount the sections in this solution.	colorless to violet or purple . . . . Cellulose Violet . . . . Mucilaginous Yellow to . . . . . Cutinized, yellowish Suberized, brown Lignified	

(This treatment also colors starch blue to purple, and protoplasmic contents yellow to brown.)

4. Chlorophyll Soak sections for 1 hr in the dark in a fresh alcoholic solution of chlorophyll.	Green	Cutinized, Suberized

5. Sudan III (0.01 g of Sudan III in 5 g of 95% EtOH (ethyl alcohol) and 2 g of glycerin.) Keep tightly closed. Leave sections in stain for 1 hr; rinse quickly in 50% EtOH and mount in glycerin.	Red Reddish brown	Cutinized Suberized

(This treatment also stains red: oils, fats, resins, and oleoresins.)

6. Sulfuric acid (concentrated)	Dissolves Does not dissolve	Cellulose Lignified or suberized

(The above tests are more apparent if the sections are first cleared in chloral hydrate dissolved in two parts of water; blot sections to free from surplus chloral hydrate before proceeding with stains.)

Project **11**   Flagellated cells

Contents

Introduction

This project is designed to acquaint you with the basic kinds of swimming, flagellated cells of plants. You will observe their modes of swimming and flagellar action with improvised darkfield microscopy and study flagellar and flagellar apparatus structure by staining techniques.

Project

I. Organisms for study

  A. *Gonium*. Each cell of a colony has two apical whiplash flagella.
  B. *Chytrid zoospores or Allomyces gametes and/or zygotes and zoospores*. Each motile cell has a posteriorly attached and directed whiplash flagellum.
  C. *Euglena or Peranema*. These unicellular organisms have an anterior, one-sided tinsel flagellum. The lateral hairs of a tinsel flagellum are called mastigonemes.
  D. *Zoospores of a water mold* (e.g., *Pythium* or *Saprolegnia*). Each spore has an anteriorly directed, two-sided tinsel flagellum and a posteriorly directed whiplash flagellum. (The two flagella are laterally attached on the zoospore body of *Pythium* and the secondary zoospore of *Saprolegnia* and other water

molds. The two flagella are subapically attached on the primary zoospore of *Saprolegnia*.)

Notes: (1) In each of the above you may find the following contaminating organisms: *Protozoan* (unidentified), with an anterior, two-sided tinsel flagellum; *Eubacteria* (unidentified), some with many bacterial flagella, others with a single bacterial flagellum, and others with a polar tuft of "flagella." (2) To clean slides, dip new slides in 95 per cent alcohol. Drain. Wipe vigorously with two layers of lens paper or unstarched, lint-free cloth.

II. Mode of swimming and action of the flagellum

Make either a thick mount or an uncovered mount of the motile cells of the organisms provided. A covered thick mount is best made by making a circle of silicone gum on a glass slide, placing a drop with motile cells in the center of the circle, and putting a cover slip on the circle of silicone gum. Silicone gum is inert, nontoxic, and immiscible with water. It keeps the slide from drying out (strongly retards evaporation) and at the same time allows the diffusion of CO_2 and O_2, preventing the accumulation of CO_2 and the depletion of O_2.

With your microscope set up for an improvised low-power *darkfield* and using $\times 15$ oculars, observe the swimming cells. Note that many or most cells are not actively swimming. Follow the path of swimming. If possible, observe flagellar action, looking for the "double image" and/or "single image" of the rapidly undulating flagellum (Fig. 15-4). Determine whether the flagellum or flagella of a cell beat in one plane or in spiral path. Make appropriate sketches.

III. Structure of the flagellum and flagellar apparatus

A. *Iodine flagellar stain*. Iodine is such a weak stain that it should be used only when it is inconvenient to use the other techniques described below. With this technique, bacterial flagella, tinsels on the tinsel flagellum, and the lash tip of a whiplash flagellum are almost never seen.
   1. Put a small drop with a large number of swimming cells on a glass slide.
   2. Mount and check with low power to see if there are a suitably large number of swimming cells.
   3. Kill and stain in one operation by adding I_2KI solution to one edge of the cover slip and letting it diffuse under.
   4. You may then wish to ring the cover slip with wax to prevent drying out and floating around of the cells in water currents.

B. *Crystal violet stain for whiplash tip*
   1. Put 1 small drop containing motile cells of a chytrid or of *Allomyces* on a clean slide and kill and fix by the fumes of 2 per cent OsO_4 (osmic acid) for 1 minute (refer to Project 10: I.B.11.b, p. 58).
   2. Put 1 drop of 1 per cent crystal violet near the drop with spores; then, using an unbent paper clip, add stain to the drop of spores until the solution is dark.
   3. Mount, blot off any excess water, and observe, first with high dry and then with oil immersion. (You may wish to ring the cover slip with wax before observation to prevent the movement of the spores in water currents caused by evaporation of the mount.)

C. *Stain for flagellar apparatus*
   1. Put a drop with the motile cells of a chytrid or of *Allomyces* on a clean

slide and kill with the fumes of 2 per cent osmic acid (see p. 58).

2. Stain with crystal violet as in B.2.
3. Air dry, if you wish, by placing slide close to a hot incandescent lamp and in the gentle breeze of a fan, which speed the drying.
4. Wash: Flood slide with water for 1 minute, drain, rinse with fresh water, and dry under lamp.
5. Add iodine solution (I_2KI) for 5 minutes.
6. Rinse with water.
7. Dry under lamp. Drive off the last bit of moisture in the flame of an alcohol lamp.
8. Destain differentially in clove oil. In general, extraction in several changes of clove oil for a few minutes beyond the time when stain extraction is no longer apparent to the naked eye will produce satisfactory results.
9. Pour off clove oil. Rinse in xylene. Clear in a fresh change of xylene for 3 minutes.
10. Mount in balsam, clarite, or other mounting medium.

D. *Löffler's stain for tinsels*
1. Put 2 or 3 drops with many motile cells bearing tinsel flagella on a very (very) clean side. (Mix together a small drop from each culture.)
2. Kill in 2 per cent osmic acid fumes for 1 minute (see p. 58).
3. Air dry, as in C.3.
4. Wash, as in C.4. (This is especially important in this procedure.)
5. Dry, under lamp (and fan for speed).
6. Add as much of the mordant (a solution used to fix the coloring) as the slide will permit. Allow it to remain there for 2 minutes, while heating the slide gently, to steaming but not to boiling. Add more mordant while heating if too much evaporates.
7. Wash gently by dipping the slide in a large bowl of water.
8. Stain with 4 per cent aniline water crystal violet. Warm gently as for mordant; leave stain on slide for 1–2 minutes.
9. Wash quickly.
10. Dry under lamp. Drive off the last bit of moisture in the flame of an alcohol lamp.
11. Mount in balsam, clarite, or other mounting medium.

Mordant	1. 20 per cent aqueous tannic acid	10	parts
	2. Ferrous sulfate, saturated aqueous solution, at room temperature	5	parts
	3. Basic fuchsin, saturated solution in 95 per cent alcohol (Filter before using.)	1	part
Stain	1. Aniline oil	0.5 ml	
	2. 95 per cent alcohol	4.5 ml	
	3. Water	20.0 ml	
	4. Crystal violet (Filter just before using.)	1.0 g	

E. *Lee's stain for bacterial flagella*
1. Put a drop of swimming bacteria (preferably a mixture of *Spirillum* and *Bacillus*) on a very clean slide.
2. Kill in 2 per cent osmic acid fumes for 1 minute (see p. 58).

3. Air dry, as in C.3.
4. Wash, as in C.4. This is an especially important step.
5. Flood slide with freshly mixed stain (see 11).
6. Let remain for 60 seconds.
7. Pour off stain and expose tilted slide to air for 7–30 seconds.
8. Wash in water.
9. Dry under lamp and drive off the last bit of moisture in flame from alcohol lamp.
10. Mount in balsam, clarite, or other mounting medium.
11. The stain:
    a. Solution A: Magnesium sulfate, 7 g; tannic acid, 8 g; distilled water, 110 ml; acetic acid (5 per cent), 40 ml. Dissolve the sulfate and the tannic acid in the water with the aid of gentle heat. When solution is complete, add the acetic acid.
    b. Solution B: Basic fuchsin, C.I. No. 676 or 677, 1.5 g; alcohol, 95 per cent ethyl, 100 ml.
    c. To prepare the stain for use, add 1 part of Solution B to 5 parts of Solution A. (The mixed stain is somewhat labile but will give excellent results for 1 day. The separate solutions may be kept undefinitely.)

Project 12   Making slides or mounts

Contents

Introduction

This project will acquaint you with techniques for making temporary and permanent slides of plant materials—both whole mounts and sections. Directions are given for making temporary and semipermanent mounts as well as permanent mounts of stem sections, delicate algae and fungi, and cleared leaves.

Project

I. Temporary mounts: GAW

Mount on a glass microscope slide plant material directly from water or from fixative into GAW [1:1:1 glycerine, 95 per cent EtOH (ethyl alcohol), distilled water].

Seal the cover slip with beeswax or nail polish.

This technique is good for gross morphological structure. Cytoplasm becomes plasmolyzed, though plasmolysis is reduced in fixed material. If carefully prepared, these mounts may last several months; the advantage over water mounts is that they do not dry out as quickly.

II. Semipermanent (nonhardening) mounts

A. *Lactophenol* (This is the best semipermanent mounting medium for fungi.)

Phenol	20 g
Lactic acid	20 g
Glycerin	40 ml
Distilled water	20 ml

Dissolve the above ingredients by heating in a hot-water bath. Add a small amount of cotton blue or acid fushsin to stain fungi (0.5 g or a few granules in a dropping bottle). Some fungi stain best with cotton blue and others stain best with acid fuchsin.

1. Mounting living aquatic fungi: Mount the fungus in water on a slide. Add a cover glass (cover slip) and observe to be sure the material is good enough for preservation. Add 2 or 3 drops of lactophenol at the edge of the cover glass, under which it will soon be drawn. Thus, the fungus is mounted in dilute lactophenol. Now let the mount dry.
2. Mounting nonaquatic fungi: Either mount as above or mount the fungus directly in lactophenol and dry.
3. Mounting fungi from fixing solutions: Mount directly in lactophenol and dry.
4. Drying: Dry slides for several weeks, preferably in an oven or on a slide-warming stage at 50°C. (As the lactophenol dries it will decrease in volume. If this results in an air space under the cover glass, add more lactophenol and continue to dry.)
5. Stabilizing mount: Clean the dried slide at the edges of the cover glass and seal by ringing the cover glass with a thick layer of clear fingernail polish (lacquer).

B. *Glycerin and glycerin jelly* (especially good for blue-green algae, protozoa, small invertebrates, sporangia, etc.)

1. Bring material to distilled water.
2. Stain in 1 per cent aqueous aniline blue for 2–3 minutes.
3. Wash out stain; then fix stain for 15 minutes in 1 per cent HCl; wash out HCl with 2 rinses of distilled water.
4. Transfer to 10 per cent glycerin. Place in incubator or on warming stage at 40°C to hasten the evaporation of water and concentration of glycerin.
5. Mount in glycerin and seal with nail polish, or mount in glycerin jelly:

Distilled water	30 ml
Gelatin	5 g
Glycerin	35 ml
Phenol (dissolved in 10 drops HOH)	5 g

Dissolve the gelatin in the water at 35°C; then add the other ingredients. Filter while still warm through glass wool or fine silk (or coarse filter paper?).

6. To make a slide from material dehydrated by the glycerin method, place a piece of glycerin jelly about as large as a matchhead on a clean, dry slide, and warm until melted.

7. Remove a quantity of material from pure glycerin, draw off excess glycerin with a piece of filter paper, and put the material into the melted jelly. Add a warmed cover slip carefully.
8. Allow to cool away from heat. Seal with nail polish.

III. Permanent mounts

A. *Stem sections—simple technique*
  1. Safranin—Methyl Green Stain Technique:
     a. Stain fresh or fixed sections in Safranin O solution (0.5 g of Safranin in 100 cm^3 of 50 per cent alcohol) for 3–5 minutes.
     b. Rinse in 70 per cent EtOH.
     c. Stain in methyl green solution (0.5 g in 100 cm^3 of 70 per cent EtOH) for 20–60 seconds.
     d. Rinse in 95 per cent alcohol for 2 minutes.
     e. Proceed as outlined for balsam mount. (This double stain colors lignified walls red and walls only with cellulose green.)
  2. Canada balsam or "Permount" or other mounting:
     After the proper stain or stains:
     a. Wash out excessive stain with 95 per cent alcohol (EtOH) for 2 minutes. This also takes out much of the water (dehydrates).
     b. Dehydrate further by placing the sections in absolute alcohol for 1 minute.
     c. Clear in xylol for 1 minute.
     d. Mount in Canada balsam that has been thinned with xylol (or mount in Permount) and add a cover glass.

B. *Stem sections—more complicated technique*
  1. Fix $\frac{1}{2}$-in. pieces of stem material in FAA:

95 per cent EtOH	50 ml
Glacial acetic acid (or propionic acid—FPA)	5 ml
Formalin (i.e., formaldehyde solution, about 40 per cent	10 ml
Distilled water	35 ml

  This fixative is the standard fixative for cytological study of plant materials. It is a 50 per cent alcohol solution; occasionally it is made up as a 70 per cent alcohol solution. Materials may be stored in this fixative for years.
  2. (No need to wash out the fixative.) Cut sections and put into 50 per cent alcohol.
  3. Stain 10 minutes (or more, depending on the material) in 1 per cent Safranin O, in 50 per cent EtOH, or in

Safranin O	2 g
Methyl Cellosolve (ethylene glycol monomethyl ether)	200 ml
95 per cent EtOH	50 ml
Sod. acetate	2 g (to intensify)
Formalin	4 ml (mordant)

  Methyl Cellosolve is frequently used to dissolve alcoholic stains.
  4. Rinse in distilled water to remove excess stain. Safranin has a tendency to overstain, hence:

5. Differentiate in acidified 50 per cent alcohol [or in a saturated (0.5 per cent) solution of picric acid], 5 drops HCl/100 ml, for 2 minutes.
6. Transfer to 70 per cent EtOH containing a few drops of NH_4OH for 5 minutes.
7. Counterstain in 1 per cent fast green made up in equal parts of methyl Cellosolve and 95 per cent alcohol for 5 minutes.
8. Absolute alcohol, plus two changes; 2 minutes, 5 minutes, 2 minutes.
9. Absolute alcohol:xylene series, 5 minutes each:
   absolute alcohol : xylene

3	:	1
1	:	1
1	:	3

   Pure xylene, two changes.
10. Mount in piccolite, or some other xylene-soluble mountant (like Canada balsam).

C. *Whole mounts of delicate algae and fungi*
   1. Fixation:
      a. Stock solution of FAA or FPA:

50 per cent ethyl alcohol	90 ml
Glacial acetic acid or	
propionic acid	5 ml
Commercial formalin	5 ml

      Note: Decoloration of algae can be prevented by adding 1 g of copper acetate per 100 ml of solution.
      b. For use: FAA or FPA   1 part
                   Water   1 part
      c. Fixation time: 12 hours or longer.
   2. Wash: Place material on a 1-in. square of filter paper in a stendor dish, and wash two times with distilled water. The filter paper prevents excessive loss and more delicate handling of material. Use 3 droppersful for each washing. Remove the solution to be discarded with a dropper.
   3. Staining:

10 minutes		*15 minutes*
1 per cent aqueous aniline blue	or	Harris's hematoxylin
		(for formula, see 10)

   4. Wash: Three rinses in distilled water.
   5. Differentiation:

1 per cent HCl	15 minutes–1 hour	Acidified water 2 minutes
		(5 drops/100 ml)

   6. Rinse: Distilled water   Ammoniated tap water
                                    (2 drops/100 ml)
   7. Dehydration, 1–2 minutes each:
      a. 5 per cent EtOH b. 10 per cent EtOH c. 15 per cent EtOH d. 20 per cent EtOH e. 30 per cent EtOH f. 40 per cent EtOH g. 50 per cent EtOH.
      Continue dehydration in standard TBA (tertiary butyl alcohol) series: 5 minutes each (if stained with aniline blue, only 3 minutes).

	H_2O	95% EtOH	TBA	Abs. EtOH
h.	50 ml	40 ml	10 ml	—
i.	30 ml	50 ml	20 ml	—
j.	15 ml	50 ml	35 ml	—

k.   —   45 ml   55 ml   —
l.   —   —   75 ml   25 ml
m.   Pure TBA, three changes, 5 minutes each

8. Transfer dehydrated material to a 10 per cent solution of balsam in TBA.

9. Allow TBA to evaporate from TBA-balsam mixture, until consistency is greater than the mounting medium (balsam is sold as a 50 per cent solution in xylene), in order to prevent plasmolysis when mounting in a drop of the mountant.

   If the TBA–balsam mixture is first placed in a 1-ounce jar, half-full, and allowed to evaporate for 24 hours, then slightly concentrated balsam can be transferred to a 60- by 15-cm (small) petri dish and allowed to evaporate further. The proper consistency will be reached after 5–8 hours.

10. Note: Harris's hematoxylin (self-mordanting)
    1 liter of 50 per cent alcohol
    1 g of aluminium chloride
    2 g of hematoxylin crystals
       Heat on water bath until dissolved. Add 6 g of mercuric oxide (use only the red powder).
       Filter. Add 1 ml of HCl.

D. *Whole mounts of cleared leaves.* Use either fresh, fixed, or dried leaves.

   1. Wash fixed material thoroughly to remove fixative. Dry and fresh material should be boiled 10–15 minutes in 70 per cent alcohol on a water bath.

   2. Transfer whole leaves to 5 per cent NaOH (for thick leaves or rapid clearing) or 2.5 per cent for thinner material to remove cell contents and soften cell walls. Let stand 3–5 days (process can be accelerated with heat). Leaves should be opaque. Brown stains are removed later by bleach.

      Since the NaOH softens cell walls, delicate trichomes such as the peltate scales in *Eleagnus* will come off; material such as this should be cleared as rapidly as possible.

   3. Rinse four times in distilled water, 10 minutes each.

   4. Bleach with full-strength Chlorox, several seconds to 5 minutes (but no longer, since leaf tissue disintegrates).

   5. Wash four times in distilled water to remove bleach, 10 minutes each.

   6. Dehydration series, 15–30 minutes each.
      30 per cent EtOH
      50 per cent EtOH
      70 per cent EtOH
      95 per cent EtOH
      absolute EtOH; change should be left overnight.

   7. Stain in 1 per cent Safranin O in absolute alcohol:xylene, 1:1, for 15 minutes to 1 hour, depending upon the material. Destain in absolute alcohol:xylene, 1:1.

   8. Final clearing to render material transparent: xylene plus a few drops absolute alcohol. Then transfer to pure xylene, and one change, $\frac{1}{2}$-hour each.

   9. Mount in xylene soluble medium such as piccolite.

      For more precise work, material should be left in each solution 4–5 hours; bleaching should be done in chloral hydrate (250 g/100 ml of water, allowing 2 days to dissolve).

Cleared leaves, because of the removal of cell contents and staining of lignified tissue, show venation patterns, and in some instances guard cells, specialized cells, and occasionally some types of trichomes and inclusions that retain the stain.

Project **13**   Making replicas of
leaf surfaces

Contents

Introduction

Leaf surfaces offer an interesting array of features that are fascinating to observe. The features may or may not be of use taxonimically—depending on the group of plants. These features are

A. *Stomates.* Usually present on lower surface only in dicots; on both surfaces in monocots.
B. *Arrangement of guard cells.* Of different types; may be distributed in clusters, or scattered; may or may not be oriented to the main axis of the leaf.
   1. Anomocytic type: several ordinary epidermal cells arranged around the stoma. Examples: Ranunculaceae, Ericaceae.
   2. Anisocytic type: three subsidiary cells, one distinctly smaller than the other two. Example: Cruciferae.
   3. Paracytic type: one or more subsidiary cells flank the stoma parallel with the long axis of the guard cells. Examples: Rubiaceae, *Vaccinum, Gaylussacia.*
   4. Diacytic type: one pair of subsidiary cells with their common walls at right angles to the long axis of the guard cells. Example: Caryophyllaceae.
C. *Shape of epidermal cells.* May differ from upper to lower surface in size and shape; size and shape are environmentally influenced: sinuous-walled epidermal cells are more often characteristic of the lower surface of species growing in damp habitats, whereas straight-walled cells are more common in species in dry habitats.
D. *Specialized cells*
   1. Papillose: especially in lower epidermis; in some cases confined to cells surrounding stomates. Examples, certain species of *Celtis* (hackberry), *Kalmia latifolia* (mountain laurel).

71

2. Bulliform cells (like blisters): grasses.

E. *Ornamentation of the cuticle.* Cuticular patterns: cuticle may be smooth (no pattern), have striations limited to cells surrounding the stomates, have intra-cullar striations, or may completely obscure the outline of epidermal cells except for the guard cells.

    1. Cuticular patterns, if present, may occur on the lower surface only, or on both surfaces.

    2. Striations radiate from stomates (sometimes) or from hairs; striations run longitudinally above veins.

F. *Trichomes* (hairs, etc.): *unicellular or multicellular*

    1. Hairs: *Rhododendron, Solanum, Halesia.*

    2. Scales: *Eleagnus,* hickory, walnuts.

    3. Glands: stalked or sessile *(Gaylussacia, Rhododendron, Lyonia).*

Project

I. Preparation of replicas

A. Fresh or dried leaves may be used.

B. If leaves are thin, they should be fastened to a piece of tape (masking tape) to prevent curling.

C. With a glass rod, apply a coating of USP Flexible Collodion to the surface of the leaf and allow to dry thoroughly.

D. Peal off the collodion replica with forceps. Trichomes will adhere to the replica and can be removed in this way and the surface recoated with collodion to see surface structure.

E. Cut replica into small flat pieces; mount in air, attaching a cover slip with a dab of mounting medium at the corners of the cover slip.

Project 14   Squash or smear techniques for studying chromosomes

Contents

Introduction

In this project are directions for staining and squashing plant tissues. You will stain root tips with acetocarmine and the Feulgen reaction for detecting DNA in chromosomes and for the study of mitosis. You will learn how to prepare pollen mother cells of anthers and spore mother cells of moss sporophytes for studying meiosis. Finally, directions for making permanent slides from squash preparations are given.

Project

I. Onion root tips *(Allium)*

A. *Acetocarmine technique for studying mitosis*
Introduction. Many variations of this method have been devised to study the dividing plant cell by squashing macerated tissues between cover slip and slide and staining with suitable dyes. Root tips are a convenient source of cells in mitotic division and are used here with acetocarmine dye.

The use of the alkaloid, colchicine, also facilitates the study of chromosomes. Colchicine is an extract of the autumn crocus, *Colchicum autumnale*. When freshly excised root tips are placed in 0.1–0.2 per cent aqueous colchicine for several hours, spindle formation in dividing cells is inhibited, effectively halting mitosis at metaphase. In addition, the chromosomes become abnormally shortened. Colchicine treatment thus facilitates both the counting of chromosomes and the study of chromosomal morphology.

1. Materials
    a. Acetocarmine

Glacial acetic acid	45 ml
Distilled water	55 ml
Carmine, alum lake	2 g

    Combine acetic acid and water and bring the material to a boiling temperature. Allow the solution to cool slightly and add carmine, very slowly, to prevent foaming. Heat gently for 30 minutes, preferably using a reflux condenser. Cool and filter. Some persons prefer to add iron to the stain. This may be done by placing a rusty nail in the solution while refluxing, but care must be taken not to overdo this and bring about precipitation of the stain. A better method is to add a small pinch of ferric acetate to the stain solution while refluxing.

    b. Acid–alcohol (for clean slides)

95 per cent ethyl alcohol	99 ml
Concentrated HCl	1 ml

    c. Carnoy's solution

Glacial acetic acid	10 ml
Chloroform	30 ml
Absolute alcohol	60 ml

    Materials should be transferred to 70 per cent ethanol after 24 hours fixation in Carnoy's solution.

    d. Colchicine

    Colchicine solutions are prepared in various concentrations by dissolving in distilled water. (Be very careful when you prepare colchicine solutions. Colchicine is poisonous!)

    For plants, commonly 0.5 per cent solution.

    For animal tissue cultures, 0.02 per cent solution.

2. Procedure
    a. Snip off all the root tips that have grown out from the base of the onion since it was placed in water culture. (Note: For the best way to grow onion root tips to obtain the highest number of mitotic figures, refer to Willey's *Microtechniques*, cited in Project 9, p. 55. Onion bulbs are often chemically treated to prevent sprouting in storage, and they usually provide a very poor yield of new roots. Onion sets are much better by far.) Use a razor blade and detach the roots at the base to eliminate later collection of root stumps, which might be confused with normal root tips. Discard those roots that are longer than 2 cm. Place half in 0.2 per cent colchicine and the remainder in Carnoy's solution. Be sure that the root tips do not become dry at any time during this process or in later steps. Be cautious in the use of colchicine. It is poisonous.

    b. After some hours in Carnoy's solution, remove four root tips and place them in the 1:1 alcohol:HCl macerating solution. Time this step carefully and at 2-minute intervals remove the root tips to vials containing 45 per cent acetic acid and marked 2, 4, 6, and 8 minutes. The root tips should remain in 45 per cent acetic acid for at least 15 minutes.

c. Place a small drop of acetocarmine on a clean slide and transfer the root tip macerated for 2 minutes into the carmine. Use the fine-pointed needle (made from an insect pin clamped in the chuck of an inoculating needle) to remove the terminal 1 mm of root tip. Discard the rest of the root, adding additional acetocarmine to the tip if necessary. Hold the tip with a Nichrome dissecting needle and tease it apart with a steel needle. You will note that the acetocarmine turns slightly purple during the teasing process. This is advantageous since it intensifies the staining reaction with chromatin. If, however, exposure to the steel needle is prolonged, unnecessarily, the dye will form a dark precipitate that ruins the preparation. Proceed with care.

d. Lower a clean cover slip over the root-tip tissue, adding acetocarmine to fill out the space under the cover. Carefully invert the slide over a clean paper towel and press gently down to flatten the cells under the cover slip. Do not let the slide slip sideways!

e. Heat the slide gently, specimen side up, over an alcohol flame to differentiate the staining (the chromosomes become more deeply stained and the cytoplasm should clear), but take care not to boil the acetocarmine preparation!

f. Tap the cover slip with the rubber tip of a pencil to further flatten the cells. Take care not to displace the cover slip laterally.

g. You may at this point wish to ring the cover slip with gum-mastic paraffin, using a hot needle to seal the edges.

h. Examine the slide under the microscope, using a green filter for greater clarity. If the cells are clumped and seem not to be flattened, discard the slide and repeat the entire procedure using the root that was macerated 4 minutes. If this one is not satisfactory, perhaps the root tips that were macerated for longer periods will prove satisfactory. Usually, however, prolonged maceration results in failure of the nucleus and chromosomes to take up the stain.

Do not try to make slides by the assembly-line technique. Make them one at a time and do not try to hurry. Save your best slides for later study. If they are to be kept for more than 2 or 3 days, it is best to place them in a petri dish containing a small bit of wet paper. Petri dish and slides should then be stored in a refrigerator. Normally the slides improve in contrast during the first several days after they are prepared!

i. Root tips placed in colchicine should be removed after 6 hours and placed in Carnoy's solution to fix. Following fixation they may be squashed and stained in acetocarmine in the same way as ordinary root tips.

j. (Optional) The chromosome number of the common onion, *Allium cepa*, is $2n = 16$. Find a cell in a colchicine-treated root tip clearly showing all 16 chromosomes, preferably well separated from each other. Make a camera lucida or careful freehand drawing of the chromosomes and prepare an idiogram. An idiogram is a diagrammatic representation of a chromosome complement arranged serially in order of size. The position of centromeres and other peculiarities should be shown.

B. *Feulgen reaction for DNA, chromosomes, and studying mitosis*

Introduction. The Feulgen stain in its original form was devised by Robert

Feulgen in the early 1900s. The stain is a decolorized basic fuchsin, and it reacts specifically with DNA to form a crimson-colored complex. In this exercise the stain will be used first to show the complex formation with purified DNA, and then to localize DNA within the cells of onion root tips.

1. Materials

   Feulgen stain (dissolve 1 g of basic fuchsin in 100 ml of boiling water; cool to 50°C and filter; add 10 ml of 1 N HCl followed by 0.5 g of potassium metabisulfite).

   Carnoy's fixative (ethanol: glacial acetic acid, 3:1)

   70 per cent ethanol

   1 N HCl

   DNA standard

   Oil-immersion lens

   Glass slides, cover slips, needles, etc.

   Hot-water bath

   Test tubes

   Small vials with caps

   Young roots of onion (*Allium*)

2. Procedure

   a. Place 5 ml of DNA standard solution into a test tube. Add 5 drops of 1N HCl and heat in a hot-water bath until all precipitate has dissolved. Add 5 drops of the Feulgen stain and wait for the color complex to appear. Describe it.

   b. Cut young onion roots and place in Carnoy's fixative overnight. Transfer and store in 70 per cent ethanol. Prior to staining, place roots into hot 1N HCl for about 5 minutes. Replace HCl with fresh 70 per cent ethanol.

   Place roots into a vial of Feulgen stain. Shake occasionally and wait for deep color to appear. Cut away the most intensely stained portion of the tip. Place this in a drop of water on a glass slide, cut into two portions, and smear each separately. Affix cover slip and observe first under low power, then under high dry, and then under oil. (Note: It may be necessary to try again if at first you don't succeed.)

   Note: Refer to the previous exercise (A) for an amplification of certain details of procedure.

   What percentage of the cells are actively dividing? Locate various mitotic chromosome configurations. Can you count the chromosomes in any of the cells?

II. **Pollen mother cells of anthers**—acetocarmine technique for studying meiosis

   A. *Selection of anthers.* When choosing anthers for pollen mother cells in the process of meiosis, remember that there are definite daily cycles of division in some plants. Usually specimens fixed about midday are good for meiosis. Anthers taken about 2 weeks before they would normally shed any pollen are usually good. A test squash will soon show whether the desired stages are present. *Tradescantia* (spiderwort) and *Zebrina* (wandering jew) are excellent.

   B. *Procedure* (refer back to I.A. for certain details of the procedure)
      1. Fix anthers in Carnoy's solution. (Large anthers should be cut open at one end to enhance the fixation process.)

2. The fixed material is placed in a drop of acetocarmine on a slide and squashed with a scalpel. If it does not squash readily, it can be teased out with mounted needles into longitudinal strips. Anthers can be cut in half and the pollen mother cells squeezed out by pressing from the uncut end with a curved mounted needle. The debris is removed from the slide and a cover glass applied.

The slide should be gently heated by passing it over the flame of an alcohol lamp. The preparation must not boil.

Chromosomes in acetocarmine squashes show up more clearly if viewed through a green filter.

III. **Spore mother cells of moss sporophytes**—aceto-orcein technique for studying meiosis

(Modified from the method of L. E. Anderson, Duke University)

A. *Materials*
1. Carnoy's fixative: ethanol: glacial acetic acid, 3:1.
2. Aceto-orcein dye:
   Orcein, synthetic (National Biological Stains) 1.5 g
   45 per cent acetic acid   100.0 ml
   Shake well, filter, store. Filter periodically. Stain improves with age!
3. a. Select a moss bearing sporophytes that are well formed. Meiosis and consequent formation of spores are delayed in mosses until the capsule is fully formed. Examine them and look for a faint reddish-brown color in the annulus. This is the indicator for the "cytological condition" in mosses. The capsules have a glossy-translucent appearance. (*Mnium* and *Aulacomnium* are two excellent genera for this technique. The chromosomes stain well and the spore mother cells spread easily. The chromosomes themselves separate well!)
   b. Fortunately for the moss cytologist, meiosis is delayed in moss capsules until the capsule is fully formed. One can observe color changes in the capsule as it matures and can recognize (or discover) the proper stage for meiotic divisions. In most capsules the following color changes occur in the wall of the capsule: grass green, shiny green, lettuce green, dullness, translucent, yellowish, completely yellow, and muddy! Sometime between the dull to translucent stage the annulus becomes colored! This is often an excellent indication that the capsules are in "cytological condition."
B. *Procedure.* The following technique should yield excellent results if you utilize care and patience in the preparation of slides. Never attempt to mass produce slides! Never allow material to dry once you have begun the process.
1. Select a well-formed healthy capsule with faint color in the annulus. Use this as a guide for obtaining the proper stage. You may find that experimenting is necessary!
2. Place the capsule on a slide. Thoroughly cleanse of dirt, sand, etc., by flooding with fixative. Scrape the capsule very lightly, if necessary, with a scalpel. Take care not to remove the operculum.
3. Remove the calyptra (if present) with pointed forceps. Move the capsule to a clean slide and flood immediately with more fixative.

4. Cut off the operculum with a fine needle or clean razor blade. Make the cut just below the annulus. Keep flooded with fixative. Squeeze the columella out the cut end by applying pressure from the base of the capsule.
5. Remove the clinging mass of white spore mother cells from the columella and discard the columella. Remove all other debris.
6. Allow fixative to evaporate but leave moist. Do not let the spore mother cells dry out at this critical stage.
7. Apply 1 drop of aceto-orcein. Apply a cover slip gently.
8. With a flat object (new pencil eraser) press down on the cover slip. Do not allow it to slip. If you are not steady, turn the slide upside down on a paper towel and press the bottom of the slide, again taking care not to slip the mount. Here, you are attempting to obtain a single layer squash of flattened spore mother cells. If you squash too hard . . . the walls will break! You should now check your slide! Try again if necessary!
9. Seal with Vaseline or make the slide permanent by the dry-ice technique.
   Slides may be kept a few days without sealing if they are kept on moist filter paper in a petri dish or other chamber.

IV. Making permanent slides from squash preparations

A. *Materials*
1. Block of dry ice (solid CO_2).
2. Acetic acid, ethyl alcohol mixtures, 1:3 and 1:9 (one dropper bottle each per four students).
3. Absolute ethyl alcohol (one staining jar full per four students).
4. Absolute ethyl alcohol, xylol, 1:1 (one staining jar full per four students).
5. Clove oil, xylol, 1:3 (one staining jar full per four students).
6. Xylol (one staining jar full per four students).
7. Kleermount or Permount (in dropper bottles).

B. *Procedure*
1. Acetocarmine squashes can be made permanent, but the procedure requires patience. Place the slide on a piece of dry ice. When frost appears, pry off the cover slip with a razor blade. If cover slips have been wiped with silicone-treated paper, such as Bausch and Lomb Eye-eeze, they will usually come off cleanly. Immediately place the slide in the bottom of a petri dish and flood gently with 1:3 acetic acid, ethyl alcohol. Pour this off and replace with 1:9 acetic acid, alcohol. Gently lower the slide into absolute alcohol and in 10 minutes transfer the slide to a staining jar of clove oil–xylol. After 10 minutes in xylol the slide can be placed face up on a piece of paper towel and a cover slip may be mounted over the tissues in Kleermount or other mounting medium. Allow the slide to dry for 10–15 minutes before examining it under the microscope. If the preparation is clear without any trace of moisture under the cover slip, it may be put aside to dry further. Slides should not be stored vertically until they have dried for at least 1 week. If moisture is present in the preparation, return the slide to xylol until the cover slip falls off, then place the slide in ethyl alcohol and repeat the subsequent steps. Good luck!
2. Label the slide, noting the material, the date, technique, and name of the preparator.

V. **Wittman's aceto-iron-haematoxylin stain for chromosomes—combined with Hoyer's mounting medium**

A. *Plant materials.* This technique has been used successfully for meiosis in slime molds, *Tradescantia,* and other plants; for mitosis in such algae as *Oedogonium* and *Eremosphaera*; and for mitosis in onion, *Tradescantia,* and other plants. (For additional procedural information, see Willey's *Microtechniques,* cited in Project 9, p. 55.)

B. *Staining solution*
   1. Dissolve 2 g of haematoxylin (National Aniline, cert. No. NH 15 has been used with excellent results) in 50 ml of 45 per cent acetic acid.
   2. Add 0.5 g of iron alum (ferric ammonium sulfate).
   Notes: (1) The stain, prepared at room temperature, should not be used during the first 24 hours. (2) The stain keeps from 4–6 months when refrigerated.

C. *Hoyer's mounting medium*
   1. Dissolve 30 g of gum arabic in 50 ml of distilled water.
   2. Dissolve 200 g of chloral hydrate in this.
   3. Add 20 ml of glycerine.

D. *Procedure with algae*
   1. Place plant material directly in a drop of stain on a microscope slide for 2–20 minutes. Length of staining time varies with the organism. Chromosomes of *Eremosphaera* may stain in 2–3 minutes and those of *Oedogonium* may require 20 minutes.
   2. Drain stain from slide.
   3. Wash with 45 per cent acetic acid until all traces of stain precipitate are removed.
   4. Transfer material with a minimum of acetic acid to a drop of Hoyer's medium on a slide.
   5. Add a clean cover slip.

Part Three
Special cultural studies

The purpose of this part is to help you to have highly successful, intimate experiences with plants in culture. It is a text and manual combined.

To ensure your full success and high achievement, information and directions are given in great detail even though the procedures are really quite simple. The large number of drawings of developmental features, materials, and techniques help you to understand the way.

In Project 15 you will study the controlled development, life cycle, and environment of the zoosporic plant *Allomyces*. In Project 16 you will study the genetics and development of a mold that grows in nature on dung—*Sordaria*. In Project 17 you will study the wood decay mushroom *Schizophyllum*.

Project **15**   A zoosporic plant

Controlled development, life cycle,
and environment of a zoosporic plant:
Allomyces, water mold, a phycomycete

Contents

Introduction

Students find *Allomyces* to be an exciting microorganism. Although it is a stationary
plant, it has swimming parts. Although it is many celled, its body is composed of
branching filaments that are one cell in thickness; thus *Allomyces* is excellent for
easily observing cytological features of growth, differentiation, and sexual and
asexual reproduction. An added advantage lies in its type of life cycle, which is
typical for plants: a spore-producing phase alternating with a gamete-producing
phase.

   In nature *Allomyces* grows in water and in soil on plant and animal remains and
is relatively easy to collect. In the laboratory at ordinary room temperatures it grows
and develops slowly enough to allow plenty of time for detailed study, but rapidly
enough to follow its entire developmental and reproductive life in about 1 week.

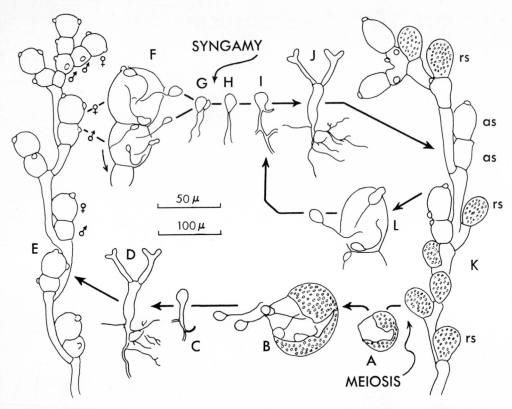

Fig. 15-1 Life cycle of *Allomyces arbuscula*.
(A) Germinating resistant sporangium with
outer wall split and a discharge papilla forming
on the inner wall. (B) Zoospores (meiospores)
emerging from the germinated resistant
sporangium. (C) Germling. (D) Young
gametophytic plant. (E) Hyphal portion of
mature gametophytic plant bearing male and
female gametangia. (F) Female and male gametes
emerging from a pair of gametangia.

(G) Gametes prior to fusing. (H) Biflagellate
planozygote. (I) Germinated zygote or diploid
germling. (J) Young sporophytic plant.
(K) Hyphal portion of mature sporophytic plant
bearing thin-walled asexual zoosporangia (as)
and heavy-walled resistant sporangia (rs).
(L) Zoospores (asexual zoospores) emerging from
a zoosporangium. *(Based on a figure in
Emerson, 1941.)*

Three types of life cycle have been discovered in *Allomyces*. Most interesting is
the long-cycled type (Fig. 15-1) in which sexual reproduction is accomplished
through the alternation of a haploid thallus (gametophyte) with a diploid thallus
(sporophyte). The *n* and *2n* vegetative thalli look alike (called isomorphic), but they
are easily distinguished when their reproductive structures develop. Three
commonly collected species display this alternation of haploid and diploid generations: *Allomyces arbuscula, A. X javanicus,* and *A. macrogynus.*

This project consists of three experiments. Although fullest understanding will
come by doing all three, each experiment stands alone. Although each can be done
easily without the others, Experiment 1 should be accompanied by either Experiment 2 or Experiment 3.

Experiment 1 will acquaint you with where *Allomyces* and other water molds
grow and with the simple but special technique for collecting water molds on "baits"
in soil-and-water cultures.

In Experiment 2 you will take *Allomyces* through its entire life cycle by a simple seed-in-water culture method. Also, you will learn how to grow *Allomyces* for drying and storing so that you can have your own viable dried material for use at a later time—even years later!

In Experiment 3 you will grow both the spore-producing phase and gamete-producing phase in nutrient broth and learn how to trigger the change from vegetative growth to reproductive growth. From your diploid culture you will see asexual zoospores differentiate inside developing sporangia, swim out and away, encyst, and germinate, and you may watch the development of the drought-resistant resting sporangia, where meiosis occurs. From your haploid culture you will see gametangia develop and discharge their motile gametes, and you will observe what may be your first view of the actual fusion of sex cells. Also you will see zygotes swim, encyst, and germinate.

The procedures are really quite simple, but information and directions are given in great detail to ensure your full success and high achievement.

Materials each student needs for doing the three experiments

Most of the materials are found in even modestly equipped laboratories. In addition, seeds for Experiments 1 and 2 are obtained from biological supply companies or from such local sources as grocery stores. Also available from biological supply companies are dried sporophytes (living) for Experiment 2, axenic cultures for Experiment 3 (either as stock cultures or in ready-to-use form), and culture media for Experiment 3 (either as ingredients or in ready-to-use form).

Necessary for all three parts

1. Compound microscope (preferably having as part of its optical components an oil-immersion objective lens).
2. Bottle of immersion oil with applicator (if an oil-immersion objective lens is available for use).
3. Microscope slides and cover slips.
4. Dropping bottle with distilled water.
5. One glass-marking pencil (for writing on culture dish lids).
6. One scalpel.
7. Two dissecting needles.
8. One forceps.

Desirable for all three parts

1. Dissecting microscope (with a glass stage and a mirror, allowing for observations with transmitted light).
2. Box of Kim-wipes or cloth towel.
3. One bunsen burner or alcohol lamp for flaming (flame sterilizing) implements.
4. (Optional) One screw-cap bottle of 70 per cent alcohol (for sterilizing implements).

For Experiment 1. Collecting soil, baiting soil-and-water cultures, identifying, and subculturing

1. Ten Whirl-pak plastic bags (or other suitable containers for soil collections).
2. A teaspoon or tongue depressor (or other suitable soil-digging tool).
3. Twenty-one 10-cm petri dishes (one for seed cutting, ten for baiting, and ten for subculturing). (Preferably sterile petri dishes.)
4. One single-edge razor blade (for cutting seeds).

5. Twenty hemp (or similar) seeds (for baiting). (Other suitable seeds: cucumber, pumpkin, squash, sunflower, and radish.)
6. Eight hundred milliliters distilled water (for soil-and-water cultures and for subcultures). (Preferably sterile distilled water.)
7. One plastic or glass wash bottle containing distilled water (for washing seed cultures of collected water molds prior to subculturing).

For Experiment 2. Life cycle starting with dried sporophyte

1. One piece of filter paper with dried sporophyte (inoculum).
2. Four 10-cm petri dishes (one for seed cutting, one for growing gametophyte from dried sporophyte, one for growing sporophyte from gametophyte, and one for drying sporophyte). (Preferably sterile petri dishes.)
3. Six hemp (or similar) seeds (substrate). (Other suitable seeds: cucumber, pumpkin, squash, sunflower, and radish.)
4. One single-edge razor blade (for cutting seeds).
5. One hundred milliliters distilled water (for growing *Allomyces*). (Preferably sterile distilled water.)
6. One plastic or glass wash bottle containing distilled water (for washing seed cultures prior to subculturing). (Preferably sterile distilled water in the wash bottle.)

For Experiment 3. Synchronous development of reproductive structures starting with agar plate cultures

A. *List of materials*
1. One 1-week-old sporophytic (2*n*) agar plate culture (for inoculating broth).
2. One 1-week-old gametophytic (*n*) agar plate culture (for inoculating broth and from which gametangia will be scraped).
3. Two razor blades.
4. One narrow spatula (for transferring mycelial agar cubes).
5. Fifty milliliters of sterile broth (for growing mycelia).
6. Two sterile, 10-cm petri dishes (for growing mycelia in broth).
7. One 10-cm petri dish (for making a slide humidity chamber). (Preferably sterile.)
8. Two pipettes (with rubber bulbs) (for removing broth and picking up germlings).
9. Three hundred milliliters of distilled water (for washing mycelial mats). (Preferably sterile distilled water.)
10. One filter paper disc (9 cm in diameter) (for making a slide humidity chamber).
11. One bunsen burner or alcohol lamp for flaming (flame sterilizing) implements.

B. *About sterile materials*
1. Agar culture plates of *Allomyces*. (These can be purchased from Carolina Biological Supply Co. and will be received in a condition ready for starting Experiment 3.) If you make your own agar plate cultures (starting with stock cultures), make media (see C for ingredients) and sterilize in Pyrex glassware in an autoclave or pressure cooker (15 lb of pressure for 15 minutes).
2. Culture dishes (petri dishes). Sterile, disposable, plastic culture dishes cost very little, but if you use glass culture dishes, either dry sterilize in an oven (175–190°C for 2–5 hours) or wrap them with paper or foil and autoclave or pressure cook (15 lb of pressure for 15 minutes).

3. Razor blade. Hold a single-edge razor blade with forceps, flame sterilize (use bunsen burner or alcohol lamp), and let it cool before using, making sure not to touch the blade's cutting part to any surface that is not sterile.
4. Transfer spatula. Flame sterilize (use bunsen burner or alcohol lamp).

C. *Ingredients of culture media* (commercially available)

1. YPSS Agar (Difco brand Emerson YpSs Agar):

Bacto-yeast extract	4.0 g
Soluble starch, Difco	15.0 g
Dipotassium phosphate	1.0 g
Magnesium sulfate	0.5 g
Bacto-agar	20.0 g
Distilled water	1 liter

2. PYG Broth (Difco brand Cantino PYG Broth):

Bacto-peptone	1.25 g
Bacto-yeast extract	1.25 g
Bacto-dextrose	3.0 g
Distilled water	1 liter

Cultures to be provided (commercially available)

(None for Experiment 1)

For Experiment 2. Life cycle starting with dried sporophyte

One dried sporophyte, a $2n$ thallus that had been grown on a halved hemp seed in water for 3 weeks to 1 month and then dried on filter paper in a petri dish and stored. (Only the resting sporangia—meiosporangia—survive drying, and many will remain alive in the dried condition for many years!)

For Experiment 3. Synchronous development of reproductive structures starting with agar plate cultures

Two agar plate cultures (1 week old). In petri dishes of sterile agar medium that had been poured thin (1–2 mm deep):
1. Gametophyte (n)
2. Sporophyte ($2n$)

Schedule

The days on which the procedures are to be carried out are given in the left margin of the directions on the following pages. The recommended schedule if all three parts are to be done is

First week: Do Experiments 1 and 2.
1. Collecting Soil, Baiting Soil-and-Water Cultures, Identifying, and Subculturing
2. Life Cycle Starting with Dried Sporophyte
Second week: Do Experiment 3.
3. Synchronous Development of Reproductive Structures Starting with Agar Plate Cultures.

Study directions

Study *Allomyces* during the next 2 weeks by following the directions outlined on the following pages. You will learn more if you make many large well-labeled drawings, make notes freely on your pages of drawings, and study the available literature. Figure 15–1 is a summary of the life cycle. The other figures show more details of structure, growth, development, and reproduction. Before you begin these experiments, carefully study these figures.

You will not be able to see all the cytological details shown in some of the figures unless your microscope is a very good one and is outfitted with an oil-immersion objective lens. Do not let this discourage you. You will have no trouble seeing the important features.

Project

I. Experiment 1. Collecting soil, baiting soil-and-water cultures, identifying and subculturing

Refer back to the section dealing with materials each student needs.

Day 1

A. *Collecting soil*
   1. Obtain ten or more containers for collecting soil. Whirl-pak plastic bags are excellent for this purpose, but other small plastic bags, paper bags, wide-mouth jars, etc., are quite satisfactory.
   2. Make ten or more collections of soil from different locations. Do not include leaf litter on the surface of the ground. A few teaspoons of soil from each location is plenty. *Allomyces* frequently grows on bits of dead organic matter in the upper inch of soil beneath cultivated shrubs. Give each collection a number, for future reference, and record the date and the specific location of each collection.

B. *Baiting soil-and-water cultures*
   1. Put 1 teaspoonful of soil in one side of a sterile petri dish. Spread out the soil so that it covers one half of the dish. Add about 35 ml of sterile distilled water to the other half of the dish. Make sure that all the soil is fully covered with water.
   2. Put twenty or more seeds in a sterile petri dish and cut the seeds in half with a single-edge razor blade.
   3. Bait each of your soil-and-water cultures by submerging four seed halves on the side of each culture where there is no or very little soil.
   4. With a glass-marking pencil put the collection number and date baited on each culture dish lid.

Days 3–7

C. *Identifying.* In from 2 days to 1 week, water molds growing out from some of the seed halves will appear. Often the most commonly collected water mold in soil-and-water cultures baited with seeds is *Achlya* or some other genus, but there is a chance that you have *Allomyces*. Even if you do not collect *Allomyces*, you should collect water molds of some sort. Thus, you will be successful in gaining a clear concept of where *Allomyces* lives in nature and will be able to surmise its role as a decay organism.

   How to identify *Allomyces*. Place your culture dish (lid off) on the stage of your microscope. Examine the mycelium only with the low-power ($\times 10$) objective lens; i.e., do not use the high-dry objective. *Allomyces* is distinct from other water molds by the following feature:

1. *Hyphae* that branch *dichotomously* and have *septa* (Fig. 15-6G). Other distinctive features are

2. If you have the gametophyte, it will develop *orange male gametangia* that are smaller than the colorless female game-tangia (Fig. 15-1E).

3. If you have the sporophyte, it will develop colorless asexual zoosporangia and usually many more *brown resting sporangia* (Fig. 15-1K).

D. *Subculturing*

1. After reproductive structures have appeared or begun to appear, with forceps take out a seed with its mycelial fringe and place it in a sterile petri dish.

2. Wash off contaminating bacteria and protozoa using a jet of sterile water (use wash bottle).

3. Place the washed mycelium in another sterile petri dish.

4. Add 20–30 ml of sterile distilled water.

5. Add two halved seeds (Four halves).

6. With a glass-marking pencil put the collection number and date subcultured on the dish lid.

II. Experiment 2. Life cycle starting with dried sporophyte

Refer back to the section dealing with materials each student needs.

Day 1   A. *Inoculating seeds with meiozoospores* (for growing gametophytes)

1. Place a piece of filter paper with a dried sporophytic thallus in a sterile petri dish.

2. Add about 20–30 ml of sterile distilled water.

3. Add two halved seeds (Four halves).

4. With a glass-marking pencil put the time and date on the dish lid.

Day 2   5. Study gametophytic thalli growing out from the halved
et seq.   seeds, intermittently starting after about 24 hours. (For some isolates, 4 days are required for gametophytic thalli to appear.)

Days 2–3   B. *Meiosporangial germination.* When hyphae first appear on the halved seeds, you know that R.S. (resting sporangium) germination has occurred and probably still is taking place.

1. Remove the filter paper (with germinating R.S.) and place it on a microscope slide.

2. Remove the old seed and add a cover slip to the R.S. still adhered to the filter paper.

3. Study with high dry (see Fig. 15-2a–j). Look for and draw
   a. Ungerminated sporangium.
   b. Sporangium discharging its meiozoospores.
   c. Empty sporangium after discharge (see Fig. 15-2k).

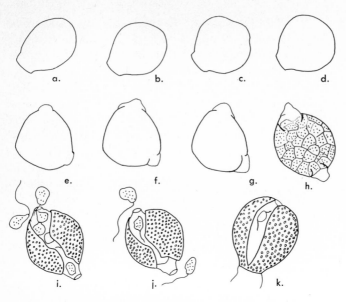

Fig. 15-2 Germination of the resistant sporangium (meiosporangium) and the release of meiozoospores. (a) Mature sporangium that has been in water about 20 minutes. (b)–(d) Pictures at three 2-minute intervals showing the rapid swelling of the sporangium. (e)–(g) Time intervals of about 10 minutes revealing the appearance and formation of the two discharge papillae developed from the inner, thin sporangial wall. The thick, pitted outer wall has cracked. (h) Forty-five minutes later. Cleavage of meiozoospores completed. (i) and (j) Spores escaping. The cracks in the thick outer wall become clearly visible. × 500. (k) Empty resistant sporangium, not the same as the one in the previous series. The pits in the outer wall and the discharge pore of the inner wall are clearly seen. × 560. *(Drawn from photomicrographs.) (Based on figures in Emerson, 1941, 1954.)*

Days 2–8   C. *Inoculating seeds with planozygotes* (for growing sporophytes)
  1. After the gametophytic thalli on seeds have matured gametangia, with forceps take out a seed with its mycelial fringe and place it in a sterile petri dish.
  2. Wash off contaminating bacteria and protozoa using a jet of sterile water (use wash bottle).
  3. Place the washed gametothallus in another sterile petri dish.
  4. Add about 20–30 ml of sterile distilled water.
  5. Add Four halved seeds (eight halves).
  6. With a glass-marking pencil put the time and date on the dish lid.
  7. Study sporophytic thalli, growing out from the halved seeds, intermittently starting after about 24 hours.

Days 21–28   D. *Growing sporophytes for drying and storing*
  1. Let your sporophytic cultures grow for 3 weeks to 1 month.
  2. Place a 9-cm disc of filter paper in a sterile petri dish.

3. Without washing the sporophytic thalli, with forceps place them on the filter paper.
4. With a glass-marking pencil put the date on the dish lid.
5. Leave the lid on while the sporophytic thalli dry.

III. Experiment 3. Synchronous development of reproductive structures starting with agar plate cultures

Refer back to the section dealing with materials each student needs.

    A. *Outline of schedule for Experiment 3*

        Day 1: Inoculate dishes of broth with sporophytic (2*n*) and gametophytic (*n*) mycelial agar cubes (see B.1 and C.1).

        Days 1–2: Study the 2*n* and *n* mycelia growing out from the agar cubes (see B.2 and C.2).

        Day 2: Wash both 2*n* and *n* mycelia growing out from the agar cubes (see B.3 and C.3 and study).

        Day 8 or anytime: Scrape gametangia off surface of an *n* agar plate culture and put scrapings in a drop of water for the study of gamete discharge and syngamy (see D).

    B. *Production of asexual zoosporangia and zoospores, from mycelium growing from agar blocks in nutrient broth*

Day 1

1. Inoculum
   a. With a sterile razor blade, cut 25 tiny, 1-mm cubes from the outer 5 mm of growth of sporophytic mycelium growing in a petri dish on agar. (The agar medium has been poured to a depth of about 1–2 mm and was inoculated 1 week ago.) Comment: The inoculum will also contain some mature sporangia, and some of these are likely to liberate zoospores that will germinate in the broth.
   b. With a narrow, sterile spatula, put the 25 mycelial-agar cubes in a 10-cm petri dish containing about 25 ml of broth (to a depth of about 4 mm).
   c. Record the time and date.

Days 1–2

2. For vegetative growth
   (Grow for up to about 18–24 hours.)
       Study: Examine your petri-dish culture (top off) with low power (compound microscope) intermittently for 6–24 hours. Record the time you make each observation. Also at each of these times, mount on a slide and study from high power mycelial growth from one of the agar blocks. (Do not return the block to the culture dish.)
   a. Vegetative cytology (see Fig. 15-3 a and b). Using oil immersion of a very thin mount of actively growing hyphae, observe the tip of a hypha and draw the following: lipid globules, nuclei, mitochondria, and vacuoles. The mitochondria tend to be very thin or filamentous. Farther back on a hypha observe the septum or cross wall. Look for a

relationship between the positions of septa and points of branching. Look for an oblique view of a septum and note that it is unevenly thickened and incompletely formed. (See Burnett, 1968, p. 22, Table 2.3 for the principal chemical components of the cell wall of hyphae.)

   b. Vegetative morphology. Notice especially the secondary or adventitious rhizoids growing out from the new mycelium. Note the differences in the rhizoids and the mycelium:
   (1) Monopodial vs. dichotomous branching (draw).
   (2) Determinant vs. indeterminant growth.
   (3) Anucleate vs. nucleate.
   (4) Aseptate vs. septate (draw).

Day 2

3. For zoosporangial differentiation and zoospore discharge
   a. After about 18–24 hours of mycelial growth in broth, wash the mats with distilled water as follows:
   (1) Pipette off the broth.
   (2) Nearly fill the petri dish with distilled water, let stand about 1 minute, and pipette off the wash water. Repeat two times (three washes in all).
   b. (1) Add about 12 ml of distilled water to the 10-cm petri dish containing the washed mycelial mats. (Record time.)
   (2) Leave for 2 hours and then start a series of observations.
   (Alternative Procedure):
   a. After about 18–24 hours of mycelial growth in broth, wash 15 of the mycelial mats as follows:
   (1) Nearly fill a 10-cm petri dish with distilled water.
   (2) Using forceps, gently remove from the broth culture, one at a time, 15 of the mycelial mats and place them in the dish of distilled water. (Leave the other 10 mycelial mats in the broth culture. They will continue to grow and will produce an abundance of resting sporangia.)
   b. (1) Pipette off the wash water (in the dish with the 15 mycelial mats).
   (2) Add about 12 ml of distilled water. Leave for 2 hours and then start observations.

Days 2–3

Study: Examine with the compound microscope intermittently between 2 and 5 hours after washing and also about 24 hours after washing.
   (1) Draw zoosporangia in the following stages of development, noting the changes that occur during maturation.
   (a) Presporangium stage: lipid accumulation in hyphal tip (Fig. 15-3b).
   (b) Sporangium delimitation state or granular stage: septum formation (Fig. 15-3c and d).
   (c) Lipid ringlet stage or gamete origin stage: lipid globules in a sphere around nuclei (Fig. 15-3e).

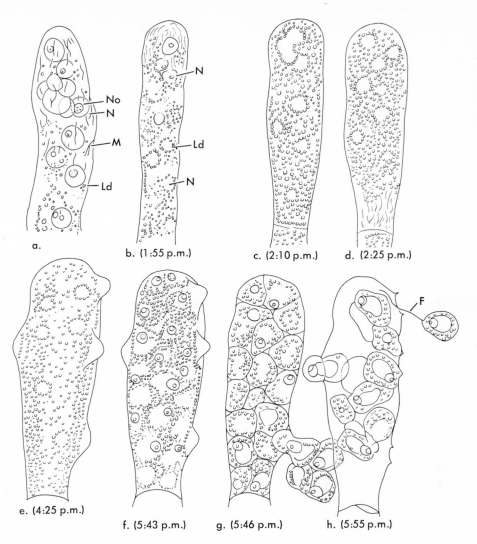

Fig. 15-3 Hyphal tip and zoosporogenesis. (a) Hyphal end showing mitochondria (M), nuclei (N), nucleoli (No), and lipid droplets (Ld). × 1525. (b) Cytoplasm and inclusions moving into the swelling apex. (c) and (d) Sporangium delimited by a septum or crosswall. (e) Maturing sporangium. Rings of lipid droplets surround nuclei. Central vacuole larger and more distinct. (f) Zoospores forming. Thin clear regions forming between spore initials. Cleaved spores are polyhedral. Note eccentric nucleoli, condensed nuclear cap, flagella not visible. (g) and (h) Exit of zoospores. Flagellum (F) formed inside sporangium. *(Based on figures in Ritchie, 1947.)*

     (d) Predischarge stage: zoospores cleaved and fully differentiated; flagella wrapped around spore bodies (Fig. 15-3f).

     (e) Zoospore discharge stage: (Fig. 15-3 g and h).

   (2) Mode of swimming and zoospore structure

     (a) Swimming (Fig. 15-4).

       Using low-power darkfield microscopy, observe the way zoospores swim by placing a drop containing

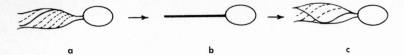

a   b   c

Fig. 15-4   Rapidly swimming zoospore as seen with darkfield microscopy. The "double image" (a and c) of the rapidly undulating flagellum changes to a "single image" (b) because of rotation of the swimming cell as it moves forward. Gametes and zygotes swim in the same manner.

zoospores on a slide and spreading the drop to make it thin. Do not put on a cover glass. (Directions for improvising a darkfield microscope with an ordinary light microscope are given in Project 9: V.)

Record your observations with drawings. How do you account for the "double image" (Fig. 15-4a and c) and the "single image" (Fig. 15-4b) made by the rapidly undulating flagellum?

(b) Internal structure (Fig. 15-5). Place a small drop containing zoospores on a slide and add a cover glass. Study from high dry and oil immersion. Look for the flagellum, nucleolus, nucleus, nuclear cap, and an anterior and a posterior cluster of lipid globules. Note that the nuclear cap is at the opposite pole from the nucleolus and place of flagellar attachment.

Fig. 15-5   (a) Living zoospore. (Drawn from a photomicrograph). × 3,400. F, flagellum; GM, giant mitochondrion; L, lipid globules; M, mitochondria; N, nucleus; NC, nuclear cap; NO, nucleolus; V, vacuole; R, rhizoplast. (b) Diagram of the *Allomyces* type of motile cell. *(Based on figures in Koch, 1961, 1969.)*

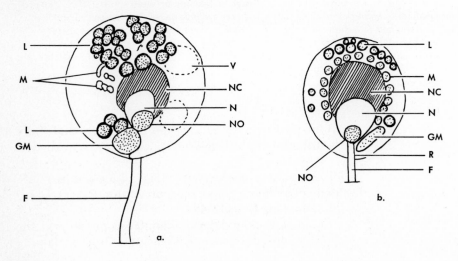

94

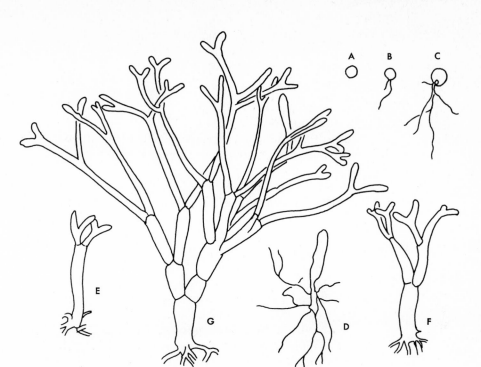

Fig. 15-6 (A)–(D) × 220; (E)–(G) × 55. States in the germination and development of a zoospore. (A) Quiescant and rounded spore about to germinate. (B) and (C) Young germlings with slender, tapering, rhizoidal germ tubes. (D) Older germling with rhizoidal system and stout hyphal tube. (E) and (F) Young plants. (G) Nearly mature thallus showing the characteristically regular dichotomy. Zygotes, zoospores, and R. S. zoospores (meiozoospores) of all long-cycled species of *Allomyces* develop in this manner. *(Based on a figure in Emerson, 1941.)*

(3) Spore germination. After about 24 hours notice the encysted spores and the germlings on the bottom of the dish. Mount, after picking up with a pipette. Draw, as observed with oil immersion. Look for germlings that have formed a single, tiny zoosporangium instead of a mycelium (monocentric thallus!) and draw (see Fig. 15-6).

C. *Production of gametangia, planogametes, and planozygotes from mycelium growing from agar blocks in nutrient broth*

Day 1

1. Inoculum

   a. With a sterile razor blade, cut 25 tiny, 1-mm cubes from the outer 5 mm of growth of gametophytic mycelium growing in a petri dish on agar. (The agar medium had been poured to a depth of about 1–2 mm and was inoculated 1 week ago.) Comment: The inoculum will have mature gametangia, and some of these will germinate when placed in broth.

    b. With a narrow sterile spatula, put the 25 mycelial-agar cubes in a 10-cm petri dish containing about 25 ml of broth (to a depth of about 4 mm).

    c. Record time and date.

Days 1–2

2. For vegetative growth
(Grow up to about 18–24 hours)

    Study: Examine your petri dish culture (top off) with low power (compound microscope) intermittently between 6–24 hours.

    a. After 6 hours in broth, some of the gametangia introduced with the inoculum may have germinated and a few may still be germinating. Quite a few planonts are seen swimming in the broth. There are no gametangia differentiated on the new vegetative hyphal tips.

    b. After about 16 hours, some of the hyphal tips of the new mycelial growth may have differentiated gametangia, and in the broth there may be quite a few sporophytic germlings growing from encysted planozygotes. Pick some of these up with a pipette and mount them. Draw, as observed at all magnifications. Note the bushy, primary rhizoidal system and the relatively broad basal cell from which arises the ordinary, dichotomously branching mycelium (mycelium with secondary or adventitious rhizoids) (see Fig. 15-7; also refer back to Fig. 15-6, A–G).

3. For gametangial differentiation, gametic discharge, and gametic fusion (syngamy: plasmogamy and karyogamy)

    a. After about 18–24 hours, wash with distilled water as follows:

      (1) Pipette off the broth.

      (2) Nearly fill the petri dish with distilled water, let stand for about 1 minute, and pipette off the wash water. Repeat two times (three washes in all).

    b. (1) Add about 7 ml of distilled water to the 10-cm petri dish containing the washed mycelial mats. (Record time.)

      (2) Leave for 2 hours and then start a series of observations. Comment: You will find that there are copious planogametes and planozygotes after 5–7 hours. Many planonts (swimming motile cells) are on the bottom of the dish, but all have flagella and are amoeboid. None are encysted. After 4 hours, planonts are sparse. After 24 hours, gametes and zygotes are still copious, and most of the gametangia have discharged.

Days 2–3

    c. Study: Examine with the compound microscope intermittently between 2–5 hours after washing and also about 24 hours after washing. Make as many drawings of the following as you can:

      (1) Anisogametangia. Note that the male is above the female (see Fig. 15-8a) in *AllomycesX javanicus* and *A. macrogynus,* while in *A. arbuscula* the male gametangium

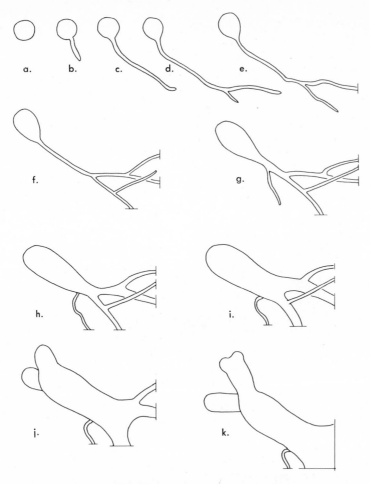

Fig. 15-7 Early development of the zygote during the first 10 hours. (a) The zygote has lost its flagellum and rounded up. (b) About 20 minutes later the first rhizoidal germ tube has appeared. (c)–(e) At 40-minute intervals showing growth and rhizoidal branching. (f)–(i) The intervals here are longer, about 100 minutes. Enlargement of the main body of the zygote is followed by elongation of the initial hyphal tube. (j) Sixty minutes after the previous figure showing the first dichotomy of the hyphal tube. (k) Second dichotomy after another 60 minutes. ×735. *(Drawn from photomicrographs.) (Based on figures in Emerson, 1954.)*

is below the female (Fig. 15-8, b–g). Only the male gametangia are pigmented, and the pigment (carotene) is localized in the lipid globules.

(2) Gametangial differentiation. Study gametangia in various stages of development (see Fig. 15-8, b–g). The maturation of gametangia is like that of asexual sporangia; therefore, refer back to the study directions in B.3 for the stages to look for. Draw at least two stages.

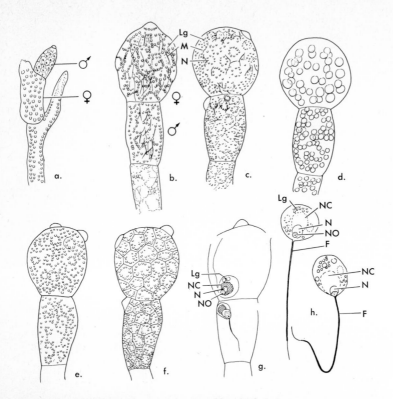

Fig. 15-8 (a) *Allomyces javanicus*, tip of hypha bearing a terminal golden-orange male gametangium and a subterminal colorless female gametangium. (b)-(g) Gametogenesis in *Allomyces arbuscula*. × 900. (b) Hyphal tip vitally stained with Janus green showing distribution of mitochondria and lipid granules. The ''granular stage'' of gametogenesis. Note the male and female gametangia. (c) Nuclei displaced peripherally and outlined by lipid granules. (d) ''Gamete origin'' state showing relative number and size of nuclei in gametangia. (e) ''Disappearance'' stage. Lipid granules more scattered. Outline of nuclei lost. (f) Cleaved gametes. (g) Male and female gametes each with a nucleus, nuclear cap, and lipid granules. (h) Female gametes. × 1875. Note whiplash type of flagellum. [*Figure 15-8(a) based on a figure in Sparrow, 1960; others based on figures in Hatch, 1935.*]

(3) Discharge. Prior to gametic discharge through one or more discharge pores, the discharge papilla is filled with a discharge plug. These expand and ultimately break or dissolve as the first few gametes are rapidly pushed out as a result of internal gametangial pressure. Later gametes come out slowly, partly swimming and partly amoeboidly. Draw at least one stage (see Fig. 15-3 g and h, which show zoospore discharge).

(4) Syngamy (see Fig. 15-9, a–e). Observe whether syngamy is anterior, posterior, or lateral. Try to observe

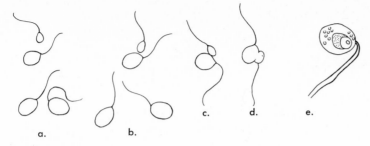

Fig. 15-9 Syngamy in *Allomyces macrogynus.* × 500. A sequence covering 14 seconds and showing (a) a male gamete approaching three females from above, (b) making contact with one of the females, (c) undergoing copulatory movements, and (d) beginning the actual process of syngamy. (e) Motile zygote. × 1,000. *(Drawn from photomicrographs.) (based on figures in Emerson, 1954.)*

that there is fusion of nuclei and nuclear caps but not of the flagella. Draw at least two stages.

(5) Gametes and zygotes (see Figs. 15-4, 15-5, and 15-8h). Look for the flagellum, nucleolus, nucleus, nuclear cap, and an anterior and a posterior cluster of lipid globules. Note that the nuclear cap is at the opposite pole from the nucleolus and the attachment of the flagellum. (The mitochondria here are small and subspherical, whereas in the vegetative hyphae they are long and linear.)

(6) After 24 hours, find and draw a germling sporophyte that has formed a single, tiny zoosporangium instead of a mycelium (monocentric thallus!).

D. *Synchronous production of planogametes and zygotes from gametangia growing on agar plates*

Slide technique. In gametangia formed on agar media, gametogenesis is temporarily delayed in the lipid ringlet stage (gamete origin stage). Many gametangia develop just above the agar surface and can be readily detached without damage to them.

Day 8 or anytime

With a scalpel, scrape gametangia off the surface of a 1- to 2-week-old agar culture. (Try not to scrape up any agar medium.) Mount the scrapings in a couple of drops of distilled water on a glass slide. Put the slide in a damp chamber (10-cm petri dish with a 9-cm wet filter disc) and leave for 1 hour and longer. After about 1–$1\frac{1}{2}$ hours (or even longer), when syngamy is well in progress (i.e., after many gametes have been discharged), make your study.

Study (see Fig. 15-10, a–e):

1. Make low and high dry observations on the uncovered material.
2. Add a cover slip for high dry and oil immersion observations of syngamy.

99

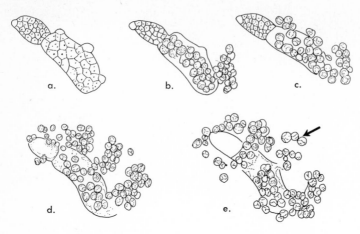

Fig. 15-10   Gametic release and syngamy. × 250. Scenes taken at about 1-minute intervals. (a) A pair of mature gametangia that have been in water for 55 minutes. A small discharge papilla shows at the apex of the darker epigynous male gametangium and three larger papillae are on the female. (b) Female gametes are starting to emerge from the bottom papilla. (c) Dishcarge is occurring from all three female papillae. (d) Male gametes are being released and can be detected by their smaller size. (e) Gametic fusions are taking place rapidly. Three zygotes are indicated by the arrow. *(Drawn from photomicrographs.) (Based on figures in Emerson, 1954.)*

Comment: This material is excellent for following the study directions in C.3.c (3), (4), and (5).

References

The most important references for you in the list below are preceded with an asterisk.

*ALEXOPOULOS, C. J. 1962. *Introductory Mycology,* 2nd ed. Wiley, New York. (pp. 100–104 and especially pp. 119–123, Fig. 45).

BURNETT, J. H. 1968. *Fundamentals of Mycology.* St. Martin's, New York. (p. 22, Table 2.3, principal components of hyphal cell wall) 546 pp., illus.

EMERSON, R. 1941. An experimental study of the life cycles and taxonomy of *Allomyces. Lloydia 4:* 77–144, 16 figs. (Figs. 3, p. 93, and 12, p. 122).

*————. 1954. The Biology of Water Molds. Chap. 8 (pp. 171–208) in *Aspects of Syntheses and Order in Growth,* ed. by D. Rudnick, Soc. Study Develop. and Growth, 13th Symposium. Princeton University Press, Princeton, N.J., Plates 2–8.

———— and E. C. CANTINO. 1948. The isolation, growth, and metabolism of *Blastocladia* in pure culture. *Am. J. Botany 35:* 157–171, 9 figs.

HATCH, W. R. 1935. Gametogenesis in *Allomyces arbuscula. Ann. Botany (London) 49:* 623–649, 33 figs. pp. 626–636 and Figs. 1–8.

KOCH, W. J. 1961. Studies of the motile cells of chytrids. III. Major types. *Am. J. Botany 48:* 786–788, 8 figs. Fig. 7.

*————. 1969. (Photomicrographs of living zoospores.) Studies of the motile cells of chytrids. 6. The Monoblepharidales and Blastocladiales types of posteriorly uniflagellate motile cell. *Mycologia 61 :* 422–426.

MACHLIS, L. 1953. Growth and nutrition of water molds in the sub-genus Euallo- myces. II. Optimal composition of the minimal medium. *Am. J. Botany 40:* 450–460, 12 figs. p. 45.

———— and E. OSSIA. 1953. Maturation of the meiosporangia of *Euallomyces*. I. The effect of cultural conditions. *Am. J. Botany 40:* 358–365.

*RITCHIE, D. 1947. The formation and structure of the zoospores in *Allomyces*. *J. Elisha Mitchell Sci. Soc. 63:* 168–206, plates 22–26.

*SPARROW, F. K. 1960. *Aquatic Phycomycetes,* 2nd ed. University of Michigan Press, Ann Arbor, Mich. pp. 613–630 and Figs. 40, 41.

Project **16**   A mold

Development and genetics of
Sordaria fimicola,
ascomycete dung mold

Contents

Introduction

Sordaria is an ascomycete that occurs in nature in dung. On the dung of such herbivorous animals as horses, rabbits, and field mice it forms vase-shaped ascocarps known as perithecia (Fig. 16-4). *Sordaria fimicola* is the commonest species and the one that most investigators have studied. Its sole reproductive spore is its meiospore, the ascospore, eight of which are produced within each ascus in a linear series (Fig. 16-4a).

Students find *Sordaria* to be an exciting organism for genetic study because it reveals easily how genetic segregation at meiosis takes place. All the products of meiosis persist and display themselves in the ascus as a linear, ordered series of ascospores, allowing one to see the order of genetic segregation. One can tell from simply looking at the ascospores in an ascus whether or not crossing over occurred (Figs. 16-4a, 16-8).

Sordaria is excellent for studying ascomycete development because it develops slowly enough to allow plenty of time for study but rapidly enough to complete its life cycle in 8 days. One can follow the entire developmental life of *Sordaria* in the laboratory at ordinary room temperatures on an agar culture medium containing ingredients commonly used for growing fungi.

Sordaria is classified in the Pyrenomycetes of the Euascomycetes and is a very close relative of another genetically famous fungus, *Neurospora*. Both genera are placed in the family Sordariaceae. They have the same number of chromosomes ($n = 7$) and similar chromosome morphology. When a heterothallic species of *Sordaria* is paired with a heterothallic *Neurospora* or *Gelasinospora*, a sexual reaction, the development of empty perithecia, may occur at the line of contact between opposite mating types, but no asci or ascospores are produced.

Although *Sordaria fimicola* is *homothallic,* it will cross by *hyphal anastomosis* (Fig. 16-1e) with color mutant strains and form hybrid asci. Hyphal fusion here is simply anastomosis, a very common phenomenon in Ascomycetes and Deutero-mycetes, and is not exactly sexual in nature. However, anastomosis does establish hyphae that are heterokaryotic (i.e., with genetically different nuclei for spore color). When these heterokaryotic hyphae form perithecia and the two nuclei of an incipient ascus have different genes for spore color (Fig. 16-3), the ascus is indeed a hybrid ascus, and the linear series of ascospores resulting from meiosis allows one to observe the results of first- and second-division segregation of the genes for spore color (Fig. 16-8).

This project consists of two experiments. Although fullest understanding will come by doing both, each experiment stands alone.

In Experiment 1 you will use a simple agar-block slide culture technique for following ascospore germination, mycelium development, hyphal anastomosis, and perithecium and ascospore development (Figs. 16-1 through 16-4).

In Experiment 2 you will make (or have provided for you) a cross plate and will examine hybrid asci and count them to determine the percentages of first- and second-division segregations (Figs. 16-5 through 16-8). From these percentages you can calculate the chromosome map distance of a spore color locus from its centromere (gene-to-centromere distance).

Cultures and culture media to be provided (commercially available, e.g., from Carolina Biological Supply Co.)

(Also refer to the lists of materials at the beginnings of the directions for Experiments 1 and 2.)

For Experiment 1: Slide-culture Study of Development: From Ascospores to Mature Perithecia. (Each student makes four slide cultures.)

Cultures: Two agar-slant stock culture tubes (stock culture tubes that are 2 weeks old or older will contain thousands of discharged ascospores:

1. Tan-spored (t) mutant strain.
2. Gray-spored (g) mutant strain.

SC culture medium: If you make your own SC (slide-culture) agar medium, use the following formula (the same one that stock cultures are grown on):

Difco cornmeal agar (dehydrated)	17.0 g
Glucose	2.0 g
Yeast extract	1.0 g
Distilled water	1 liter

Note: Pour the sterilized SC medium into standard size (10 cm wide and 15 mm deep) sterile culture plates (petri dishes), putting about 30 ml of culture medium in each dish. Mark SC on each of the poured plates.

For Experiment 2: Hybrid Ascus Study of Genetic Segregation and Crossing Over. (Each student makes or has provided for him two cross plates.)

Cultures:

A. If mature cross plates are to be provided, they must be 8–10 days old (not younger and not older). Usually 9-day-old cross plates are best.

B. If you inoculate your own cross plates, three agar plate cultures (about 5 days old) are needed:

    1. (+) Wild type (dark-spored).

    2. (t) Tan-spored mutant.

    3. (g) Gray-spored mutant.

    CR culture medium: If you make your own CR (cross-plate) agar medium, use the following formula:

Difco cornmeal agar (dehydrated)	17.0 g
Sucrose	10.0 g
Glucose	7.0 g
KH_2PO_4	0.1 g
Yeast extract	1.0 g
Distilled water	1 liter

    Note: Pour the sterilized CR medium into standard-size (9 cm wide and 15 mm deep) sterile culture plates (petri dishes), and pour them fairly deep (with about 30 ml of culture medium in each dish). Mark CR on each of the poured plates.

Schedule

    Below is the recommended schedule if both experiments are to be done, including the inoculation of cross plates for Experiment 2.

Day 1   1. Inoculate cross plates (Experiment 2).

                  2. Inoculate slide cultures (Experiment 1).

Days 1–8   Study ascospore-to-mature perithecium development using your slide cultures (Experiment 1).

Day 9 (8–10)   Make ascus counts for study of genetic segregation and crossing over (Experiement 2).

Study directions

    Study *Sordaria fimicola* during the next 8–10 days following the directions outlined in the experiments. You will learn more if you make many large well-labeled drawings, make notes freely on your pages of drawings, and study the available literature. Study the drawings in this project before you begin these experiments.

Project

I. **Experiment 1. Slide culture study of development: from ascospores to mature perithecia**

        A. *Making slide cultures*

            1. Materials (Refer back to the section dealing with cultures and media to be provided)

                a. Sterile water: Two 5-ml portions in two vials or test tubes.

                b. Cultures (2 weeks old or older agar-slant stock cultures):

                    (1) (t) Tan-spored mutant.

                    (2) (g) Gray-spored mutant.

c. Slide humidity chambers. Make four slide humidity chambers as follows: Put a V-shaped piece of glass tubing in each of four glass petri dishes, preferably deep ones (22 mm). Put an ordinary glass microscope slide on each of the V-shaped pieces of glass tubing. Put the tops on the petri dishes and dry sterilize the assembled slide humidity chambers. Let them cool.

d. Agar medium for cutting agar blocks to be inoculated. A standard size (9 cm in diameter) culture plate (petri dish) containing about 30 ml of sterile SC medium (slide-culture agar medium).

Day 1

2. Inoculation

a. Add 5 ml of sterile water to the surfaces of each of the two 2-week-old or older agar-slant stock cultures: (t) and (g).

b. Shake each to obtain an ascospore suspension.

c. Using these ascospore suspensions, make slide cultures of both strains as follows:

(1) Cut the plate of sterile SC agar medium into 10- to 15-mm squares (blocks).

(2) Remove the cover of a slide humidity chamber, and with a flame-sterilized spatula place a block of agar on the glass slide. Put cover back on. Repeat three times, i.e., put a block of SC agar on the slide in each of the other three slide humidity chambers.

(3) Inoculate two agar blocks with (t) ascospores and the other two agar blocks with (g) ascospores. (Inoculate by drawing a sterile loop with its load of spores over the surface of the agar several times.)

(4) Place a new, clean cover glass over one of the agar blocks inoculated with (g) spores and one with (t) spores. (For each of the two strains, one slide culture will have a cover glass on the inoculated agar and the other slide culture will not.)

(5) To the bottom of each culture dish, add several milliliters of sterile water. (The V tube will prevent wetting of the slide and the water will prevent drying out of the culture.)

(6) With a wax or other glass-marking pencil indicate on the top or lid of each slide humidity chamber: (a) the strain of ascospores: (t) or (g); (b) date; (c) time of day; (d) your name.

B. *Study of development: from ascospores to mature perithecia*

1. Supplement your study of later stages of development using perithecia growing in cross plates.

2. You can expect the following approximate schedule of development:

Stage 1 (2–6 hours) Germ tube or bleb stage

Stage 2 (6–12 hours) First hyphae stage

Stage 3 (12–36 hours) Branching mycelium stage
Stage 4 (36–48 hours) Ascogonium or protoperithecial initial
    stage
Stage 5 (2–3 days) Protoperithecium stage
Stage 6 (4–6 days) Meiotic perithecium stage
Stage 7 (7–8 days) Mature perithecium stage

Days 1–2   a. Ascospore germination and mycelial development (Stages 1–3) (Fig. 16-1). Study ascospore germination and mycelium development, including hyphal anastomosis.

Days 2–4   b. Ascogonium-protoperithecium development (stages 4 and 5) (Figs. 16-1e, 16-2). Most difficult to find will be the ascogonium or protoperithecial initial. (A gold ascospore goes to the person who finds one!) Ascogonia develop beneath the agar surface (beneath the dung surface in nature) and you are more likely to find them in your slide cultures lacking cover slips. Young ascogonia are short, curved to coiled, lateral hyphae perpendicular to main hyphae (Fig. 16-1e).

Days 4–5   c. Staining for nuclei in meiotic perithecia (stage 5). Use alcholic toluidine blue (0.5 per cent toluidine blue in 70 per cent ethyl alcohol). Usually, meiosis starts on the fourth day after inoculating a cross plate, and it is completed in all asci of a perithecium during the fifth to sixth day.

Remove a few perithecia in various stages of development from the culture and put them in a drop of water on a microscope slide. Put a cover slip on top and (with your thumb) press it lightly, without squashing the perithecia to bits, to crack the perithecial wall and release the developing ascal clusters. Using a needle, lift off the cover slip, leaving the material on the slide. Under a dissecting microscope, put another drop of water close by and make a trail of water with a needle. Using a needle tip, push the ascal rosettes or clusters to the clean drop of water. (These procedures are diagrammed in Fig. 16-6.)

After transferring several ascal clusters, free of debris, put a drop of 0.5 per cent toluidine blue dissolved in 70 per cent ethyl alcohol on the center of a clean cover slip and invert this over the preparation of rosettes. Blot off the excess liquid and examine. Nuclei will stain purple and be clearly seen with the oil immersion objective. Notice how large the meiotic nuclei are when compared with the ordinary nuclei, such as the two nuclei easily seen in the developing or young ascospores.

Days 4–8   d. Ascus and ascospore development (stages 6 and 7) Figs. 16-3, 16-4). Mount perithecia in various stages of development as described above (B.2.c), but do not add stain. Note the pseudoparenchyma tissue of the perithecial walls.

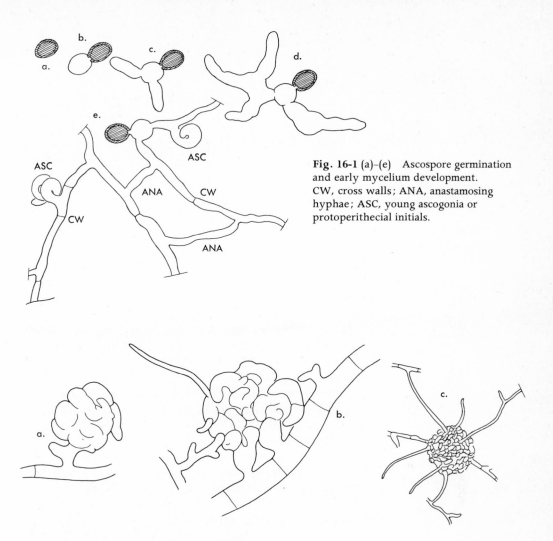

Fig. 16-1 (a)–(e) Ascospore germination and early mycelium development. CW, cross walls; ANA, anastamosing hyphae; ASC, young ascogonia or protoperithecial initials.

Fig. 16-2 (a)–(c) Protoperithecial development [(c) is at a lower magnification)].

Fig. 16-3 Development of young asci from a coil of an ascongonium within a young perithecium.
(a) Curved, multinucleate ascogonium becomes septate and dikaryotic. (b) Ascogonium proliferates croziers directly (no multicellular ascogenous hyphae). (c) Beginning of ascal multiplication by proliferation from a crozier.

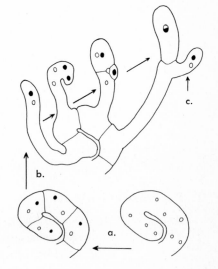

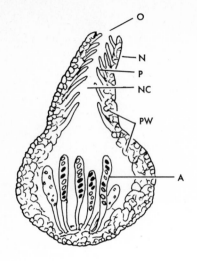

Fig. 16-4 Longitudinal section of a mature perithecium. O, ostiole; N, neck; P. periphyses; NC, neck canal; PW, perithecial wall (pseudoparenchyma); A, cluster of asci.

From oil immersion, study details of the three major stages of ascal development:

(1) Young, procleavage ascus containing clearly visible tiny lipid globules and vacuoles. Find a crozier (hook) at the base of the young ascus.

(2) Young ascosporic ascus: Find epiplasm; colorless young ascospores in linear sequence, each with a thin wall, vacuoles, and tiny lipid globules; and ascus apex thickened around the place (pore) where ascospores will be discharged.

(3) Mature ascus: Find epiplasm; mature ascospores with thick walls (inner wall pigmented and outer wall colorless or hyaline, much thicker, and "gelatinous"); and discharge pore.

Note that ascospores grow as they mature; a recently cleaved ascospore is smaller than a mature ascospore.

C. *Ascospore discharge.* In 10-day and older cross plates you can see masses of discharged ascospores adhered by their gelatinous walls to the inner surface of the culture dish lid.

Days 8–10   Try to observe the liberation or forcible discharge of ascospores from mature perithecia. Observe your slide cultures or cross plates and use low and high power of the dissecting microscope with reflected light. Note that the perithecial neck was meristematic for a time and was positively phototropic. Ingold, 1965, Chap. 3, gives excellent accounts of techniques used for experimenting and of the effects of light, temperature, and humidity on spore discharge in *Sordaria*.

II. Experiment 2. Hybrid ascus study of genetic segregation and crossing over

A. *Inoculation of cross plates*

1. Materials (Refer back to the section dealing with cultures and media to be provided)

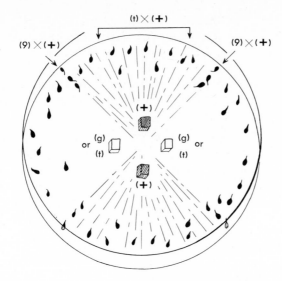

Fig. 16-5 How to inoculate and where to collect hybrid perithecia. Arrows indicate positions of the heaviest concentrations of hybrid perithecia.

    a. To be inoculated: Two standard size (9 cm in diameter) culture plates (petri dishes) each containing about 30 ml of sterile CR medium (cross-plate agar medium).

    b. Inoculum: The following three agar plate cultures, about 5 days old:

        (1) (+) Wild type (dark-spored).

        (2) (t) Tan-spored mutant.

        (3) (g) Gray-spored mutant.

Day 1

2. How to inoculate

    a. Cut the (+), (t), and (g) inoculum plates into $\frac{1}{2}$- to 1-cm-square blocks. Flame sterilize the cutting implement (transfer spatula, razor blade, or scalpel) before cutting each culture.

    b. Inoculate the two culture dishes of cross-plate medium as follows (see Fig. 16-5):

        (1) Toward the center of each agar plate place two blocks of (+) inoculum $1\frac{1}{2}$–2 cm apart.

        (2) In one of these plates, place two blocks of (g) inoculum the same distance apart and at 90° to the two (+) blocks.

        (3) In the other plate, do the same with two blocks of (t) inoculum.

    c. With a wax or other glass-marking pencil, indicate the identities of the inocula on the bottoms of the cross plates.

    d. On the top or lid of each cross plate, write: (1) cross made: (+) × (g) or (+) × (t); (2) date; (3) time of day; (4) your name.

B. *Making ascus counts*

    1. When to count. Although 8-day-old cross plates will have hybrid perithecia with ascospores mature enough for counting, 9-day-old cultures are better because more mature hybrid

asci are available for counting. Ten-day-old cross plates are also good, even though some asci are discharging their spores.

2. Positions of hybrid perithecia. Because *Sordaria fimicola* is homothallic, you must select only clusters of hybrid asci for observation. The position in your cross plates of the heaviest concentrations of hybrid perithecia are indicated in Fig. 16-5. Note that the positions for the (t) × (+) cross are different from the positions for the (g) × (+) cross.

Day 9
(8–10)

3. Making a slide for ascus counts. With a needle or scalpel remove several (6–8) mature perithecia from a region where hybrid perithecia occur in a cross plate (Fig. 16-5) and put them in a drop of water on a microscope slide. Put a cover slip on top and with your thumb press it lightly, without squashing the perithecia to bits, in order to crack the perithecial wall and release the ascal clusters. Lift off the cover slip, leaving the material on the slide.

Under a dissecting microscope, put another drop of water close by and make a trail of water with a needle. Using a needle tip, push the ascal clusters to the clean drop of water. (These procedures are diagrammed in Fig. 16-6.)

Now gently place a cover slip over the selected clusters. This causes each ascal cluster to spread out into a rosette. Sometimes it is helpful to gently press the cover slip with the tip of a needle over the ascal rosettes needle to further spread out the rosettes and make ascus counting easier.

4. Identifying a rosette of hybrid asci. From low power search your slide for a cluster of asci with spores of two colors in a single line (within an ascus) (see Fig. 16-7). All the asci in this rosette are likely to be hybrid asci.

5. Counting hybrid asci

   a. Identifying first- and second-division segregations. For each of your crosses, if no crossing over occurred, segregation of the gene for spore color took place during the first division of meiosis (MI) and the linear sequence of ascospores will be as in Fig. 16-8a (MI segregation = 4:4). If crossing over occurred, segregation took place during the second division of meiosis (MII) and the order of the ascospores will be as in Fig. 16-8b (MII segregation = 2:2:2:2 and 2:4:2).

   b. How to count

   (1) Count from high dry. From this magnification the different colors of even immature ascospores can be determined. (Very young ascospores have no pigment and are colorless.)

   (2) Count 200 hybrid asci. An orderly way to count the asci of an ascal rosette is indicated in Fig. 16-7. Go all the way around counting first-division segregations (4:4) first, and then go around again, this time counting second-division segregations (2:2:2:2 and 2:4:2).

110

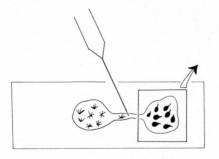

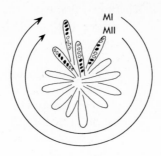

Fig. 16-6 Making a slide for studying ascus development and counting ascus genotypes (see directions).

Fig. 16-7 How to count hybrid asci. First count MI asci, in which segregation of the genes for spore color took place during the first division of meiosis [see Fig. 16-8(a)]. Next count MII asci, in which segregation took place during the second meiotic division [see Fig. 16-8(b)].

Fig. 16-8 (a) Ascospore sequences of hybrid asci in which there had been *no crossovers*. (b) Ascospore sequences of hybrid asci in which there *had been crossovers*. *(Figures 16-6, 16-7, 16-8 based on notes of L. S. Olive.)*

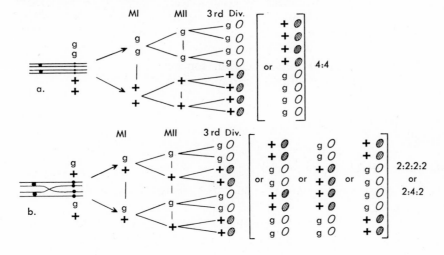

C. *Tabulation and interpretation*

1. Tabulate your counts and calculate as follows (a set of summary data from previous student experiments has been filled in):

	M I	M II	Total	% M II (M II/total)	$\frac{\% \text{ M II}}{2}$ = map distance (from centromere)
(g) × (+)	291	519	810	64%*	32 units on chr. 1**
(t) × (+)	292	404	696	58%	29 units on chr. 3

*Not significantly less than 66.7%.
**This really should be 33.3 or more units (see C.2, Interpretation).

2. Interpretation. More second-division (MII) asci indicate that a gene is farther from the centromere than a gene that displays fewer second-division asci. The gene for gray spores (g) is known to be more crossover units from its centromere than is the gene for tan spores (t).

The distance of the spore color locus from its centromeres (gene-to-centromere distance) is determined (approximately) by determining the percentage of MII asci and dividing this value by 2. One divides by 2 because only 1 pair—one half— of the terad of chromatids is involved in the crossing over (Fig. 16-8b), and since only half the strands in the second division asci have recombined, the recombination percentage is only half the percentage of second division asci.

The final value percentage recombination represents the number of crossover units between the locus and the centromere. If a value of 33.3 (66.7% MII) is obtained, this means only that the locus may be anywhere between 33.3 crossover units and an indeterminate distance from the centromere. If significantly less than this value, the number is a fair reflection of the distance.

Large numbers of counts from crossover experiments dealing with many loci indicate that (g) and (t) are actually the following number of crossover units from their centromeres:

(g) about 60 units on chromosome 1.
(t) about 26 units on chromosome 3.

References

The most important references are preceded with an asterisk.

*ALEXOPOULOS, C. J. 1962. *Introductory Mycology*, 2nd ed. Wiley, New York. p. 238, Fig. 88; pp. 305–307.

BARNETT, H. L., and V. G. LILLY. 1947. The effects of biotin upon the formation and development of perithecia, asci, and ascospores by *Sordaria fimicola*. Ces. and de Not. *Am. J. Botany 34:* 196–204.

BRETZLOFF, C. W., JR. 1954. The growth and fruiting of *Sordaria fimicola*. *Am. J. Botany 41:* 58–67.

BURNETT, J. H. 1968. *Fundamentals of Mycology*. St. Martin's, New York. 546 pp., illus. p. 159 and p. 160, Fig. 6.7: spore liberation.

*CARR, A. J. H., and L. S. OLIVE. 1958. Genetics of *Sordaria fimicola*. II. Cytology. *Am. J. Botany 45:* 142–150.

——— and L. S. OLIVE. 1959. Genetics of *Sordaria fimicola*. III. Cross-compatibility among self-sterile and self-fertile cultures. *Am. J. Botany 46:* 81–91.

DOQUET, G. 1960. Contribution a l'étude du noyau du *Sordaria fimicola*. *Rev. Cytol. Biol. Végetales 22:* 109–130.

INGOLD, C. T. 1958. On light-stimulated spore discharge in *Sordaria*. *Ann. Botany (London) 22:* 129–135.

———. 1960. Spore discharge in Pyrenomycetes. *Friesia 6:* 148–163.

*————. 1965. *Spore Liberation*. Oxford University Press, New York. 210 pp., illus. (pp. 52–74: spore discharge in *Sordaria*).

———— and V. J. DRING. 1957. An analysis of spore discharge in *Sordaria*. *Ann. Botany (London) 21:* 465–477.

———— and S. A. HADLAND. 1959. The ballistics of *Sordaria*. *New Phytologist 58:* 46–57.

————, and B. MARSHALL. 1962. Stimulation of spore discharge by reduced humidity in *Sordaria*. *Ann. Botany (London) 26:* 563–568.

———— and B. MARSHALL. 1963. Further observations on light and spore discharge in certain Pyrenomycetes. *Ann. Botany (London) 27:* 481–491.

*OLIVE, L. S. 1956. Genetics of *Sordaria fimicola*. I. Ascospore color mutants. *Am. J. Botany 43:* 97–106.

———— and A. A. FANTINI. 1961. A new, heterothallic species of *Sordaria*. *Am. J. Botany 48:* 124–128. (Refers to pairing of *S. brevicollis* with heterothallic *Neurospora* and *Gelasinospora*).

*RITCHIE, D. 1937. The morphology of the perithecium of *Sordaria fimicola* (Rob.) Ces. and de Not. *J. Elisha Mitchell Sci. Soc. 53:* 334–342. (Development from ascospore).

Project **17**   A mushroom

Culture, controlled development, and
life cycle of a bracket mushroom:
Schizophyllum, a wood decay
basidiomycete

Contents

Introduction

Schizophyllum is a small gill fungus known as "split gill." It is a common bracket
mushroom found on dead trees and shrubwood, and can be collected in all parts
of the world. Although there are several species, *Schizophyllum commune* is the
type species and is by far the most widespread and common.

   Schizophyllum is heterothallic and is best known for what has been revealed
about its complicated genetic control of sexual development. Perhaps more is
known about the genetics of sexuality in *Schizophyllum* than in any other organism.

   Because of its widespread distribution, its ease of culture, and its rapid and
normal development to reproductive maturity in axenic culture at ordinary room
temperatures, *Schizophyllum* is an excellent organism for class study and experi-
mentation.

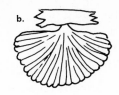

The basidiocarp (fruit body or "mushroom") of *Schizophyllum* (Fig. 17-1) is remarkable because it rolls up its spore-producing lamellae or gills during dry weather (Fig. 17-2a). This keeps alive, in a dormant state, the hymenium or spore-producing layer of basidia. During wet weather the gills unroll and new basidia produce more basidiospores (Figs. 17-2b, 17-9).

In dead wood basidiospores develop primary or haploid (n) mycelia (Fig. 17-4).

Sexual fusion of hyphae (somatogamy) of opposite mating types establishes the dikaryotic ($n + n$) condition (Fig. 17-5), after which the dominant secondary ($n + n$) mycelium (Figs. 17-7, 17-8) grows and permeates the wood. This secondary mycelium develops basidiocarps (Fig. 17-6) in most cases on the sides or bottom of the wood.

Dry basidiocarps collected on wood can be stored in the laboratory and used for starting cultures at a later time—even years later! The living material you will use for starting your cultural studies is a dry basidiocarp.

This project consists of three experiments. Fullest understanding will come by doing all three, but this is not necessary.

In Experiment 1 you will follow the full life cycle of this mushroom during 1–2 weeks. You will have a basidiocarp shed some of its spores on the surface of an agar culture plate (Fig. 17-3). You will watch these spores germinate to produce primary (n) mycelia (Fig. 17-4) and from them secondary ($n + n$) mycelium and the progress of basidiocarp development and the discharge of basidiospores (Figs. 17-5 through 17-10).

In Experiment 2 you will make single-spore cultures by isolating young primary mycelia (Figs. 17-3, 17-11) and noting the lack of basidiocarp formation by the primary mycelium that grows out from a single spore. Experiments 1 and 2 together are a controlled experiment designed to provide you with insight into the heterothallic nature of *Schizophyllum*.

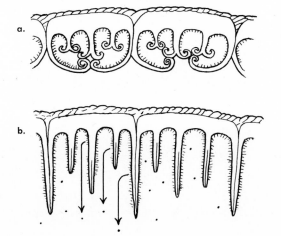

Fig. 17-2 (a) Section of basidiocarp during dry weather showing each half of a split gill curled back in opposite directions, protecting the spore-producing layer of basidia (the hymenium). (b) Same during wet weather. The many short lines represent basidia. The arrows represent the paths of discharged, falling basidiospores. *(Figures 17-1 and 17-2 based on figures in Buller, 1909.)*

Experiment 3 is an experimental study of the effect of gravity on basidiocarp development.

The procedures are really quite simple, but information and directions are given in great detail to ensure your full success and high achievement.

Living and culture materials each student needs (commercially available, e.g., from Carolina Biological Supply Co.)

A. (For Experiments 1–3) A living, dry basidiocarp of *Schizophyllum*.
B. (For Experiments 1–3) Nine plates (petri dishes 10 cm in diameter) of sterile agar medium, either PDA or CMDP (two agar plates for Experiment 1, four for Experiment 2, and three for Experiment 3).

Note 1. Ingredients of culture media:

1. PDA (potato-dextrose agar). You can use Difco brand and make according to directions. The ingredients are

Infusion from potatoes	200 g
Dextrose	20 g
Bacto-agar	15 g
Distilled water	1 liter

2. CMDP (cornmeal-dextrose-peptone agar)

Difco cornmeal agar	17 g
(Ingredients: Infusion from cornmeal	50 g
Bacto-agar	15 g)
Dextrose	10 g
Peptone	2 g
Distilled water	1 liter

Note 2. If you make your own culture medium and pour your own culture plates, pour each plate deep (with about 30 ml) of the sterilized and cooled (to about 40–45°C) agar medium. Sterile, disposable, plastic culture dishes cost very little, but if you use glass culture dishes, either dry sterilize in an oven (175–190°C for 2–5 hours) or cover with paper or foil and autoclave or pressure cook (15 lb of pressure for 15 minutes).

C. (For Experiment 2) A microspatula for cutting tiny blocks of agar, each containing a young primary mycelium. The cutting end of the microspatula is flame sterilized, using a bunsen burner or alcohol lamp.

Schedule

Day 1
1. Starting Procedures
   a. Make humidity chamber, moisten basidiocarp, and place moist basidiocarp in humidity chamber (for Experiment 1–3).
   b. Inoculate six culture plates with basidiospores (for Experiments 1–3).
2. Study mature basidiospores (Experiment 1).

Days 1–2
1. Study young primary mycelia (Experiment 1).

Days 2–3
1. Make three single spore culture plates (Experiment 2).
2. Study older primary mycelia looking for plasmogamy (somatogamy) (Experiment 1).

Days 4–7
1. Study dikaryotic mycelium and early development of basidiocarps (Experiment 1).

Days 8–11   1. Study expanding and gill formation stages of basidiocarp development (Experiment 1).

Days 11–21   1. Study mature basidiocarp structure, basidiospore development, and basidiospore discharge (Experiment 1).
2. Study asexual spores (Experiment 1).
3. Study the effect of gravity on basidiocarp formation (Experiment 3).

Starting procedures

Refer back to the section dealing with living and culture materials.

A. *Preparing a dry basidiocarp for spore discharge*
1. Submerge a dry basidiocarp in sterile distilled water (Fig. 17-3a) in a sterile container (e.g., petri dish) for 10 minutes. (By this time the gills will have unrolled.)

Fig. 17-3   Ballistospore method for depositing basidiospores on an agar plate. (a) Dry basidiocarp placed in distilled water. (b) Moistened basidiocarp attached by its dorsal surface to the lid of a humidity chamber. (c) Basidiocarp discharging basidiospores onto a clean microscope slide. (d) Basidiocarp discharging basidiospores onto the surface of sterile culture medium. (e) The agar surface of a culture plate properly inoculated with basidiospores. AD, adhesive; AM, agar culture medium in petri dish; DB, dry basidiocarp placed in water; MB, moist basidiocarp; SP, basidiospores; SL, glass microscope slide; W, water.

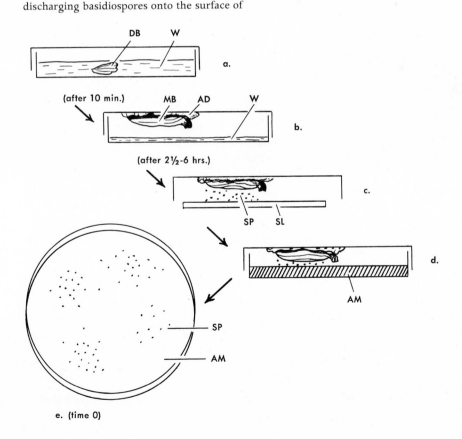

Note: Tests have shown that basidiocarps (fruit bodies) can remain stored in a dry state for 25 years and then, after wetting, freely liberate viable spores (see Fig. 17-2).

2. Make a high-humidity ballistospore chamber by putting about 5 ml of sterile distilled water in a sterile petri dish (culture plate).
3. On the underside of the lid, add eccentrically a big blob of petrolatum.
4. Remove the wetted basidiocarp and with a clean cloth blot up the excess water, especially from the ventral (gill) surface.
5. Firmly attach the moistened basidiocarp by its dorsal surface to the blob of petrolatum on the petri dish top (Fig. 17-3b). With a wax pencil mark on the petri dish top the time of day and the date.
6. Place this top over the bottom part of the humidity chamber (Fig. 17-3b). Check to be sure that the basidiocarp is hanging down well above the surface of the water in the humidity chamber. Leave the top on for $2\frac{1}{2}$–6 hours (some specimens may require longer). By this time basidiospore production should be prolific and will so continue for 8 or more hours. The rate of basidiospore discharge is relatively low after 16–24 hours.

B. *Inoculating six culture plates with basidiospores*

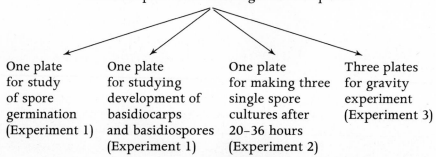

Follow the directions below for making
six multispore-inoculated agar culture plates

| One plate for study of spore germination (Experiment 1) | One plate for studying development of basidiocarps and basidiospores (Experiment 1) | One plate for making three single spore cultures after 20–36 hours (Experiment 2) | Three plates for gravity experiment (Experiment 3) |

1. Some time after $2\frac{1}{2}$–6 hours, remove from the humidity chamber the top with the discharging basidiocarp and place it over a clean microscope slide (Fig. 17-3c). Let spores fall on the slide for 5 seconds. Examine it with the compound microscope to make sure that only one to a few spores are in a single field of view with the high dry objective lens. If there are too many spores, reduce the exposure to 2 seconds. If there are too few spores, increase the exposure from 10 seconds to 1 minute. The exposure time that you need is one that will produce on an agar plate a scattering of basidiospores widely enough spaced for making single-spore isolates. A properly exposed plate may have 50 or more basidiospores on the surface of the agar.
2. Now place the top with its basidiocarp over a sterile culture plate (Fig. 17-3d) (PDA or CMDP) for the proper length of time (above). Rotate the top of the petri dish just enough to place the basidiocarp over uninoculated agar and leave it in position again for the proper length of time. Repeat as many times as needed to expose a maximal area of the agar surface to spores (Fig. 17-3e).
3. Remove the lid with the adhered basidiocarp and replace it over the botton of the humidity chamber.
4. Observe the exposed agar plate with the compound microscope, making sure that the density of spores is adequate. Immediately put the lid back on the dish.

5. Make five more multispore cultures (six culture plates in all, each with about 50 basidiospores on the surface of the agar).

6. With a wax pencil mark on the culture dish tops (a) the time of day that the plates were inoculated with spores, (b) the date, and (c) your name.

7. Put three of these multispore cultures in the culture cabinet by the directions given in Experiment 3 (Effect of Gravity on Basidiocarp Development).

8. Invert and put two more of these multispore cultures in the culture cabinet for use in your study of basidiocarp and basidiospore development (Experiment 1) and for making single-spore cultures (Experiment 2).

9. Use the sixth multispore culture for studying basidiospore germination (Experiment 1).

Study directions

Study *Schizophyllum* during the next 2–3 weeks following the directions outlined in the experiments. You will learn more if you make many large well-labeled drawings, make notes freely on your pages of drawings, and study the available literature.

Two plates of figures are provided. Study them before you begin these experiments.

Project

I. **Experiment 1. Life cycle starting with a dry basidiocarp** (agar-plate culture study of development: from basidiospores to primary mycelia to secondary mycelium to basidiocarps)

Day 1   Notes: (1) Refer back to the starting procedures section. They will tell you how to make the ballistospore-inoculated agar plates for beginning this study. (2) Unless otherwise specified, observe basidiospores, germinating spores, and mycelial development in situ, with the lid of the culture dish removed.

Day 1   A. *Mature basidiospores* (Fig. 17-4a). Observing with the high dry objective, draw several spores, which are hyaline, cylindric,

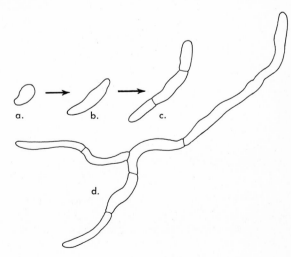

Fig. 17-4 Basidiospore germination and development into a young primary (*n*) mycelium. (a) Mature, ungerminated basidiospore. (b) Very young sporeling (germling) having bipolar germination. (c) The same sporeling a few hours later, now with two septa. (d) Young, branched, primary mycelium, in this case twenty hours old.

ellipsoid, or slightly kidney-bean shaped, and with a tiny nipple subbasally. These spores are about 7.5 microns long.

Days 1–2

B. *Germination of basidiospores—primary mycelium* (Fig. 17-4b–d).
  1. After about 8–12 hours. Study and draw several young sporelings. Spores germinate from one end or both ends; that is, spores have monopolar or bipolar germination.
  2. After about 12–18 hours. Study sporelings. Notice that the germ tubes are growing on the surface of the agar.

    Looking through a dissecting microscope at about X40, with a small spatula cut out a small block of agar that has many germlings on it, place the block of agar on a microscope slide in a small drop of water, gently add a cover slip, and press the mount to a thinness suitable for observation with an oil-immersion objective lens.

    Study and draw several germlings. If your optical system is good, you can see clearly the cross walls and many tiny lipid globules or granules in each cell. You can see less clearly several vacuoles in each cell. and you can see a nucleus (distinguishable from a vacuole by its large but only faintly visible nucleolus) in most of the cells.
  3. After 20–28 hours. Study and draw young primary mycelia from high dry. You can see that the branches come out from the initial hyphae predominantly at right angles and that these branches, along with the tip portions of the initial hyphae, usually penetrate the agar at an angle. (Hyphae or portions of hyphae that are in air above or on the surface of the agar are more refractive than those within the agar.) Find faintly visible cross walls and lipid granules or globules.

  Note: This is about the time to make mycelial cultures of single-spore origin if you do Experiment 2 (see directions in Experiment 2).

Days 2–3

C. *Plasmogamy* (*somatogamy*) (Fig. 17-5). After 30–48 hours. Find the place in your culture plate where the young mycelia are most crowded. Observe this portion of your culture plate with high dry of the compound microscope. Look for the fusion of hyphae derived from different spores; but do not be disappointed if you do not find this sexual hyphal fusion, because it is rare at this early stage, especially since one mycelium can fuse with only 25 per cent of the other mycelia owing to the tetrapolar sexuality of *Schizophyllum*. Read the discussion of this in Alexopoulos, 1962, 436–438.

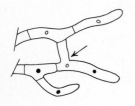

Fig. 17-5 Sexual hyphal fusion (somatogamy) between primary mycelia of opposite mating types. Arrow indicates point of fusion.

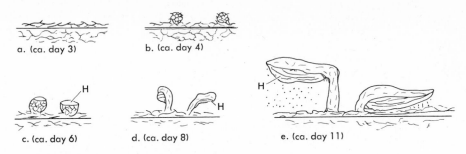

Fig. 17-6   Normal basidiocarp development from secondary
mycelium when agar plate is kept in upright position.
(a) Cross section of agar culture showing $n+n$ mycelium above
surface of agar. (b) Protobasidiocarp (cotton ball) stage.
(c) Shallow-cup (apothecium-like) stage. (d) Gill-formation stage.
(e) Mature stage with basidiocarps shedding basidiospores.

Days 4–5
or later

D. *Young secondary (dikaryotic) mycelium* (Figs. 17-6b, 17-7).

1. Using low power of the dissecting microscope, with a small
spatula cut out a small, thin block of agar, about 1 mm^2,
including one ball-like weft of aerial mycelium (one protobasidiocarp) on the block of agar. Observing with low power
of the dissecting microscope, place this small block in a drop
of water on a microscope slide. Press the aerial mycelium
under the water with the spatula, driving out all the air that
you can with the spatula. Add a cover slip and press it down
with many, short taps, driving out more air and making the
mount very thin.

2. Study the secondary mycelium on the agar around the clump
of aerial mycelium. Note cell lengths and widths and the mode
of branching. Find clamps at the positions of hyphal septa.
Notice that there is no correlation between hyphal width and
whether or not cell division by clamp formation has occurred.
Notice that in most cases the septum or cross wall in the clamp
itself is nearly but not quite parallel with the hypha and that it

Fig. 17-7   Tip of young secondary $(n+n)$ hypha
showing cell division by clamp formation. Note
spiral arrangement of clamps.

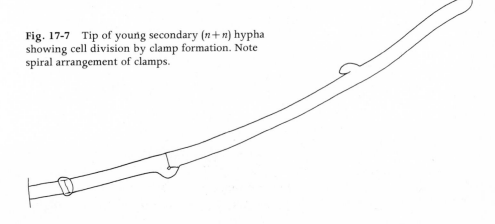

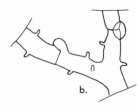

Fig. 17-8 (a) Stub type of hypha.
(b) Peg type of hypha.

is in the anterior part of the clamp. Notice that most clamps are not exactly parallel with their hyphae; this is best seen when looking down on top of a clamp. Also notice that successive clamps tend to come out from different parts of the circumference of a hypha. Find a clamp in side view that shows clearly the nearly circular space between the clamp and the hypha. Find an occasional clamp from which has started to sprout a branch hypha, a "clamp branch." Draw several clamps on their hyphae.

Days 4–5 or later

E. *Protobasidiocarp* (*cotton-ball stage*) (Figs. 17-6b, 17-8). Using the same slide, study the ball-like weft of aerial, dikaryotic mycelium Notice that two hyphal types have differentiated: (a) stub hyphae or hyphae that are thicker and somewhat more curved and branched; (b) peg hyphae or hyphae with many peglike growths. Draw both of these hyphal types, including enough of each mycelium to show about a dozen cells. (Notice also the crystalline material among the hyphae.)

Days 5–7 or later

F. *Shallow-cup or apothecium-like juvenile stage* (Fig. 17-6c).
1. With a dissecting microscope (low and high powers) and using reflected light, study the clumps of aerial mycelia on the surface of your culture plates of multispore origin after 5, 6, and 7 days of growth. Find tiny yellowish, smooth, shallow cups with fuzzy, slightly involuted rims. Draw.
2. With a razor blade, make a thin section of one of these and make a water mount of the section. Draw, showing cellular details (as viewed with the compound microscope), especially noting the hymenium. Find a basidium with sterigmata and basidiospores. (It seems to be bizarre for a juvenile basidiocarp of a mushroom to produce mature basidiospores!)

Days 8–11

G. *Expanding and gill-formation stages* (Figs. 17-6d and e).
1. Study and draw enlarging basidiocarps in 8- 11-day-old cultures that are developing gilled hymenial surfaces by a downward folding of the smooth hymenial surface of the

122

shallow-cup, juvenile stage. Cooke, 1961, describes this maturation process as follows:

"As the cup enlarges peripherally, certain segment grow more rapidly than others. As the principal radiating segments elongate, they also expand laterally. Both the radial and lateral growth patterns are symmetrical. If, as happens in some cases, the point of attachment of the pileus is central, a perfectly round fruit body will develop. This will be divided into segments for almost the length of the radius of the pileus. Some pilei will show these segments as separate branches, the 'digitatum' or the 'radiatum' type of pileus. Other pilei will develop so that these segments will be shown to be separate only after careful observation or by observing tangential sections through the margin or mid-parts of the pilei. Lines of major development branch dichotomously so that each of these primary divisions of the pileus may become partially divided 2, 4 or 8 times. The secondary, tertiary and other successive partitionings of the hymenophoral branches do not completely split the context, and may even be so shallow that the 'brevilamellatum' type of development occurs."

2. In your cultures you will see many expressions of abnormal development. These forms may be environmentally or genetically induced. [Raper and Krongelb (1958, p. 717) show photomicrographs of genetically controlled morphological types of basidiocarps, as viewed from below: Normal (fig. 3); Abnormal (Medusoid) (figs. 4, 5); Cauliflower (fig. 6); Bugs Ear (figs. 7 and 8); Coralloid (fig. 9); Microcoralloid (fig. 10); and Haploid (fig. 11).]

Days 11–15 or later

H. *Basidium development and basidiospore discharge* (Fig. 17-9). Make very thin sections, using a new razor blade, of gills with hymenia containing basidia in all stages of development. A basidiocarp that is shedding spores will reveal all stages. Use a basidiocarp grown in culture or use a dried one that has been remoistened and is discharging basidiospores.

1. Basidial development. Mount sections in a drop of water, add a cover glass, and, using the highest-power objective, find basidia in different stages of development.

All the hymenial cells of *Schizophyllum* are so small that it is difficult to see clearly what happens during their maturation. An oil-immersion objective lens is needed for seeing much. Draw as many development stages as you can find.

2. Basidiospore discharge (Fig. 17-9E). Put freshly cut sections on a slide (not in a drop of water) and add a cover glass. Ring three sides of the cover glass; i.e., plug the space between three edges of the cover glass and the slide with a little petrolatum. This prevents excessive loss of water vapor.

Look to find the forcible discharge of basidiospores. Is it true that the spores of a basidium are discharged successively

123

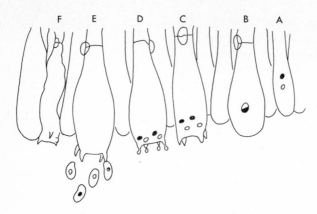

Fig. 17-9 Portion of the hymenium of a mushroom gill diagramming basidium development and basidiospore discharge. (Dark and light circles indicate nuclei of opposite mating types.) (A) Dikaryotic incipient basidium. (B) Diploid basidium. (C) Basidium after meiosis and with four sterigmata developing. (D) Basidium initiating basidiospores, one from the tip of each sterigma. (E) Basidium forcibly discharging its basidiospores. (F) Collapsed basidium after spore discharge.

—never simultaneously? Notice the small bubble (water or gas?) that develops on the apiculus, which is directed toward the axis of the basidium. The bubble persists for only a few seconds and disappears during spore discharge.

Draw what you observe.

Days 15–21   I. *Asexual spores* (Fig. 17-10).

1. In a drop of water on a microscope slide mount some of the aerial mycelium (dikaryotic or secondary) growing between protobasidiocarps and basidiocarps of a 2- to 3-week-old culture. Add a cover slip, pressing to force out air, and study at all magnifications.

2. Draw several of the 1- to several-cell-long sections of the aerial hyphae that contain condensed and thickened protoplasts which serve as asexual spores when they break away from the adjacent cells that are empty of protoplasm. (Incidentally, take note of the great lengths of the empty vegetative cells and the clarity of their clamps. If your observations of clamp connections are incomplete, this is excellent material with which to complete and also to confirm your knowledge of clamp formation.) If these spores are the same size and shape as the vegetative hyphal cells, they are called arthro-

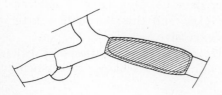

Fig. 17-10 Thick-walled asexual spore dense with protoplasm, and adjacent cells empty of protoplasm.

124

spores; whereas, if these spores are enlarged, rounded up, or with thickened walls, they are called chlamydospores. The asexual, dikaryotic spores of *Schizophyllum* may be either arthrospores or chlamydospores, as you should see. Find chlamydospores that have formed after the protoplast has withdrawn from the end walls, reminiscent of endospore formation in bacteria! In *Schizophyllum*, chlamydospores are comparable to the gemnae of Saprolegniaceae and arthrospores are comparable to the macroconidia of *Neurospora* and many other Ascomycetes and Fungi Imperfecti.

II. Experiment 2. Single-spore agar-plate culture study of development

Is *Schizophyllum* heterothallic?

Day 1 A. The ballistospore-inoculated agar plate, from which you will cut out young primary mycelia derived from a single basidiospore, is made by following the directions in the starting procedures section.

Days 2–3 B. *Make three single-spore culture plates* (from a 20- to 36-hour-old culture)
1. Using your small microspatula and with × 40– × 60 of a dissecting microscope, cut out three tiny blocks of agar, each with a single, 20- to 36-hour-old primary mycelium derived from a single basidiospore (Fig. 17-11).
2. Place each of the three blocks, with its mycelium of a single genotype, in the center of an agar plate of the same medium. Give each stock culture a number and put your name on the plates. Such stock cultures could be used for experimentally determining mating types and other developmental activities (see IV on pp. 71–73 in Koch, 1966).
3. Into the culture cabinet return the agar-plate culture of multispore origin and also place the three single-spore cultures. (Remember to keep these cultures inverted.)

Days 11–21 4. If basidiocarps do not develop in these single-spore cultures and if they do develop in your multispore cultures, heterothallism is indicated. You could test your working hypothesis

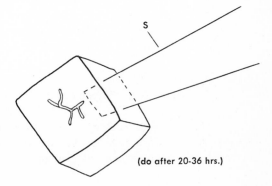

Fig. 17-11 Block of agar medium with a young primary mycelium derived from a single basidiospore. S, tip portion of a microspatula with which block was cut and is transferred to a fresh agar plate.

(do after 20-36 hrs.)

(*Schizophyllum* is heterothallic and not homothallic) through the experiment detailed on pp. 71–73 in Koch, 1966.

III. Experiment 3. Effect of gravity on basidiocarp development

Day 1

    A. *Inoculation.* Follow the directions given in the starting procedures.

    B. *Incubation.* All students are to incubate the cultures together in three groups: an up group, a down group, and a vertical group. Place in the culture cabinet one culture with the agar surface up. Similarly place one culture with the agar surface down. Using transparent tape, hold together the top and bottom of the third culture plate and place it on edge with the agar surface vertical.

Days 15–21

    C. *Study.* During the second and third weeks of growth, study basidiocarp formation. Compare your cultures with those of your classmates. Answer the following questions on the basis of class results:

1. Is it true that carpophore formation is most abundant in the vertical culture and least in the cultures with the agar surface up?
2. Is it true that more normal development occurs when the agar surface is down?
3. Is it true that more abnormalities in development occur when the agar surface is up?
4. Is it true that the pileus is sessile when the agar surface is down, shelflike when the agar surface is vertical, and stiped when the agar surface is up?
5. What other observations can you make? Draw and otherwise record your observations.

References

ALEXOPOULOS, C. J. 1962. *Introductory Mycology*, 2nd ed. Wiley, New York. (p. 10, Fig. 7; pp. 436–438; p. 516).

BULLER, A. H. R. 1909–1924. *Researches on Fungi*, Vols. 1–3. Longmans, Green, and Co., Ltd., London; Hafner, New York.

BURNETT, J. H. 1968. *Fundamentals of Mycology*. St. Martin's, New York. 546 pp., illus. (p. 22, Table 2.3, hyphal wall components; pp. 135–139, biochemical morphogenesis of basidiocarp).

COOKE, W. B. 1961. The genus *Schizophyllum*. *Mycologia 53:* 575–599. (pp. 575–589, taxonomy).

CORNER, E. J. H. 1948. Studies in the basidium. I. The ampoule effect, with a note on nomenclature. *New Phytologist 47:* 22–51, 9 figs. [Seven stages in the development of the living basidium of a typical gill mushroom, *Oudemansiella canarii* (*Collybia apalosarca*) and in some other typical gill mushrooms].

EHRLICH, H. G., and E. S. MCDONOUGH. 1949. The nuclear history in the basidia and basidiospores of *Schizophyllum commune* Fries. *Am. J. Botany 36:* 360–363, 28 figs. (Cytology of developing basidia studied from stained sections of paraffin embedded material).

INGOLD, C. T. 1939. *Spore Discharge in Land Plants.* Oxford University Press, New York. 178 pp., illus. (Pages 74–92 discuss the drop-excretion mechanism of basidiospore discharge and summarize theories explaining forcible basidiospore discharge).

————. 1953. *Dispersal in Fungi.* Oxford University Press, New York. 208 pp., illus. (Pages 68–95 discuss balistospore liberation in basidiomycetes and other fungi).

————. 1965. *Spore Liberation.* Oxford University Press, New York. 205 pp., illus. (See pp. 85–86 for *Schizophyllum* and Chap. 6, Toadstools, Their Form and Function, for updated discussion of basidiospore discharge).

————. 1971. *Fungal Spores: Their Liberation and Dispersal.* Oxford University Press, New York. 302 pp., illus.

KOCH, W. J. 1966. *Fungi in the Laboratory.* The Book Exchange, Chapel Hill, N.C. 113 pp. (Pages 71–73: heterothallism genetics experiment.)

OLIVE, L. S. 1964. Spore discharge mechanism in basidiomycetes. *Science 146:* 542–543, 1 fig. (Evidence for a "gas-bubble mechanism" of forcible basidiospore discharge).

PARAG, Y. 1965. Common-B heterokaryosis and fruiting in *Schizophyllum commune. Mycologia 57:* 543–561, 9 figs., 1 table.

RAPER, A. and J. R. RAPER. 1964. Mutations affecting heterokaryosis in *Schizophyllum commune. Am. J. Botany 51:* 503–512, 15 figs., 5 tables.

RAPER, J. R. 1966. *Genetics of Sexuality in Higher Fungi.* Ronald, New York. 283 pp., illus. (The authoritative reference source in the field of fungal incompatibility — interrelations between genetic factors, mating patterns, and morphogenetic sequences).

———— and G. S. KRONGELB. 1958. Genetic and environmental aspects of fruiting in *Schizophyllum commune* Fr. *Mycologia 50:* 707–740, 11 figs. (Basidiocarp morphogenesis).

SINGER, R. 1962. *The Agaricales in Modern Taxonomy,* 2nd ed. J. Cramer, Weinhein; Hafner, New York. 915 pp., illus. (pp. 178–180, Taxonomy).

WELLS, K. 1965. Ultrastructural features of developing and mature basidia and basidiospores of *Schizophyllum commune. Mycologia 57:* 236–261, 25 figs. (Electron micrographs of developing basidia).

Part Four
Survey of the major groups of plants

The purpose of this part is to help you to become acquainted with the major groups of plants. It is a text and manual combined.

Project 18 is an introduction, with two tables and a map, designed to help you gain a general perspective of the major plant groups, the classification of these groups, when different kinds of plants arose, and how they function in our biosphere. Each of the other projects (19–45) deals with a distinctive group of plants and consists of an introductory statement about the group, with illustrations, and directions for laboratory investigations.

Blue-green algae and bacteria are treated first because they are generally agreed to be primitive and closely related, and they are the only prokaryotic organisms. The eukaryotic algal groups are treated after fungi so that their study will precede the study of the other autotrophic plants: bryophytes and vascular plants.

Project 18   Introduction to the survey

Contents

Introduction

There is fantastic diversity in the over 400,000 known species of plants. Botanists conceive of different ways to group these species into larger categories, and as a result we have quite a few different systems of plant classification. But we can agree that there are 27 distinctive groups of plants that have living members.

Project

I. Study of Table 18-1

Refer to Table 18-1. To the left is a list of the common names for the 27 distinctive plant groups. They are numbered according to the number of the project in which each group is treated in Part Four. Following the common names in parentheses are the technical or scientific names that have been given to these groups. In general, evolutionarily more primitive groups are toward the first of the list and more advanced groups are toward the end. Because these 27 groups of plants are classified variously into larger categories, to the right are

131

Table 18-1 Outline of the major groups of plants

19. Blue-green algae (Cyanophyta, Cyanophycophyta, or Schizophyceae)
20. Bacteria (Schizophyta, Schizomycophyta, Schizomycota, or Schizomycetes)
21. Cellular Slime Molds (Acrasiomycetes, Acrasieae, Acrasiales, or Dictyostelia and Acrasia)
22. Plasmodial Slime Molds (Myxomycota, Myxomycophyta, Myxomycota, or Myxomycetae)
23. Phycos or Alga-like Fungi (Phycomycetes, Phycomycophyta, or Phycomycota)
24. Ascos or Sac Fungi (Ascomycetes, Ascomycophyta, or Ascomycota)
25. Basidios or Club Fungi (Basidiomycetes, Basidiomycophyta, or Basidiomycota)
26. Imperfect Fungi (Form-Group Deuteromycetes, Deuteromycota, or Fungi Imperfecti)
27. Lichens or Symbiotic Fungus–Alga Plants
28. Green Algae (Chlorophyta, Chlorophycophyta, or Chlorophyceae)
29. Stoneworts (Charophyta or Charophyceae)
30. Euglenoids (Euglenophyta or Euglenophycophyta)
31. Xanthophytes, Chrysophytes, and Diatoms (Chrysophyta or Chrysophycophyta—including Xanthophyta)
32. Dinoflagellates and Relatives (Pyrrophyta or Pyrrophycophyta)
33. Brown Algae (Phaeophyta or Phaeophycophyta)
34. Red Algae (Rhodophyta or Rhodophycophyta)
35. Liverworts (Hepaticae or Hepatophyta, which includes No. 36)
36. Hornworts (Anthocerotae)
37. Mosses (Musci or Bryophyta, in this sense excluding Nos. 35 and 36)
38. Lycopods (Lepidophyta, Lycopodophyta, Microphyllophyta, Lycophyta, or Lycopsida)
39. Horsetails (Calamophyta, Arthrophyta, Sphenophyta, or Sphenopsida)
40. Ferns (Filicophyta, Pterophyta, or Filicineae—including Psilotaceae)
41. Cycads (Cycadophyta)
42. Ginkgo or Maidenhair Tree (Ginkgophyta)
43. Conifers (Coniferophyta)
44. The Gnetum or Gnetum–Ephedra–Welwitschia Group (Gnetophyta)
45. Flowering Plants or Angiosperms (Anthophyta or Angiospermae)

Bracketed groupings (shown as nested brackets alongside the list):

- **(Prophyta) (Monera) Prokaryotes** — Nos. 19–20
- **Eukaryotes** — Nos. 21–45
  - **Thallophytes** — Nos. 21–34
    - **Mycetozoans** — Nos. 21–22
    - **True Fungi** — Nos. 23–26
    - (27. Lichens)
    - **Eukaryotic Algae** — Nos. 28–34
  - **Embryophytes** — Nos. 35–45
    - **Nonvascular Plants (Atracheata)** — **Bryophytes** — Nos. 35–37
    - **Vascular Plants (Tracheata)** — Nos. 38–45
      - **Pteridophytes** — Nos. 38–40
        - **Microphyllae**
        - **Megaphyllae (Pteropsida) (Pterophyta)**
      - **Seed Plants (Spermatophytes)** — Nos. 41–45
        - **Gymnosperms** — Nos. 41–44
- **Cryptogams**
- **Phanerogams**

132

shown the names that are often used for different assemblages of the major plant groups. These assemblages represent either evolutionary levels or evolutionary lines and some represent both. Some are natural or phylogenetically related assemblages and others are artificial, used only for convenience. It is important for you to become acquainted with as many of the groups of plants listed to the left as time permits, but it may not be essential for you to know the reasons behind the establishment of all the various assemblages indicated at the right. Your efforts should be directed to becoming acquainted with the distinctive groups of plants and toward learning and understanding the system or systems of classification used by your teacher and text.

II. Study of Table 18-2

Refer to Table 18-2, the geologic timetable. Information about the fossil record is included. Acquaint yourself with the geologic eras and periods, when they began and how long they lasted, the important events that occurred, and the dominant organisms.

III. Study of Map 18-1

Refer to Map 18-1, which shows an estimation of the primary productivity of the land masses and the seas of our biosphere. Primary production is quantified in terms of the number of grams of carbon fixed by autotrophic plants on each square meter during each year (g of C/m^2). One gram of carbon/m^2 is approximately equal to 2.5 g of dry matter/m^2. From this map one can calculate that approximately 50 per cent of primary production occurs on land and 50 per cent in the sea. Can you detect any other patterns of productivity? You will become acquainted with the kinds of plants that account for this primary production in the various parts of our biosphere.

IV. Scanning the plant groups and reference books

A. *The plant groups*
   1. Read the introductory statements and look at the illustrations for all the major groups of plants in Projects 19–45. Do this in a rather casual way without concern for remembering or understanding details. Later, as you make your own investigations in the laboratory, you will gain depth of understanding. At the present time you are simply after a general perspective of the exciting studies ahead of you.
   2. Each introduction includes comments about (1) the taxonomy of the group (nomenclature, distinguishing features, classification, and phylogeny), (2) biological and economic importance, (3) habitats and distribution, (4) vegetative or nonreproductive features (body structure and distinguishing cytological, morphological, and functional features), (5) asexual reproduction, and (6) sexual reproduction, including life cycles.
B. *Reference Books*
   Look through the available reference books to get some idea of how each can be of use to you throughout your survey of the major groups of plants.

Table 18-2 *Geologic timetable*

ERA	PERIOD	TIME *(millions of years since beginning)*	IMPORTANT EVENTS	DOMINANT ORGANISMS
Cenozoic	Quaternary — Recent			Age of herbs and man
	Quaternary — Pleistocene	1	Repeated glaciation. Social man appears. Rise of modern herbaceous angiosperms. Herbaceous angiosperms widespread. Angiosperm forests restricted.	
	Tertiary	63	Angiosperms continue to spread. Worldwide angiosperm forests in early Tertiary. Rise of herbaceous angiosperms. Gymnosperms decline. Herbaceous lycopods and horsetails almost extinct.	Age of angiosperms, mammals and birds
Mesozoic	Cretaceous	135	Rapid evolution and spread of angiosperms to world-wide dominance. Earliest known pines.	Age of higher gymnosperms and reptiles
	Jurassic	181	Origin of angiosperms (?). Gink-goales, Coniferales, Cycadales dominant. Great cosmopolitan flora.	
	Triassic	230	Cycads, ginkgoes and conifers on increase. Seed ferns becoming extinct.	
Paleozoic	Permian	280	Climate dry. Dwindling of ancient groups. Decline and extinction of arborescent lycopods and horsetails (great coal-forming swamp forests). First cycads and conifers.	Age of lycopods, seed ferns and amphibians
	Pennsylvanian (CARBONIFEROUS)	310	Great coal-forming swamp forests. Arborescent lycopods, horsetails, true ferns, seed ferns, and gymnosperms. First moss.	
	Mississippian (CARBONIFEROUS)	345	Land floras well established. Rise of arborescent lycopods and horsetails. Bryophytes on increase. Early coal deposits.	
	Devonian	395	Early land plants. First forests. First liverwort. Rise of lycopods, horsetails, ferns, and seed ferns. A gymnospermous tree common in late Devonian.	Age of early land plants and fishes
	Silurian	425	Atmospheric oxygen at second critical level. Explosion of life over land. Early land plants in late Silurian. Algae dominant.	
	Ordovician	500	Marine algae (mostly calcareous).	Age of marine algae and invertebrates
	Cambrian	600	Atmospheric oxygen at first critical level. Explosion of life in the oceans. Marine algae.	
Precambrian		1200	First eukaryotic algae and fungi.	Age of bacteria and blue-green algae
		3 billion years	First prokaryotes (bacteria and blue-green algae).	
		4.5–4.8 billion years	Beginning of Precambrian.	

Map 18-1 *Map showing primary productivity (g of C/m²) of the biosphere*

(According to Lieth, 1964–1965.) (Courtesy P. Duvigneaud, Université Libre de Bruxelles.)

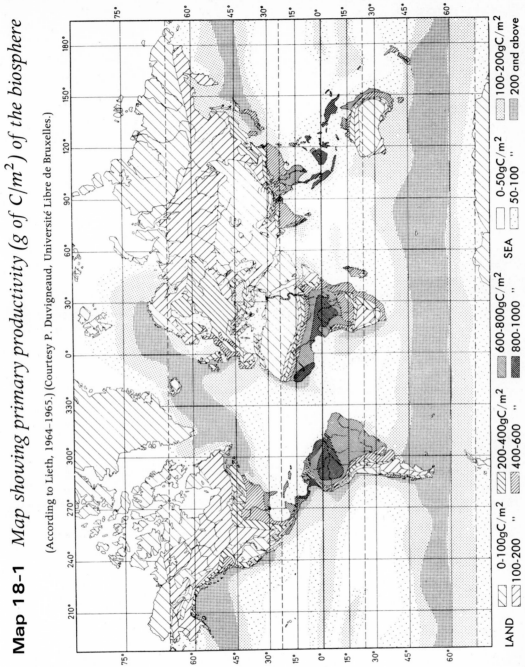

LAND
- 0-100gC/m²
- 100-200 ”
- 200-400gC/m²
- 400-600 ”
- 600-800gC/m²
- 800-1000 ”

SEA
- 0-50gC/m²
- 50-100 ”
- 100-200gC/m²
- 200 and above

References

The following reference books can be helpful aids in the laboratory as you seek a meaningful comprehension of the major groups of plants. (References for determining or identifying plants and plant groups are given in Project 1, p. 4.)

Plant kingdom textbooks

Hardback

BOLD, H. C. 1967. *Morphology of Plants,* 2nd ed. Harper & Row, New York.

BROWN, W. H. 1935. *The Plant Kingdom*. Ginn, Boston.

COULTER, M. C., and H. J. DITTMER. 1964. *The Story of the Plant Kingdom*. University of Chicago Press, Chicago.

CRONQUIST, A. 1961. *Introductory Botany*. Harper & Row, New York.

DITTMER, H. J. 1964. *Phylogeny and Form in the Plant Kingdom*. Van Nostrand Reinhold, New York.

GIBBS, R. D. 1950. *Botany, A Phylogenetic Approach*. McGraw-Hill, Blakiston Division, New York.

HAUPT, A. W. 1953. *Plant Morphology*. McGraw-Hill, New York.

RUSSELL, N. H. 1958. *An Introduction to the Plant Kingdom*. Mosby, St. Louis.

SCAGEL, R. F., et al. 1965. *An Evolutionary Survey of the Plant Kingdom*. Wadsworth, Belmont, Calif.

————. 1969. *Plant Diversity, An Evolutionary Approach*. Wadsworth, Belmont, Calif.

TRIBE, I. 1970. *The Plant Kingdom*. Grosset and Dunlap, New York.

Paperback

ALEXOPOULOS, C. J., and H. C. BOLD. 1967. *Algae and Fungi*. Macmillan, New York. (Current Concepts in Biology Series)

BELL, P. R., and C. L. F. WOODCOCK. 1968. *The Diversity of Green Plants*. Addison-Wesley, Reading, Mass. (Contemporary Biology Series)

BOLD, H. C. 1964. *The Plant Kingdom,* 2nd ed. Prentice-Hall, Englewood Cliffs, N.J. (Foundations of Modern Biology Series)

DELEVORYAS, T. 1965. *Plant Diversification*. Holt, Rinehart and Winston, New York. (Modern Biology Series)

DOYLE, W. T. 1970. *Nonseed Plants: Form and Function,* 2nd ed. Wadsworth, Belmont, Calif. (Fundamentals of Botany Series)

GOTTLIEB, J. E. 1968. *Plants: Adaptation Through Evolution*. Van Nostrand Reinhold, New York. (Selected Topics in Modern Biology Series)

HARRIS, R. M. 1969. *Plant Diversity*. William C. Brown, Dubuque, Iowa. (Concepts of Biology Series)

SALISBURY, F. B. and R. V. PARKE. 1964. *Vascular Plants: Form and Function*. Wadsworth, Belmont, Calif. (Fundamentals of Botany Series)

General reference books

AINSWORTH, G. C. and A. S. SUSSMAN, eds. 1965, 1966, 1968. *The Fungi*, Vols. I–III. Academic Press, New York.

ALEXOPOULOS, C. J. 1962. *Introductory Mycology,* 2nd ed. Wiley, New York.

ALSTON, R. E., and B. L. TURNER. 1963. *Biochemical Systematics*. Prentice-Hall, Englewood Cliffs, N.J.

ARNOLD, C. A. 1947. *An Introduction to Paleobotany.* McGraw-Hill, New York.

BELL, C. R. 1967. *Plant Variation and Classification.* Wadsworth, Belmont, Calif.

BENSON, L. 1962. *Plant Taxonomy, Methods and Principles.* Ronald, New York.

BESSEY, E. A. 1961. *Morphology and Taxonomy of Fungi.* Hafner, New York.

BIERHORST, D. W. 1971. *Morphology of Vascular Plants.* Macmillan, New York.

BILLINGS, W. D. 1964. *Plants and the Ecosystem.* Wadsworth, Belmont, Calif.

BONNER, J. T. 1966. *The Cellular Slime Molds,* 2nd ed. Princeton University Press, Princeton, N.J.

BONY, A. D. 1966. *A Biology of Marine Algae.* Hutchinson Educational, London.

BOWER, F. O. 1935. *Primitive Land Plants.* Macmillan, New York.

BRIGGS, D., and S. M. WALTERS. 1969. *Plant Variation and Evolution.* McGraw-Hill, New York.

BRAUN, E. L. 1950. *Deciduous Forests of Eastern North America.* Hafner, New York.

BROCK, T. D. 1970. *Biology of Microorganisms.* Prentice-Hall, Englewood Cliffs, N.J.

BURNETT, J. H. 1968. *Fundamentals of Mycology.* St. Martin's, New York.

CAIN, S. A. 1971. *Foundations of Plant Geography.* Hafner, New York. (Facsimile of 1944 edition).

CARLQUIST, S. 1961. *Comparative Plant Anatomy.* Holt, Rinehart and Winston, New York.

CHAMBERLAIN, C. J. 1935. *Gymnosperms: Structure and Evolution.* University of Chicago Press, Chicago. (1966. Dover, New York)

COCHRANE, V. W. *Physiology of Fungi.* Wiley, New York.

CRONQUIST, A. 1968. *The Evolution and Classification of Flowering Plants.* Houghton Mufflin, Boston.

DAUBENMIRE, R. F. 1959. *Plants and Environment,* 2nd ed. Wiley, New York.

————. 1968. *Plant Communities: A Textbook of Plant Synecology.* Harper and Row, New York.

DAVIS, B. D., et al. 1969. *Microbiology,* corrected ed. Harper and Row, New York.

DAVIS, P. H., and V. H. HEYWOOD. 1963. *Principles of Angiosperm Taxonomy.* Van Nostrand Reinhold, New York.

DAWSON, E. Y. 1966. *Marine Botany.* Holt, Rinehart and Winston, New York.

DELEVORYAS, T. 1962. *Morphology and Evolution of Fossil Plants.* Holt, Rinehart and Winston, New York.

DODD, J. D. 1962. *Form and Function in Plants.* Iowa State University Press, Ames, Iowa.

DOYLE, W. T. 1970. *The Biology of Higher Cryptogams.* Macmillan, New York.

DUVINEAUD, P. 1967. *Ecosystèmes et Biosphère,* 2nd ed. Documentation 23, vol. 2. Ministère de l'Education Nationale et de la Culture, Bruxelles.

EAMES, A. J. 1936. *Morphology of Vascular Plants, Lower Groups.* McGraw-Hill, New York.

————. 1961. *Morphology of Angiosperms.* McGraw-Hill, New York.

EATON, T. H., Jr. 1970. *Evolution.* Norton, New York.

ESAU, K. 1965. *Plant Anatomy,* 2nd ed. Wiley, New York.

FLORKIN, M. 1966. *A Molecular Approach to Phylogeny.* American Elsevier, New York.

FOSTER, A. S., and E. M. GIFFORD, JR. 1965. *Comparative Morphology of Vascular Plants,* 5th ed. W. H. Freeman, San Francisco.

FROBISHER, M. 1968. *Fundamentals of Microbiology,* 8th ed. Saunders, Philadelphia.

GRANT, V. 1971. *The Origin of Adaptations.* Columbia University Press, New York.

HALE, M. E. 1967. *The Biology of Lichens.* Edward Arnold, London.

HAWKER, L. E. 1966. *Fungi, an Introduction.* Hutchinson Educational, London.

HENNIG, W. 1966. *Phylogenetic Systematics.* Translated by D. D. Davis and R. Zangerl. University of Illinois Press, Urbana, Ill.

HEYWOOD, V. H. 1967. *Plant Taxonomy.* St. Martin's, New York.

HILL, A. F. 1952. *Economic Botany.* McGraw-Hill, New York.

HUTCHINSON, J. 1959. *The Families of Flowering Plants,* 2nd ed. Oxford University Press, New York.

INGOLD, C. T. 1961. *The Biology of Fungi.* Hutchinson Educational, London.

————. 1965. *Spore Liberation.* Oxford University Press, New York.

JACKSON, D. F. 1968. (ed.) *Algae, Man, and the Environment.* Syracuse University Press, Syracuse, N. Y.

KEOSIAN, J. 1968. *The Origin of Life,* 2nd ed. Van Nostrand Reinhold, New York.

KINGSBURY, J. M. 1964. *Poisonous Plants of the United States and Canada.* Prentice-Hall, Englewood Cliffs, N.J.

LAWRENCE, G. H. M. 1951. *Taxonomy of Vascular Plants.* Macmillan, New York.

————. 1955. *An Introduction to Plant Taxonomy.* Macmillan, New York.

LEE, A. E., and C. HEIMSCH. 1962. *Development and Structure of Plants, A Photographic Study.* Holt, Rinehart and Winston, New York.

LEEDALE, G. F. 1967. *Euglenoid Flagellates.* Prentice-Hall, Englewood Cliffs, N.J.

LEWIN, R. A. (ed.) 1962. *Physiology and Biochemistry of Algae.* Academic Press, New York.

MOORE-LANDECKER, E. J. 1972. *Fundamentals of Fungi.* Prentice-Hall, Englewood Cliffs, N.J.

MORRIS, I. 1967. *An Introduction to the Algae.* Hutchinson Educational, London.

O'BRIEN, T. P., and M. E. MCCULLEY. 1969. *Plant Structure and Development.* Macmillan, New York.

OOSTING, H. J. 1956. *The Study of Plant Communities,* 2nd ed. W. H. Freeman, San Francisco, Calif.

ORNDUFF, R. 1967. *Papers on Plant Systematics.* Little, Grown, Boston, Mass.

POINDEXTER, J. S. 1970. *Microbiology.* Macmillan, New York.

PORTER, C. L. 1967. *Taxonomy of Flowering Plants,* 2nd ed. W. H. Freeman, San Francisco, Calif.

PRESCOTT, G. W. 1968. *The Algae: A Review.* Houghton Mifflin, Boston.

ROUND, F. E. 1965. *The Biology of Algae.* Edward Arnold, London.

SAVAGE, J. M. 1963. *Evolution.* Holt, Rinehart and Winston, New York.

SMITH, G. M. 1955. *Cryptogamic Botany,* 2nd ed. Vol I. *Algae and Fungi.* Vol. II *Bryophytes and Pteridophytes.* McGraw-Hill, New York.

SOKAL, R. R., and P. H. A. SNEATH. 1963. *Principles of Numerical Taxonomy.* W. H. Freeman, San Francisco.

SOLBRIG, O. T. 1966. *Evolution and Systematics.* Macmillan, New York.

————. 1970. *Principles and Methods of Plant Biosystematics.* Macmillan, New York.

SPORNE, K. R. 1965. *The Morphology of Gymnosperms.* Hutchinson Educational, London.

STEBBINS, G. L. 1950. *Variation and Evolution in Plants.* Columbia University Press, New York.

————. 1966. *Processes of Organic Evolution.* Prentice-Hall, Englewood Cliffs, N.J.

SWAIN, T. 1963. *Chemical Plant Taxonomy.* Academic Press, New York.

TALBOT, P. H. 1971. *Principles of Fungal Taxonomy.* The Macmillan Press Limited, Houndmills, Basingstoke, Hampshire.

TIFFANY, L. H. 1958. *Algae, the Grass of Many Waters,* 2nd ed. Charles C. Thomas, Springfield, Ill.

VOLPE, E. P. 1970. *Understanding Evolution,* 2nd ed. William C. Brown, Dubuque, Iowa.

WATSON, E. V. 1964. *The Structure and Life of Bryophytes.* Hutchinson Educational, London.

WEBSTER, J. 1970. *Introduction to Fungi.* Cambridge University Press, New York.

WOLF, F. A., and F. T. WOLF. 1947. *The Fungi* (2 vol.) Wiley, New York.

Project **19**   Blue-green algae

Contents

Introduction

Taxonomy   Blue-green algae are organisms of the group technically known as Cyanophyta, Cyanophycophyta, or Schizophyceae. There are about 150 genera and 1,500 species.

Blue-green algae and bacteria are generally agreed to be primitive and closely related. They are the only prokaryotic organisms and all other organisms are eukaryotic (Table 18-1, p. 132). Prokaryotes lack true sexuality and lack organized nuclei, nuclear membranes, plastids, mitochondria, and golgi apparatuses. They are also unique in having mucopeptides as components of their cell walls. Also, the ribosomes of prokaryotes are smaller than those in the cytoplasmic matrix of eukaryotes. Prokaryotic ribosomes exist as 70S particles (about 150 A), whereas eukaryotic ribosomes are 80S particles (about 200 A). It is interesting, indeed, that the ribosomes found in the chloroplasts and mitochondria of eukaryotes are of the same smaller size of the ribosomes of blue-green algae and bacteria. Does this suggest a possible evolutionary origin for chloroplasts and mitochondria?

The fossil record indicates that present-day prokaryotes are of very ancient lineage. The oldest rocks revealing fossils are about three billion years old, and they contain only fossil prokaryotes (Table 18-2, p. 134).

Blue-green algae can be classified into three groups (orders), separated on the basis of whether or not they are filamentous and whether or not endospores

140

are produced, as follows: (1) multicellular and filamentous (Oscillatoriales); (2) regular formation of endospores (Chamaesiphonales); and (3) not strictly filamentous and not with regular endospore formation (Chroococcales).

Importance Blue-green algae are important as primary producers in food chains or webs, as plankters, and as occupants of diverse aquatic and terrestrial habitats and niches (Fig. 19-1). They build and maintain soil and water fertility and oxygenate their environment. They act as a soil binder, reduce erosion, and help to increase the water-holding capacity of soil. Some blue-green algae, like some bacteria, fix atmospheric nitrogen; that is, through a series of metabolic reactions, such genera as *Anabaena* can incorporate elemental nitrogen into their proteins. Nitrogen fixation is associated with specialized cells called heterocysts (Fig. 19-2). When nitrogen-fixing blue-green algae die, they increase the nitrogen content and thus enrich the soil or water they are growing in. Indeed, for this reason blue-green algae are cultivated in rice paddies. For all the above reasons it is easy to see that blue-green algae are important to agriculture.

Unfortunately for man, blue-green algae in large enough numbers may have an undesirable odor. They can give the water in water supplies both a bad odor and taste. Blue-green algae in large enough numbers may pollute water and be toxic to other aquatic life and man, and they may even cause death. This can be a real problem in farm ponds, fish hatcheries, and home aquaria. For example, pasture ponds may turn greenish from a "bloom" of blue-green algae, and after a cow drinks this water, death may come even within an hour. This is a common occurrence, for example, in Wisconsin. A few blue-green algae (e.g., *Lyngbya*, Fig 19-3, and *Phormidium*) are known to be attacked by viruses. Perhaps suitable algal viruses can be found and used in the biological control of algal populations in water supplies.

If water from a sewage-treatment plant is run into a lake, the resulting high level of nutrients (e.g., nitrates, phosphates, and carbon compounds) in the lake

Fig. 19-1 Pond, pasture, and woods, all of which provide many habitats for blue-green algae and many other plants. *(Courtesy Carolina Biological Supply Company.)*

Fig. 19-2 Portion of a stained filament of *Nostoc* showing the larger, clearer heterocyst cell. *(Photomicrograph courtesy Carolina Biological Supply Company.)*

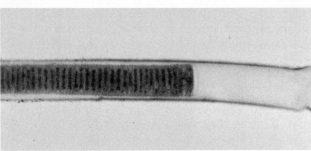

Fig. 19-3 Portion of a stained filament (trichome) of *Lyngbya* within its thick sheath. *(Photomicrograph courtesy Carolina Biological Supply Company.)*

may initiate a huge population growth of blue-green and other algae. The combination of high nutrient concentration and shallow water with heating by the sun are environmental factors that facilitate such algal population explosions. Characteristically, such an algal bloom lasts until most of the available nutrients are used up, at which time the huge algal population dies, sinks to the bottom, and rots or decays, killing fish and other animals because of oxygen depletion. Very offensive odors are also a product of such a catastrophe.

Some blue-green algae are components of lichens and, as such, aid in soil formation. Some grow in hot springs, forming extensive limestone deposits. Some calcareous blue-green algae are important in tropical reef formation.

Fig. 19-4 Three tiny globular colonies of *Gloeocapsa. (Photomicrograph courtesy Carolina Biological Supply Company.)*

Fig. 19-5 Macroscopic view of four large mucilaginous colonies (balls) of *Nostoc*. The largest one is 20 mm in diameter. *(Courtesy Carolina Biological Supply Company.)*

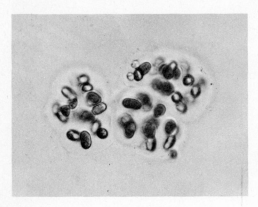

Occurrence   Blue-green algae are widely distributed—from the tropics to the poles—in fresh and salt water, attached and submerged, as well as free floating or planktonic, in hot springs, in and on soil, and on snow, leaves, bark, and rocks. They are especially abundant in stagnant water containing much decaying organic matter. Endophytic forms live in cavities of such other plants as bryophytes, ferns, and gymnosperms. Epiphytic forms live on surfaces of other algae, plants, and animals. The Red Sea is so named because of the red color of the water caused by the massive population of blue-green algae (*Trichodesmium* with its abundance of the red pigment *c*-phycoerythrin.)

Agents of blue-green algal dispersal are water (currents in bodies of water and rain on land), wind, and animals.

Vegetative features   Blue-green algae have tiny, unicellular forms that are 5 microns across and less, as well as larger forms that are globular, fan shaped, sheetlike, or irregularly shaped colonies (Figs. 19-4, 19-5, 19-12). Many blue-green algae are multicellular filaments, called trichomes, that are up to 100 microns to several centimeters long. Filamentous forms may be unbranched (Figs. 19-2, 19-3, 19-6, 19-7, 19-8), falsely branched (Figs. 19-9, 19-11), or truly branched (Fig. 19-10). Those that form mats and clumps are seen easily with the unaided eye. When viewed macroscopically, blue-green algae may appear blue-green, green, yellowish, red, blue, violet, brown, or black, as explained later.

Most blue-green algae are slimy to the touch because of the mucilaginous pectic outer walls or sheaths (Figs. 19-3, 19-4, 19-5, 19-9). The inner, more rigid wall contains cellulose and chitin, in addition to the characteristic mucopeptides, containing diaminopimelic and muramic acids, known as wall constituents only of bacteria and blue-green algae.

With the light microscope one usually can distinguish between the outer pigmented region (chromoplasm) of the protoplast and the central, irregularly shaped nuclear or DNA area (centroplasm or nucleoplasm). There is no clear separation between the pigmented and DNA regions; there is no nuclear membrane. The nucleoplasm of blue-green algae (and bacteria) contains deoxyribonucleic acid but not protein—not histone. In contrast, the DNA of the nuclei of all eukaryotic organisms, except pyrrophyte algae and some fungi, is combined with a special protein, histone.

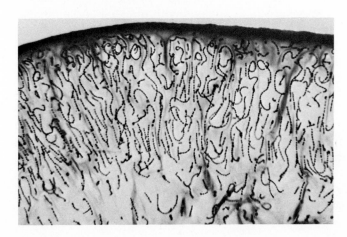

Fig. 19-6   Stained section of a portion of a gelatinous colony of *Nostoc* filaments (see Fig. 19-5). *(Photomicrograph courtesy CCM: General Biological, Inc., Chicago.)*

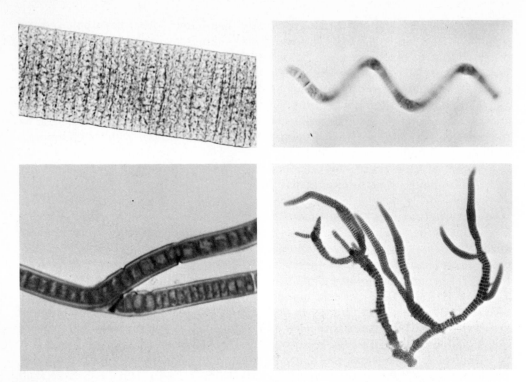

Fig. 19-7 Portion of a multicellular filament of *Oscillatoria. (Photomicrograph courtesy Carolina Biological Supply Company.)*

Fig. 19-8 Stained, multicellular, spiral filament of *Arthrospira. (Photomicrograph courtesy Carolina Biological Supply Company.)*

Fig. 19-9 Stained portion of a filamentous thallus of *Tolypothrix* showing false branching. *(Photomicrograph courtesy Carolina Biological Supply Company.)*

Fig. 19-10 Stained thallus of *Stigonema* showing true branching. *(Photomicrograph courtesy Carolina Biological Supply Company.)*

As in all cells, the blue-green algal protoplast is bounded by a living lipoprotein unit membrane called the cell membrane, plasma membrane, or outer membrane. Excess photosynthate is stored as minute granules of cyanophycean starch located in the chromoplasm. The cell *lacks* flagella, a nucleus with nucleoli and a nuclear membrane, water vacuoles (but large numbers of small gas vacuoles may be present), mitochondria (but their equivalent is present), golgi apparatus, and endoplasmic reticulum. Blue-green algae, like all organisms, do have ribosomes. With the electron microscope one can also see that the chromoplasm contains many parallel, photosynthetic membranes. The pigments found in this membranous region are chlorophyll *a* (bluish-green), carotenes and xanthophylls (yellow to orange), and two biliprotein pigments, *c*-phycocyanin (blue) and *c*-phycoerythrin (red). (As in eukaryotic plants, photosynthesis in blue-green algae involves the addition of hydrogen to carbon dioxide, and water serves as the hydrogen donar, with oxygen being released.) Pigments of various colors may be in the cell wall. One can readily understand how different amounts and kinds of the various pigments give blue-green algae a wide range of colors when they are viewed macroscopically.

144

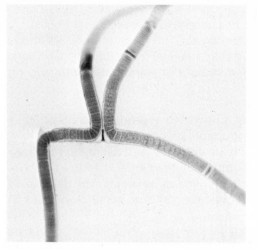

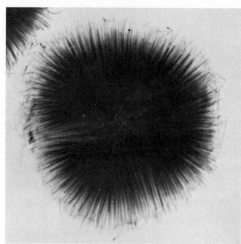

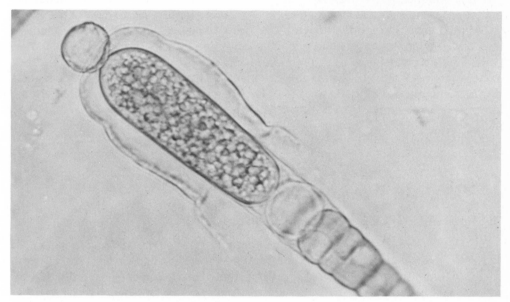

Fig. 19-11 Stained portion of a filamentous thallus of *Scytonema* showing separation discs and false branching. *(Photomicrograph courtesy Carolina Biological Supply Company.)*

Fig. 19-12 Stained globose colonies of *Gloeotrichia*. Each colony consists of hundreds of tapering filaments, each with its heterocyst and akinete in the center (see Fig. 19-13). *(Photomicrograph courtesy Carolina Biological Supply Company.)*

Fig. 19-13 Basal portion of a tapered filament of *Gloeotrichia* showing the terminal heterocyst, adjacent akinete, and sheath. *(Photomicrograph courtesy Carolina Biological Supply Company.)*

Blue-green algae that fix atmospheric nitrogen have specialized cells called heterocysts (Figs. 19-2, 19-13), and these cells are involved with the process.

No blue-green algae can swim—they lack flagella. However, many filamentous forms, especially members of the family Oscillatoriaceae (Fig. 19-7), can move slowly by gliding backward and forward, in a straight or spiral path, or by waving the terminal portion of a filament.

Reproduction Blue-green algae are not known to reproduce sexually; they have asexual life cycles only. Asexual reproduction is accomplished in unicellular forms by binary fission or cell division and in colonies and filaments by fragmentation. Multicellular segments (hormogonia) of filamentous forms may become separated and thus effect reproduction. Separation occurs at the site of heterocysts in some (Fig, 19-2), or dead concave cells or separation discs in others (Fig. 19-11).

Endospores are produced by some blue-green algae. Endospores could be called sporangiospores: the protoplasm within a cell (sporangium) cleaves into a number of units (spores) that can grow into new plants.

Many filamentous forms develop one or two specialized types of reproductive cells or asexual spores called akinetes and heterocysts (Figs. 19-2, 19-13). Ordinarily heterocysts do not germinate and thus are functionless as spores, but akinetes are asexual spores that are very effective in bringing about multiplication and dissemination. Akinetes may tide blue-green algae over unfavorable periods, as for example when the soil in which they are growing dries. Akinetes may remain alive in dry soil for many years. Actually, ordinary vegetative cells of some blue-green algae have this property or ability to withstand drying.

Project

I. **Filamentous blue-green algae** (Oscillatoriales)

    A. *Oscillatoria, Lyngbya*. Place a small amount of the alga in a drop of water on a slide, tease apart the filaments, and add a cover slip. *Lyngbya* differs from *Oscillatoria*, which lacks a sheath, in that the trichomes are surrounded by a clearly visible sheath. What are the two types of movement seen? What is the shape of an individual cell? Do the filaments branch? In the cell protoplast, can you distinguish between the central body and the peripheral region, the chromoplasm? Where are the dark or glistening reserve food granules found? Look for small discs of gelatinous material, the separation discs, where breaking of a filament often occurs. The multicellular segment delimited by separation discs is a hormogonium. Fragmentation is the only method of reproduction. Test for cellulose in the inner wall: chloroiodide of zinc reagent turns cellulose purple. (If starch were present, it would turn dark blue because of the iodine in the solution.)

    B. *Anabaena*. Place a small fragment of the water fern *Azolla* on the slide in a drop of water, add a cover slip, and crush by moving the cover slip back and forth with the eraser end of a pencil. Note the chains or filaments of cells. Is each chain a colony or an individual in your opinion? Are all the cells the same size? Can you find division stages? Are reserve food granules present? Find heterocysts, slightly larger than a vegetative cell, nearly colorless and transparent, and at maturity with thickenings of wall material forming the polar nodules at the area adjacent to the vegetative cells. The string of cells between heterocysts is a hormogonium. Look for akinetes, always larger than vegetative cells, generally cylindrical and with rounded ends, with a dense protoplast, and occurring in various places in the filament. (Note: If akinetes and/or heterocysts are not found in the living material, refer to prepared slides.)

C. *Nostoc*. Place a small piece of the colony on a slide in a drop of water, add a cover slip, and press firmly to spread the gelatinous matrix. Study and look for the same features as in *Anabaena*. Akinetes may not be found. They do not usually form until a colony is mature.

D. *Gloeotrichia, Rivularia*. Observe that the filaments taper from base to apex. Identify the terminal heterocyst and the relatively large and elongate cell, the akinete, next to it. How many akinetes do you see between the heterocyst and the vegetative cells? Akinetes are not formed by species of *Rivularia*. Observe the gelatinous sheaths. Do they enclose the entire filament?

E. *Scytonema, Tolypothrix, Stigonema*. *Scytonema* and *Tolypothrix* show false branching, whereas *Stigonema* shows true branching. Observing filaments under low power, locate instances of branching. Study from high power. Is there any relationship between the position of heterocysts and the origin of false branches?

II. Unicellular and colonial forms (Chroococcales)

Gloeocapsa, Chroococcus, Gloeothece. Note that there are occasionally individual cells but more commonly irregular colonies of cells. An individual is a single cell whose protoplast is conspicuously colored and is enveloped by a delicate cell wall. Outside the cell and enclosing it are broad layers of mucilaginous (pectic) material that has been secreted by the protoplast. (This is actually the outer wall.) The cell may divide by constriction, but the daughter cells are held together by the gelatinous matrix of the parent cell. Each daughter cell then secretes its own gelatinous sheath, which may be distinguished from the original parent matrix. By further cell divisions and continued secretions of gelatinous material, irregular colonies of cells are formed. Note that colony formation is one of the results of the abundant production of mucilage. Note especially that there are no chromatophores and that the protoplast actually has a bluish-green color (these features may not be seen well in prepared slides).

Project **20**   Bacteria

Contents

Introduction

Taxonomy   Bacteria are organisms of the group technically known as Schizophyta, Schizomycophyta, Schizomycota, or Schizomycetes. There are about 200
genera and 1,500 species.

Because bacteria and blue-green algae are the only prokaryotic organisms,
as explained in the introduction to Project 19, they are generally agreed to be
primitive and closely related.

Bacteria are classified into 10 or 11 groups (orders) and into smaller groups
on the basis of morphological and physiological differences such as form of
colonies in axenic culture (Fig. 20-1), shape and form of cells, staining characteristics, end products of respiration, ability to metabolize specific chemicals or
substrates, the host of a parasite, and the disease symptoms produced. Recently,
such biochemical features as DNA base pair ratios, expressed as %GC (guanine-
cytosine), have become taxonomic criteria.

Because the fossil record is of no aid in classifying the different kinds of bacteria, we say that bacterial classification is a phenetic system of classification, one based only on information derived from extant organisms. A phylogenetic system of classification, in contrast, would include evidence from fossil ancestors. The goal of either a phenetic or a phylogenetic system of classification is a so-called natural classification, one which shows or reflects evolutionary relationships.

A type of taxonomy known as numerical taxonomy has been introduced in order to avoid the arbitrary weighting of characters. In numerical taxonomy, a large number of characters are determined (on the order of 50-100), and with the aid of computers, groups are established on the basis of the proportion of characters shared, without giving any characters more weight than others. This laborious taxonomic approach could lead to the regrouping or modification of the present grouping of bacteria and other organisms.

The following orders of bacteria can be recognized: (1) "True bacteria" (Eubacteriales) are generally thought of as typical or relatively unspecialized bacteria. (2) Pseudomonads (Pseudomonadales), which include some of the sulfur and iron bacteria, have many members that are photosynthetic and chemo-synthetic. (3) Beggiatoas (Beggiatoales) include nonphotosynthetic, filamentous, gliding, sulfur bacteria which can easily be mistaken for colorless members of the blue-green algae. (4) Actinomycetes (Actinomycetales) are filamentous and superficially look like little fungi. (5) Myxobacteria or slime bacteria (Myxo-bacteriales) are gliding and aggregating bacteria which superficially resemble cellular slime molds. (6) Members of the Chlamydobacteriales are characteristically filamentous and with a sheath encrusted with iron or manganese oxide, and these are known as iron or manganese bacteria respectively. (7) Hyphomicrobiales has members which reproduce by budding. (8) Members of the Caryophanales are filamentous and composed of cylindrical or discoid cells surrounded by a con-

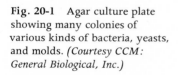
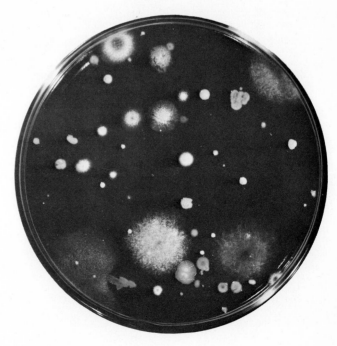

Fig. 20-1 Agar culture plate showing many colonies of various kinds of bacteria, yeasts, and molds. *(Courtesy CCM: General Biological, Inc.)*

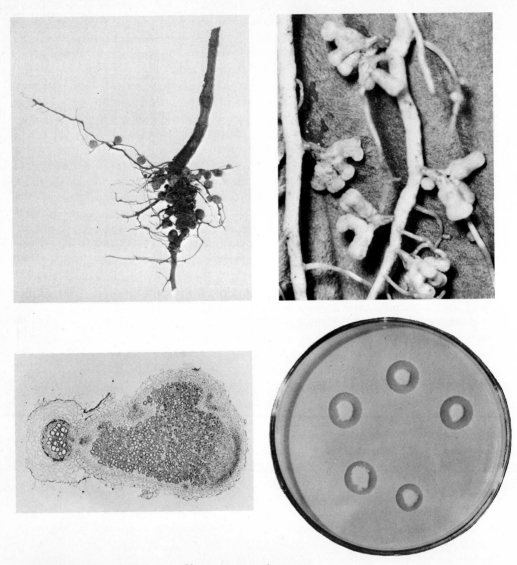

Fig. 20-2 Nodules on the roots of leguminous angiosperms
containing nitrogen-fixing bacteria *(Rhizobium).* Top left: Bean.
Top right: Clover. *(Courtesy Carolina Biological Supply Company.)*

Fig. 20-3 Stained cross section of a pea root
and nodule with its cortical cells filled with
*Rhizobium. (Courtesy Ripon Microslides
Laboratory.)*

Fig. 20-4 Agar culture plate with five colonies
of one bacterium that produced an antibiotic
substance that prevented the growth (clear
areas) of another bacterium. *(Courtesy Carolina
Biological Supply Company.)*

tinuous wall. (9) Spirochaetes (Spirochaetales) are flexuose, slender, highly motile spirals. (10) Rickettsias (Rickettsiales), which are somewhat virus-like organisms that are transmitted by arthropods, and (11) the virus-like mycoplasmas (Mycoplasmatales), including the PPLO (pleuropneumonia-like organisms), can be classified with bacteria. Viruses can be regarded as exceptionally simple micro-organisms—when they are in the cells that they infect—or as exceptionally complex chemicals—when they are outside of cells. All viruses contain a single type of nucleic acid, either DNA or RNA, and a protein coat. In addition, some viruses contain lipids and carbohydrates.

Importance Bacteria are important in maintaining soil and water fertility. Most bacteria are saprobic (saprophytic or saprotrophic) heterotrophs. They play a major role (along with fungi) in decomposing organic matter and in the gradual recycling of nutrients bound in organic matter. Some fix atmospheric nitrogen and some of these nitrogen fixers form nodules on the roots of leguminous plants (Figs. 20-2, 20-3). Some convert ammonia to nitrites and nitrites to nitrates, which are utilized by green plants. Bacteria may be aerobic or less frequently anaerobic.

Bacteria are used by man to form such industrial products as acetic and lactic acids, acetone, butyl alcohol, and many of our antibiotics, such as strepto-mycin, actinomycin, aureomycin, and neomycin (Fig. 20-4); in the retting of flax and hemp; tanning animal hides; curing tobacco; and producing butter, cheese, sauerkraut, and vinegar. However, bacteria cause millions of dollars of damage yearly by spoiling foods and crops.

Relatively few bacteria are pathogenic to man (causing such diseases as pneumonia, tetanus, syphilis, typhoid fever, tuberculosis, diphtheria, and botulism); pathogenic to animals (causing such diseases as chicken cholera, anthrax, and bang's disease); and pathogenic to plants (causing such diseases as potato and bean blights, alfalfa wilt, fire blight, and crown gall).

Escherichia coli (E. coli) of the Eubacteriales is a common inhabitant of the intestine of man, and it is routinely used as an indicator of pollution in water supplies. The number of *E. coli* cells in a given volume of water is an excellent indicator of the amount of fecal contamination. Contaminated water often causes the spread of such human pathogens as the typhoid fever bacterium.

Because of their rapid reproductive rate and ease of in vitro culture, bacteria are of considerable value in basic biological research in such areas as genetics, respiration, nutrition, and immunology. What we know and are finding out about the genetic code and how DNA functions in controlling metabolism and inheritance is due in large part to research using bacteria and viruses. *E. coli* is the major experimental organism in this important area of research.

Occurrence Bacteria are ubiquitous, found in almost any environment in which life exists. They occur in the air and thrive in all types of soils and fresh and salt water systems from the tropics to the poles—from hot springs to snow. Aquatic forms are most abundant in shallow water muds and oozes. They exist on the surfaces of all plants and animals. They are found on the human body, but particularly in respiratory passages, the throat, and the alimentary canal.

Vegetative features Bacteria are very small—the smallest plants—ranging in diameter or width from 0·5–8 microns and averaging 1–3 microns.

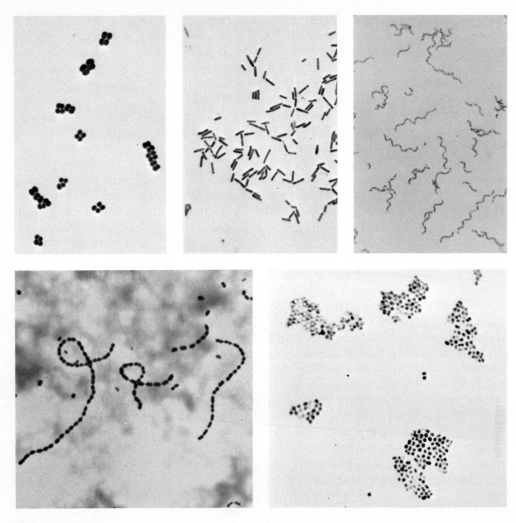

Fig. 20-5 (top of page)   Bacterial shapes. Left: Spherical (coccus form). Center: Rod-shaped (bacillus form). Right: Spiral (spirillum form). *(Photomicrographs courtesy Carolina Biological Supply Company.)*

Fig. 20-6   Stained *Streptococcus.* *(Photomicrograph courtesy CCM: General Biological, Inc., Chicago.)*

Fig. 20-7   Stained *Staphylococcus.* *(Photomicrograph courtesy Carolina Biological Supply Company.)*

Unicellular bacteria may be spherical (coccus form), rod shaped (bacillus form), spiral (spirillum form), or very short curved rods (vibrio form) (Fig. 20-5). Cells of *Rhizobium*, growing in legume root nodules, vary from typical bacillus form to X, Y or club shaped. Coccus forms may cohere to form colonies of various shapes, like chains (Fig. 20-6) and irregular clumps (Fig. 20-7), and bacillus forms may form unbranched filaments. Actinomycetes have a branching mycelium similar to, but smaller than, the mycelium of fungi.

Cell structure is of the simple prokaryotic type, and there is little to see with the light microscope. Mucopeptides, with their characteristic muramic acid, amino sugar, and often with the amino acid, diaminopimelic acid, give rigidity to the wall. Penicillin is effective as an antibiotic because it interferes with wall formation, especially with the incorporation of muramic acid into mucopeptides. Bacteria known as Gram-positive have relatively large amounts of mucopeptides. Gram-negative bacteria have relatively large amounts of lipid, proteins, and other poly-saccharides (which are found in smaller amounts in all bacterial walls). It is easy to see why penicillin is effective against most Gram-positive bacteria and usually not effective against Gram-negative bacteria. A slime layer of varying thickness and composed mainly of polysaccharides may be present immediately outside the cell wall. A thick slime layer is called a capsule.

Visible with the electron microscope are a central nuclear area or body surrounded by cytoplasm that is bounded by an outer membrane. Coiled membranes called mesosomes are usually found in the cytoplasm. Food granules in the cytoplasm may be volutin (metachromatic bodies), glycogen, or fat. The nuclear area contains a single strand of deoxyribonucleic acid (DNA). In *E. coli* the units of inheritance are all physically linked with each other; thus, the single chromosome, which is essentially a single strand of DNA, is continuous or cyclic. It appears to be linear only during the special process of conjugation.

Some bacteria can move by gliding or by swimming. Those that can swim or that have motile asexual spores bear flagella. Flagella may occur singly or in tufts, and they are variously located on the cell in different kinds of bacteria: a single flagellum on one end (monotrichous), on both ends (amphitrichous), a tuft or flagella at one or both ends (lophotrichous (Fig. 20-8), or flagella over the entire surface (peritrichous) (Fig. 20-9). Each flagellum, which is a long fibrous protein molecule, is embedded in the cytoplasm where it is terminated by a basal granule.

Unlike eukaryotic organisms, bacteria lack complex flagella (with the 9 + 2 arrangement of strands that are bounded by a common flagellar membrane), a nucleus with nucleoli and a nuclear membrane, mitochondria, golgi, and endo-plasmic reticulum. But bacteria, like all organisms, do have ribosomes; however, the ribosomes of bacteria, like those of blue-green algae, are smaller than those in the cytoplasmic matrix of eukaryotes.

Although photosynthetic bacteria lack chloroplasts, their pigments are localized in simpler structures called bacterial chromatophores. There are three bacterial photosynthetic pigments, and these are chemically similar to the chlorophylls of algae and autotrophic plants: bacteriochlorophyll (found in the purple bacteria) and two chlorobium chlorophylls (found in the green sulfur bacteria). Photosynthetic bacteria occur mainly in anaerobic habitats (the earth's early atmosphere was anaerobic), and photosynthesis in bacteria differs from photosynthesis in blue-green algae and in eukaryotic plants. The hydrogen donor is not water and oxygen is not released. For example, in photosynthetic sulfur bacteria, sulfur

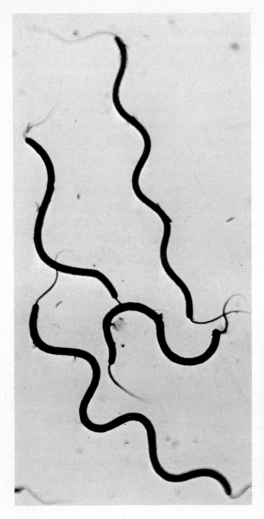

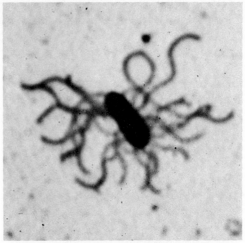

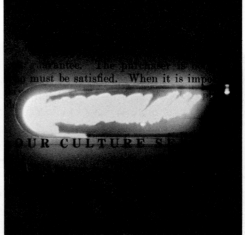

Fig. 20-8 *Spirillum volutans* stained to show tufts of flagella. *(Photomicrograph courtesy Carolina Biological Supply Company.)*

Fig. 20-9 Photomicrograph of a bacillus-form soil bacterium stained to show peritrichous flagella.

Fig. 20-10 Test-tube culture of *Photobacterium fischeri* photographed in total darkness using only light emitted by the bacterium. *(Courtesy Carolina Biological Supply Company.)*

compounds like hydrogen sulfide serve as the hydrogen donor in the reduction of carbon dioxide, and free sulfur is the by-product and is deposited as refractile granules. Beggiatoas obtain energy chemosynthetically by oxidizing H_2S, and sulfur droplets accumulate within their filaments.

The vegetative cells of some bacteria have the ability to give off light or luminesce in the dark (Fig. 20-10).

Reproduction Reproduction in most bacteria is accomplished by binary fission.

In addition, colonies and mycelia may fragment. Some bacilli can produce spores (endospores and cysts) that are resistant to heat, desiccation, chemicals, and other unfavorable conditions (Fig. 20-11). One cell produces one spore or becomes one cyst, and this spore or cyst germinates to produce a single vegetative cell. Thus multiplication is not effected in this manner. Actinomycetes produce exposed asexual spores (conidia) or spores protected by a wall (sporangiospores) that have flagella and can swim when the sporangium wall ruptures. These motile spores are called zoospores or planospores. They develop by fragmentation of hyphae contained by the sporangium wall and not by cleavage, like the sporangio spores of fungi and algae.

Unlike any other bacteria, slime bacteria (Myxobacteriales) form relatively complex, colonial structures (fruiting bodies) bearing clusters of air-disseminated spores or cysts (sori of spores). These develop by a sequence of colonial events resembling, quite remarkably, those of cellular slime molds (see reproduction in Project 21). The habitats of slime bacteria and cellular slime molds are similar, but the former are prokaryotic and the latter are eukaryotic; thus, because they are not closely related, their similarity in reproduction is said to be the result of either parallel or convergent evolution.

True sexual reproduction is unknown in bacteria; meiosis and syngamy do not occur. Bacteria, then, have asexual life cycles. However, there is a sexual-like process called meromyxis, meaning partly sexual, that gives genetic results similar to those of sexual reproduction. This involves a unidirectional transfer and incorporation into a recipient cell of a portion of the genetic material (DNA) of a donor cell. The recipient cell is a partial diploid cell, but the generations arising

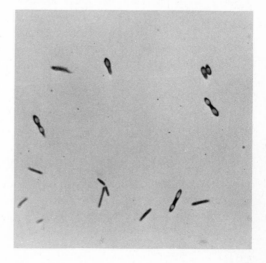

Fig. 20-11 *Clostridium* stained to show endospores. *(Photomicrograph courtesy Carolina Biological Supply Company.)*

from it are haploid. They exhibit characteristics of both the donor cell and the recipient cell. The donor cells may be living bacteria (a process called bacterial conjugation), dead bacteria (transformation), or bacterial viruses, bacteriophages or simply phages, which are really not cells (transduction).

Project

I. **"True" bacteria** (Eubacteriales and Pseudomonadales)

A. *Basic shapes:* Transfer a drop of hay or bean infusion, or a bit of *Spirogyra* or other material in a decaying condition, to a clean slide. Apply a cover slip. Examine under high power, using relatively little light. Observe the three morphological types: rod shaped (bacillus), spherical (coccus), spiral (spirillum). Supplement observations using a prepared slide or slides.

B. *Symbiotic nitrogen-fixing bacteria:* Examine the nodules on the roots of clover or other legumes. Nodules are proliferous growths of the roots. They contain numerous bacteria *(Rhizobium)* that are able to make nitrogenous compounds, using free nitrogen from the air.

1. Cross section. With a sharp razor cut a thin cross section through a nodule. Examine under low and high power. In what kind of cells and in what parts of the cells do the bacteria occur? Observe the size, shape or shapes, and motility of the bacteria. Why are the root-nodule bacteria biologically and economically important? What is the relationship between denitrification and nitrogen fixation? Are all nitrogen-fixing bacteria symbiotic? Supplement observations using a prepared slide.

2. Mashed nodule
   a. Find a tiny nodule on a root. Pluck it with forceps and place it on a clean slide in a very small drop of water. Mash the nodule to pieces with a dissecting tool. Add a cover slip and observe under high power (dry or oil immersion). Can you find more than one form or shape among the numerous bacterial cells?
   b. Staining. Make another slide as above but do not add a cover slip. Let the slide air dry. Place a drop of 1 per cent crystal violet stain on the dried bacterial material. After 2 minutes, rinse it off with tap water. Be sure to remove all large particles of the root nodule. Let the slide dry again and examine under high power.

C. *Bacterial flagella* (oil immersion): Observe a stained slide of a bacterium showing bacterial flagella. Directions for staining bacterial flagella are given in Project 11: III, E, p. 63.

D. *Endospores* (oil immersion): Observe the stained slide of a bacterium showing endospores. How many endospores are formed from a single cell? Of what advantage are spores to bacteria?

II. **Iron bacteria** (Chlamydobacteriales)

Obtain material containing iron bacteria *(Sphaerotilus).* Does it possess any sort of motility? What forms the brownish sheath? From oil immersion observe protoplasm and iron sheath. Of what special interest is the nutrition of iron bacteria?

III. Sulfur bacteria (Beggiatoales)

Obtain material containing sulfur bacteria *(Beggiatoa)*. Does it posses any sort of motility? What substance is the granular material? From oil immersion observe protoplasm and sulfur granules. Of what special interest is the nutrition of sulfur bacteria?

IV. Filamentous, fungal-like bacteria (Actinomycetales)

Cut out a thin sliver or cross-sectional piece of a portion of an agar culture of an actinomycete. Mash the covered mount, if necessary, to permit good observation from high power. Note: branching mycelium and sporangia (e.g., *Actinoplanes*) or conidia (e.g., *Streptomyces*).

V. Human pathogens

Study prepared slides showing parasitic bacteria pathogenic to man.

IV. Isolating colonies on agar plates

Contaminate nutrient agar plates by exposing them to the air, a coin, hair, pencil, soil, fingertips, lips, etc. Store these in a culture cabinet after having written with a wax pencil your name, date, and how inoculated.

During the next week examine these, at first macroscopically and then with a hand lens, under a binocular stereoscopic microscope, and with low power of the compound microscope. Account for the increase in the size of the colonies. How can you tell fungal from bacterial colonies? How can you distinguish between the different kinds of bacteria– that is, how do the different kinds compare as to gross characteristics of the colonies, such as size, color, and smoothness of surface? If time permits, examine each kind of colony microscopically from a covered mount on a glass slide with low and high power. You may find it helpful to stain with a small drop of crystal violet solution or to add a very small drop of India ink. You may also find unicellular yeast colonies that look a lot like unicellular bacterial colonies. You can easily distinguish between them from high dry because yeast cells are so much larger.

VII. Effect of antibiotics on bacterial growth

If time and materials are available, design and carry out a simple experiment to show the effects of antibiotic substances on bacterial growth.

Project **21**   Cellular slime molds

Contents

Introduction

Taxonomy   Botanists have often referred to cellular slime molds technically as Acrasiomycetes, Acrasieae, or Acrasiales. Many biologists now classify cellular slime molds with protozoa and divide them into two groups (subclasses): Dictyostelia and Acrasia. There are about 10 genera and 25 species.

Like all organisms except blue-green algae and bacteria, which are prokaryotic, cellular slime molds have a eukaryotic cell structure—are eukaryotic organisms. Protozoologists classify cellular slime molds with amoeboid protozoa in the larger group called Sarcodina, and they do seem to be related to free-living amoebae in the soil. Some biologists place cellular slime molds, plasmodial slime molds, protostelids, and often two other somewhat similar groups (Labyrinthulales and Plasmodiophorales) in a separate, larger group, which they call Mycetozoa. In some ways these interesting organisms resemble fungi and in other ways they are like protozoa. Although mycologists have made and still are making important contributions to our knowledge of cellular slime molds, most consider them to be more animallike than fungal or plantlike.

The basic life cycle of cellular slime molds involves aggregation and is like that of Myxobacteriales, and since this remarkable pattern of development and reproduction is unique to these groups, one might think that they are closely related; however, present evidence indicates that it is a matter of parallel or convergent evolution.

158

The classification of cellular slime molds, of which there are not many kinds, is based primarily on differences in their fruiting structures (sorocarps). For example, the sorocarp of *Dictyostelium* has only a terminal sorus of spores, whereas the sorocarp of *Polysphondylium* has both a terminal sorus and lateral whorls of smaller, stalked sori.

Importance   Cellular slime molds engulf and digest organic particles and microorganisms, and thus, as phagotrophs (holozoic organisms), function in the "heterotrophic ecological niche" in gradually recycling nutrients bound in organic matter. Cellular slime molds are not of economic importance, but they are important research tools for the biological scientists who are investigating the metabolism and development (morphogenesis) of organisms, especially because they start their lives as unicellular organisms (their feeding or trophic stage) and culminate their lives as a multicellular organism (a reproductive stage).

Occurrence   Cellular slime molds are widely distributed in terrestrial habitats and are found primarily in soil, humus, and dung where other microorganisms, particularly bacteria, are abundant. They are cultured in the laboratory by growing them with bacteria, or sometimes yeasts.

Vegetative features—the feeding or trophic stage   The trophic stage is amoeba-like. The uninucleate amoebae are indistinguishable from ordinary protozoan amoebae. They move in a creeping, amoeboid manner, engulfing food particles (mainly bacteria) by means of pseudopodia. The food particles are then digested in food vacuoles within the amoeboid cell. This mode of nutrition, also found in plasmodial slime molds, does not occur in true fungi and other plants. The amoebae of the Acrasia have blunt pseudopodia (lobose pseudopodia) and those of the Dictyostelia have fine pointed ones (filopodia or filose pseudopodia), and they never form flagella as do the myxamoebae of plasmodial slime molds.
   Bounded by a lipoprotein unit membrane are organelles like those found in the cells of the other eukaryotic organisms: a membrane-bounded nucleus (with chromosomes and one or several nucleoli) that divides by mitosis, mitochondria, golgi apparatus, endoplasmic reticulum, and ribosomes. Contractile vacuoles are present and, along with the nucleus, can be seen rather easily with the light microscope.

Reproduction   Reproduction is accomplished through asexual means. Amoebae multiply by fission (binary fission). Mitosis is followed by cytokinesis—two separate daughter amoebae are formed from one. The two daughter amoebae grow and then divide to form four amoebae. And so on.
   Spores that can be dispersed by wind are produced after a fascinating sequence of developmental events. Sporulation is preceded by the aggregation of amoebae to form a pseudoplasmodium. The aggregation stage occurs after all feeding has ceased. The amoebae move together in streamlike groups, converging on a central collection point or aggregation center and ultimately form a single, discrete mass of cohering but unfused amoebae. Movement of the cells toward an aggregation center is a chemotactic response to substances (first called acrasins) that are secreted by cells at the aggregation center. In dictyostelids the attractant has been identified as 3', 5'-cyclic adenosine monophosphate (cyclic AMP). The

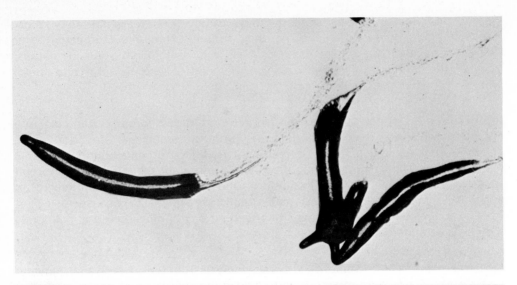

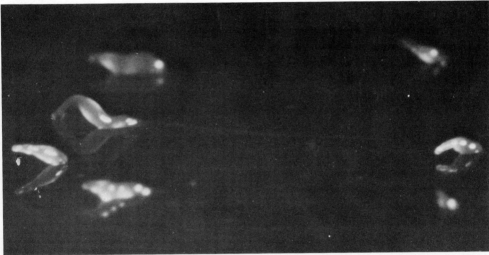

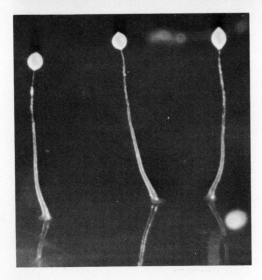

Fig. 21-1 (top) Top view of migrating pseudoplasmodia of *Dictyostelium* as seen with transmitted light. *(Courtesy Carolina Biological Supply Company.)*

Fig. 21-2 (center) Side view of migrating pseudoplasmodia of *Dictyostelium* as seen with reflected light (darkfield microscopy). *(Courtesy Carolina Biological Supply Company.)*

Fig. 21-3 (at left) Side views of sorocarps of *Dictyostelium.* *(Courtesy Carolina Biological Supply Company.)*

rounded, aggregated mass of amoebae becomes elongate—a mature, multicellular pseudoplasmodium.

The pseudoplasmodium of *Dictyostelium discoideum* and some others migrates slowly away from the place of aggregation (Fig. 21-1). This migration stage lasts for a variable length of time depending on such environmental conditions as humidity, temperature, and composition of the substratum. A migrating pseudoplasmodium (called a slug) is easily observed to have an elevated head region and a rear end, and as it migrates it leaves behind a slime track (Fig. 21-2).

Following migration, the pseudoplasmodium stops gliding, contracts in length, and becomes erect. Within the pseudoplasmodium a cellulosic cylinder (stalk tube) forms, with amoebae moving down into it as it develops and with these amoebae forming cellulosic walls around themselves. The walls become polygonal owing to mutual pressure. The stalk or sorophore lengthens as more amoebae become sorophore cells, and while this happens the other amoebae are carried up as a mass on the outside of the sorophore apex. At the tip of the completed sorophore of *Dictyostelium discoideum*, the remaining cells form a globular mass. Each of these amoebae secretes a wall, and this encysted amoeba is a spore. The globular mass of amoebae has been converted into a sorus of spores. The sorus, like the remainder of the fruiting body, has a thin sheath around it, but this breaks down by the time the spores are mature. Since there is no endogenous delimitation of spores from a common protoplasm, the sorus is not a true sporangium. The sorus and sorophore are called a sorocarp (Fig. 21-3). After spore dispersal and on a suitable substrate, such as a moist decaying leaf or an agar medium, spores germinate. A single protoplast escapes from the spore case of each to become a trophic amoeba. It is clear that multiplication is not effected through spore formation.

Sexual reproduction as a regular process is not known; however, cannibalistic engulfment and cell anastomosis may be mistaken for plasmogamy. The rare occurrence of nuclear fusion and the very low yield of genetic recombinants from cultures of mixed genotypes indicate that a parasexual process similar to that of the mold *Aspergillus* occurs in cellular slime molds.

Project

I. *Dictyostelium discoideum*

Remove the lid of an agar plate culture of this cellular slime mold, and put the culture plate on the stage of a dissecting microscope and examine. Then place the culture plate on the stage of a compound microscope and examine. Study, first using low power.

Note that this is a two-member culture: *Dictyostelium* feeding on a bacterium.

Now examine and study the various stages of development. *(Usually one can find all stages in a 2- to 3-day-old culture.)*

A. *Feeding stage* (about 1 day after inoculation). Mount some amoebae *(myxamoebae)* with bacteria, add a cover slip and possibly some water to the mount, and study with high power. Look for slowly moving pseudopodia, contractile vacuoles, nuclei (one per myxamoeba), and food vacuoles. From what you see here, do you think cellular slime molds are animals or plants?

161

B. *Aggregation stage* (after about 2 days). Using low power find a population of amoebae slowly streaming toward a center of aggregation, forming a pseudoplasmodium. What is the morphology of these aggregating amoebae; that is, what form do they take?

C. *Migration stage* (after 2–3 days)
   1. Note the morphology of a migrating pseudoplasmodium, often called a slug. Observe at intervals to detect migration and the trails slugs leave behind.
   2. Cut out a small piece of agar bearing a pseudoplasmodium and immerse it in a petri dish of distilled water while watching it under a dissecting microscope. Observe any changes that take place.
   3. Mount a pseudoplasmodium in a drop of water on a slide and add a cover slip. Study, using high power. Can you detect its internal differentiation? Are all the cells alike in the front end, middle portion, and posterior end?

D. *Culmination or fruiting stage* (after 2–3 days)
   1. Using low power find several stages in sorocarp development.
   2. Mount one or more sorocarps in a drop of water, add a cover slip, and study, using high power. Notice the cellular stalk (pseudoparenchymatous) and the cluster or sorus of spores. Note the difference in the shapes of these two types of cells. Why is this fruiting structure called a sorocarp rather than a sporangium and sporangiophore?
   3. Test a sorocarp for cellulose with chloroiodide of zinc. (Include in the mount a couple of cotton fibers to make certain that the reagent is active.) Refer to Project 10: I.A.2, p. 57. From your observations of the fruiting stage do you think cellular slime molds are plants or animals?

II. *Polysphondylium*

A. Examine a fruiting culture of *Polysphondylium*. Note the whorled arrangement of the sorocarp branches.

B. If time and materials are available, make observations on *Polysphondylium* of the sort you did above for *Dictyostelium*.

III. *Culture*

Directions for culturing *Dictyostelium* are given in Project 3: I, p. 22. If materials and time are available, start your own culture.

Project **22**   Plasmodial slime molds or myxomycetes

Contents

Introduction

Taxonomy   Plasmodial slime molds are organisms of the group technically known to botanists as Myxomycota, Myxomycophyta, or Myxomycetae. Their protozoological scientific name is Myxogastria. All biologists commonly refer to plasmodial slime molds as myxomycetes. There are about 70 genera and 450 species.

In some ways these fascinating organisms resemble fungi and in other ways they are like protozoa. Because of this, some biologists group plasmodial slime molds with cellular slime molds and related organisms in a separate larger group, Mycetozoa.

The several hundred species of myxomycetes are classified into five groups (orders) mainly on the basis of sporangial features: whether the sporangium is microscopic or macroscopic, whether spores in mass are light to bright colored or very dark to black, whether or not lime granules are present, and the presence or absence of and the nature of capillitial threads and the columella.

Importance   Myxomycetes aid in the decomposition of organic matter and thus, as phagotrophic organisms, function in the gradual recycling of bound nutrients. They are not important commercially, but they do provide biologists

163

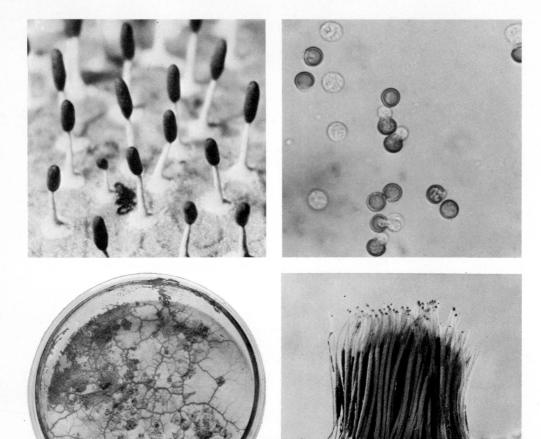

Fig. 22-1 Sporangia of *Diachea*. *(Courtesy Carolina Biological Supply Company.)*

Fig. 22-2 Haploid myxamebae of *Stemonitis* emerging from spores. *(Photomicrograph courtesy Bruno Kowalczyk.)*

Fig 22-3 Diploid plasmodium of *Physarum polycephalum* feeding on bacteria in an agar plate culture dish. *(Courtesy Carolina Biological Supply Company.)*

Fig. 22-4 Cluster of sporangia of *Stemonitis* on the surface of a decaying log. *(Courtesy Carolina Biological Supply Company.)*

with an unexcelled opportunity to study protoplasm and they are excellent for studying mitotic rhythms, DNA synthesis, inheritance mechanisms, and other fundamental life processes. Their development is of special interest in morphogenesis because, like most plants, their life cycle involves an alternation of haploid and diploid generations or phases, and their diploid reproductive phase is plantlike (Fig. 22-1), but on the other hand, their haploid and diploid vegetative or trophic phases are animallike (Figs. 22-2, 22-3).

Occurrence Myxomycetes are widely distributed throughout the world. They grow in moist, terrestrial habitats and are very common on dead wood (Fig. 22-4) and humus in shady places. Their amoeboid plasmodia feed actively on bacteria and other small organisms during periods of rain and high humidity. They occur in relative abundance in the moist decaying ground litter on forest floors, on the undersides of decaying logs, and between the bark and wood of well-decayed, felled trees. Fruiting structures are usually large enough to be seen with the unaided eye and may be found on the upper or exposed surfaces of their substrata.

Vegetative features—the feeding or trophic stages Plasmodial slime molds have more than one feeding stage. The spores of myxomycetes germinate to form flagellated cells (swarm cells) or amoebae (myxamoebae) (Fig. 22-5). A swarm cell has a characteristic appearance when it swims. It has thin pseudopodia at its posterior end and characteristically bears two, unequal, tinsel-less or whiplash flagella at the front end. (Swarm cells can be uniflagellate owing to the suppression of formation of the shorter flagellum).

Unlike the flagellum of prokaryotic cells (bacteria), the flagellum of Myxomycetes (and the flagellum and cilium of all other eukaryotic organisms) has a sheath that is a unit membrane and is continuous with the outer membrane of the motile cell. Also, the contractile fibers of the axis or axoneme of the flagellum have a 9 + 2 arrangement (2 central, single fibers and 9 peripheral, double fibers). The axoneme originates from a basal body or kinetosome. The kinetosome itself develops from a centriole.

Fig. 22-5 Flagellated cell or swarm cell of *Stemonitis* (arrow indicates the direction of swimming). Also seen are germinating spores and myxamebae. *(Photomicrograph courtesy Bruno Kowalczyk.)*

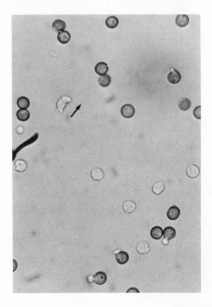

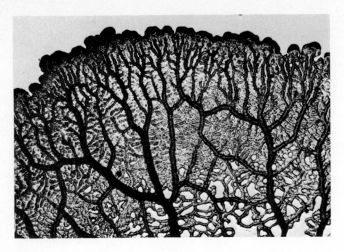

Fig. 22-6 Apical portion of a phaneroplasmodium of *Physarum polycephalum* growing on an agar culture dish. Photographed with transmitted light. *(Photomicrograph courtesy Carolina Biological Supply Company.)*

While a swarm cell swims, the longer flagellum is directed forward and the shorter flagellum is directed backward, usually closely appressed to the body of the cell. This kind of flagellated cell is unique to myxomycetes. When a flagellated cell (swarm cell) creeps on a substratum, it may engulf bacteria and other food particles by means of pseudopodia at its posterior end. Swarm cells can lose their flagella and become myxamoebae. Also, myxamoebae can grow flagella and become swarm cells.

The uninucleate, haploid myxamoebae structurally or cytologically are much like the amoebae of dictyostelid cellular slime molds (see p. 159). They are vegetative or trophic, feeding on bacteria and other food particles. However, myxamoebae either soon fuse or are converted into flagellated cells that soon fuse to form amoeboid zygotes, which initiate the dominant or major trophic phase: diploid, phagotrophic (holozoic), multinucleate, unwalled, amoeboid plasmodia. The diploid nucleus of an amoeboid zygote divides by mitosis. Subsequent nuclear divisions, along with feeding and growth, result in the formation of the multinucleate, unwalled plasmodial cell. Growing plasmodia may fuse vegetatively with zygotes and other plasmodia, especially during early plasmodial growth. This is not a sexual type of fusion because nuclei do not fuse. The multinucleate, diploid plasmodia feed in the same way as the uninucleate, haploid myxamoebae. They can even engulf and digest myxamoebae, an act of cannibalism.

Plasmodia vary in form, size, and color. They may be hyaline, white, yellow, red, violet, or black, and although this is reasonably constant in a given species, color may be affected by pH, light, temperature, or substances of the substratum.

Three basic plasmodial forms or types are recognized. (1) The protoplasmodium of *Echinostelium* and several other genera is the simplest kind. It is a tiny, multinucleate, amoeba-like protoplast that does not show rhythmic ebb and flow of protoplasm, as do the other types. (2) The aphanoplasmodium of *Stemonitis* and others is a thin and relatively inconspicuous, reticulate plasmodium. (3) The phaneroplasmodium is the most common kind and is larger, coarser, and more thickly reticulate and is the kind that is easily seen in nature (Fig. 22-6). The phaneroplasmodium of *Physarum polycephalum* can be grown in axenic culture on a chemically defined culture medium. Under these conditions food substances in the culture medium are absorbed through the outer membrane, as in the fungal mode of nutrition.

The phaneroplasmodium moves slowly in an amoeboid manner. Typical migrating plasmodia are fan shaped and are composed of a network of veinlike strands except at the advancing front. Each strand consists of a fluid inner portion, an outer gel layer, and a surrounding protective layer or sheath (not a cell wall), which is left behind the migrating plasmodium as a slime track. New sheath forms as the plasmodium grows and moves forward. Within a strand the fluid inner portion, which contains nuclei and other organelles, flows in one direction for a few seconds, slows to a stop, reverses directions, and then flows in the opposite direction. A contractile protein (myxomyosin) found in plasmodia may be responsible for this ebb and flow type of protoplasmic streaming.

Reproduction The air-dispersed spores of myxomycetes (Fig. 22-8), in a suitable habitat, come out of their spore walls or cysts as either flagellated swarm cells or myxamoebae, usually one from each spore (Figs. 22-2, 22-5). The haploid myxamoebae *multiply asexually* by fission or simple cell division followed by separation of the daughter cells. Under drying conditions, a myxamoeba can encyst, and when conditions are favorable the protoplast can escape from its cyst, engulf and digest food, grow, and divide again.

The diploid plasmodium multiplies asexually by growing into two or more parts and then fragmenting into separate thalli as the plasmodium moves forward. Under drying conditions, a plasmodium can cleave into multinucleate segments that encyst. A plasmodium that has converted itself into these hardened, resting macrocysts is called a sclerotium. Under favorable conditions a sclerotium germinates to form one or more active plasmodia.

Sexual reproduction is accomplished through an alternation of haploid and diploid generations or phases. Myxomycetes have a diplohaplontic type of life cycle, which means that vegetative growth occurs during both the diploid and haploid phases of the organism. Syngamy or sexual fusion takes places between pairs of either haploid swarmers or flagellated cells, which then are gametes. Because the two gametes that fuse are equal in size and appearance, they are called isogametes. The fusion cell or zygote initiates the plasmodial or diploid vegetative phase. Meiosis takes place in the diploid fruiting structure that develops from a plasmodium. Recent evidence (presence of synaptonemal complexes) indicates that the usual position of meiosis is within the spores just after they are cleaved. The spores of myxomycetes, then, may be called meiospores even though meiosis follows rather than precedes spore cleavage. These spores are sexual spores in the sense that they are involved with the sexual process meiosis. These spores continue the sexual life cycle, and they do not bring about asexual reproduction.

Just prior to fruiting, the well-fed plasmodium flows out or onto an exposed surface and there produces sporocarps (fruiting structures) characteristic for the species. Three major types of sporocarps are recognized: sporangia, plasmodiocarps, and aethalia. The sporangium is a relatively small, stalked or sessile mass of spores surrounded by a fragile wall called the peridium. Among the mass of spores of many species are threadlike strands, the capillitium, which is sometimes

Fig. 22-7 Several sporangia of *Arcyria* with prominent capillitia. *(Courtesy Carolina Biological Supply Company.)*

Fig. 22-8 Sporangial stalk and sporangium of *Dictydium* showing capillitium and spores being shed. *(Courtesy Carolina Biological Supply Company.)*

Fig. 22-9 Aethalial sporocarp of *Fuligo* on decaying vegetation. *(Courtesy Carolina Biological Supply Company.)*

Fig. 22-10 Aethalial sporocarps of *Lycogola* on a decaying log. *(Courtesy Carolina Biological Supply Company.)*

united to form a network. Some capillitia are accompanied by a central columnar structure, the columella. A thin, often transparent deposit of material at the base of a sporangium is called the hypothallus. Many sporangia are produced by a single large plasmodium. Species of *Physarum, Stemonitis, Arcyria,* and many other genera form sporangia (Figs. 22-1, 22-4, 22-7, 22-8). The plasmodiocarp is netlike or irregular and is derived from the main veins of the plasmodium. Certain species of *Physarum* and other genera produce spores in plasmodiocarps. The aethalium is relatively large and cushion shaped. A single aethalium develops from one plasmodium that has heaped up in a single mass. *Fuligo, Lycogola,* and other genera produce spores in aethalia (Figs. 22-9, 22-10).

Project

I. Plasmodium

Observe plasmodia in petri dish cultures on (a) filter paper and (b) agar. Note the remains of a plasmodium in its former positions. Is there any evidence of vegetative reproduction? Can you observe how the holes arise in a plasmodium? You can show amoeboid changes in a plasmodium by using a camera lucida (see Project 9: VI, p. 53) and drawing at intervals of 2–5 minutes the outline of the amoeboid front of the plasmodium. Care should be taken not to move either the paper or the culture dish from which you are drawing during this time. The paper should be taped to the table top. With this setup you can calculate the speed of movements. Look for pseudopodia at the leading edge of a plasmodium.

II. Sclerotium

A. Study the gross appearance of a sclerotium under a dissecting microscope.
B. Study a prepared slide showing individual sclerotial units.

III. Fruiting stage

A. Study the distinguishing features of the fruiting bodies of *Fuligo, Physarum, Stemonitis,* and *Lycogola,* or other common genera. (Use a hand lens or dissecting microscope.) Note the sporangium, sporangium stalk, sporangium wall (peridium), capillitial threads or network, and spore masses. The wall or peridium may not be present on many specimens since it is very fragile and usually breaks off soon, exposing the spores for wind dispersal.
B. From high power study a sporangium of *Stemonitis* mounted in water (or use a prepared slide). Note spores, capillitium, columella, and sporangium stalk.
C. Mount and study (using oil immersion) the spores of a few of the species available in order to compare spore wall characteristics.
D. Study prepared slides of sections of the fruiting bodies of *Fuligo* and *Lycogola.*

IV. Spore germination

A. *Germinating spores*
1. Remove the cover from a petri dish culture of *Physarum polycephalum* or

other plasmodial slime mold to allow sporangia to dry completely. This will take up to several days, depending on the relative humidity. (The spores of *Stemonitis* collected in nature usually germinate well.)

2. Make a circle of silicone gum or petroleum jelly on a glass slide. In the center of the circle place a drop of sterile water.
3. Using sterile forceps, transfer the dry sporangia to the drop of water, taking care to wet them thoroughly.
4. Either put the slide in a slide humidity chamber (see Project 3: VI.C.2, p. 29) or put a cover slip on the circle of petroleum jelly.
5. Flagellated gametes may emerge earlier (3–7 hours) but you can expect them after 18 hours if all goes well.

B. *Study of motile cells.* Find motile cells and note the amoeboid activity in the posterior end of a flagellated cell. Kill and fix the swimming cells with the fumes of osmic acid and stain lightly with crystal violet (see Project 10: I.B.11.b, p. 58). (Warning: Osmic acid fumes are very dangerous. Do not inhale them.) Look for the nucleus and flagella of a motile cell. Sometimes the short flagellum is very difficult to see or is absent. If you stain the cells intensely enough, you will observe (using oil immersion) that both of the flagella of a cell are of the whiplash or tinsel-less type.

V. Culture

Directions for culturing plasmodial slime molds are given in Project 3: II, p. 22. If materials and time are available, start your own culture.

Project 23   Phycomycetes or alga-like fungi

Contents

Introduction

Taxonomy   Phycomycetes or alga-like fungi are organisms of the group technically known as Phycomycetes, Phycomycophyta, or Phycomycota. There are about 270 genera and 1,400 species.

Although these lower fungi (those which are thought to still strongly resemble their early ancestors) are quite diverse and are probably a polyphyletic or unnatural group of organisms, those who study fungi (mycologists) agree that they are true fungi and that most of them are related to the higher fungi (those which are highly evolved).

Some botanists group phycomycetes variously with other fungi, algae, protozoa, and prokaryotes into a larger group called Protista and call them all protists. Others consider fungi to be a separate group or evolutionary line (Fungi) parallel with the green-plant and animal groups or evolutionary lines (Plantae and Animalia). And other botanists simply consider fungi to be plants that have their own unique characteristics.

Table 18-1 (p. 132) treats phycomycetes as plants and also, like ascomycetes, basidiomycetes, and imperfect fungi, in increasing order of specificity as eukaryotic plants, cryptogams, nonvascular plants, thallophytes, and true fungi.

171

Phycomycetes are classified into two main groups mainly on the basis of whether they are aquatic and produce motile flagellated cells (the more primitive Aquatic Phycomycetes, recently named Planomycetes) or whether they are terrestrial and incapable of forming flagellated reproductive cells (the more advanced Zygomycetes). A third, poorly known group, Trichomycetes, is composed of small filamentous forms that live in arthropods, mainly attached to their chitinous hindgut wall where they reproduce asexually by nonflagellate spores, conidia.

Planomycetes are a large, heterogeneous, artificial group that has diverse evolutionary origins, probably both in algae and protozoa. The highly diversified Planomycetes are divided into three main groups primarily on the basis of differences in their swimming motile cells (planonts). (1) Chytridiomycetes form zoospores (planospores) and sometimes motile gametes (planogametes) that have a single, posteriorly attached and directed whiplash flagellum, which is one that bears a thin tailpiece (Figs. 15-4, 15-8h). (2) Oomycetes form asexual zoospores that have two laterally attached flagella: a posteriorly directed whiplash flagellum and an anteriorly directed tinsel flagellum, one that bears two lateral rows of submicroscopic hairs (mastigonemes). (3) Hyphochytridiomycetes form asexual zoospores that have a single, 2-sided tinsel flagellum.

There are two groups of zoosporic organisms, Plasmodiophorales and Labyrinthulales, which are of uncertain affinity and can be classified either in Phycomycetes or in Mycetozoa. Members of the Plasmodiophotales, which are parasites mostly of vascular plants, are called Plasmodiophoromycetes when classified in the Phycomycetes and called Plasmodiophorida in the Mycetozoa. The motile cells of *Plasmodiophora* and the other plasmodiophorids bear two laterally attached flagella: a posteriorly directed whiplash flagellum and an anteriorly directed tinselless or whiplash flagellum. *Labyrinthula* and the other so-called net-plasmodial slime molds are common marine parasites and saprobes having motile cells essentially like those described above for Oomycetes.

Evolutionary trends relating to habitat, the thallus, and asexual and sexual reproduction indicate that Zygomycete-like fungi of past geological ages evolved into Ascomycete-like fungi of the past; thus, we now say the Phycomycetes are the ancestral group from which Ascomycetes probably evolved.

Importance   Phycomycetes as well as all other fungi are lysotrophic, which means that they grow as saprobes or parasites on or within their food sources and either dissolve them by digestion and absorb the dissolved food, or they absorb dissolved food already in the substratum (in the case of saprobes) or host organism (in the case of parasites). The saprobic (saprophytic) phycomycetes and other saprobic fungi decompose dead organic matter, and as such they are scavengers. This is extremely important in the recycling of essential elements and compounds in the environment. Phycomycetes are also of ecological importance as parasites of a wide variety of plants and invertebrate animals.

Of economic concern are the phycomycetes that live as parasites in such crop plants as potato, grape, cabbage, onion, cucumber, pea, and tobacco. A disease called late blight of potato, caused by the pathogenic water mold *Phytophthora infestans,* brought on a major famine in Ireland. The downy mildew disease of grapes, caused by a different planomycete, *Plasmopara viticola,* has threatened the wine industry of France. Another common water mold, *Pythium debaryanum,* causes a disease known as damping-off of seedlings and is a constant threat to crop and other seed plants that are in the seedling stage of development.

Fig. 23-1 A stream and a forest that provide many aquatic and terrestrial habitats for a variety of phycomycetes and other fungi and plants. *(Courtesy Carolina Biological Supply Company.)*

Some water molds are parasitic on fish, causing problems in fish hatcheries and aquaria. A few Planomycetes parasitize the aquatic larvae of mosquito and are being investigated as possible agents for the control of mosquitoes and the disease microorganisms that they carry. Water molds thus far have proved to be the best, albeit difficult, plant materials with which to study the hormonal control of sex, and they are valuable as experimental organisms in other areas of basic biological research.

Occurrence Phycomycetes are found in a wide range of habitats (Fig. 23-1), from the tropics to the poles, as saprobes and parasites. They live parasitically on other fungi and plants ranging from algae to flowering plants and less frequently on a number of invertebrate animals, from amoebae to millipedes. More kinds of phycomycetes are found in areas where man and domestic animals are than in areas undisturbed by man.

Zygomycetes are terrestrial and are abundant in soil, especially forest soil, and in dung. Planomycetes also are found in practically all soils, and of course they occur in most water habitats, but primarily freshwater ones, where they grow on such substrates as algae (Fig. 23-2), water-soaked seeds (Fig. 23-3), leaves and twigs (Fig. 23-4), pollen (Fig. 23-5), chitinic insect exuviae, and keratinic hair, feathers, and snake skin. Some planomycetes parasitize plankton algae and invertebrates. The relatively few marine forms are found mainly in estuaries and in the intertidal zones of ocean fringes.

Vegetative features The thallus (soma) of phycomycetes is relatively small. The thalli (somata) vary from microscopic, single-celled ones (Fig. 23-5) to larger, branched mycelia that appear, with or without a hand lens, as delicate mats or cottony growths (Fig. 23-3).

A few aquatic forms have unwalled thalli, but the vast majority of phycomycetes have cell walls. These walls, like those of higher fungi, are composed mainly of chitin, although Oomycetes have cellulosic walls and some other aquatics have both chitin and cellulose in their walls. Bounded by a lipoprotein membrane are organelles that are found in slime molds, in higher fungi, and in other eukaryotic organisms: a membrane-bounded nucleus (with chromosomes and a nucleolus), mitochondria, golgi apparatus (not in all), endoplasmic reticulum,

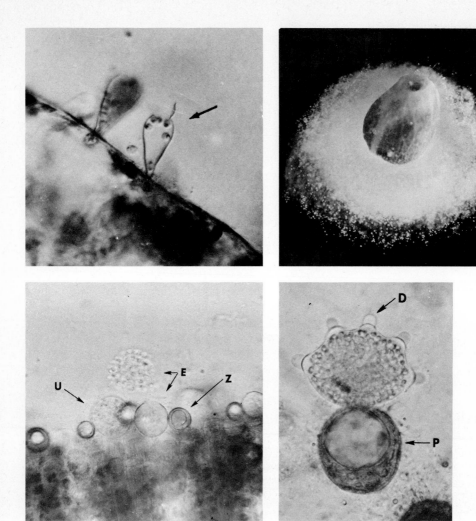

Fig. 23-2 Photomicrograph of *Chytridium sexuale*, an epibiotic and endobiotic mono-centric chytrid growing parasitically on the yellow-green alga *Vaucheria*. The arrow points to an operculate, epibiotic sporangium liberating posteriorly uniflagellate zoospores.

Fig. 23-3 Mycelium of a water mold (*Saprolegnia*) growing out from a water-soaked seed. *(Courtesy Carolina Biological Supply Company.)*

Fig. 23-4 Photomicrograph of *Chytriomyces*, an epibiotic and endobiotic monocentric chytrid growing saprobically on the edge of a dead leaf in water. U, undischarged zoosporangium; E, empty sporangium and a mass of zoospores just released; Z, zygospore (resting spore).

Fig. 23-5 Photomicrograph of a mature, zoosporangial thallus of *Phlyctochytrium*, an epibiotic and endobiotic monocentric chytrid growing on and within a pollen grain floating on water. P, pollen grain; D, one of the five papillate discharge structures through which zoospores will be liberated.

174

and ribosomes. Food is stored mainly as globules of lipid materials. An interesting feature of nuclear division of the small vegetative nuclei of phycomycetes and higher fungi is that the nuclear membrane remains intact during division, a process called endomitosis. Also, centrioles may be associated with the dividing nuclei of phycomycetes.

These diverse fungi have many types of vegetative thalli. Among the more primitive aquatic types is the simple sac (cell) with rhizoidal extensions, as found in the chytrids (order Chytridiales) *Chytriomyces* and *Rhizophydium*. Branched rhizoids grow in the food source, anchoring the thallus and absorbing dissolved food. This thallus type is called monocentric because nuclei are found only in the sac; thus there is a single control center for growth. When the sac is outside and the rhizoids are inside the food source, as in the above genera, the thallus is said to be epibiotic and endobiotic as well as monocentric (Figs. 23-2, 23-4, 23-5).

Other aquatics, like the water-mold *Allomyces,* a member of the uniflagellate Chytridiomycetes (order Blastocladiales), have a branching filamentous system, a mycelium or system of hyphae, that bears rhizoids (Fig. 15-6). Here the mycelium as well as the rhizoids may penetrate the food source and be trophic.

Most water molds, like the biflagellate *Saprolegnia* and *Achlya* (family Saprolegniaceae), have an extensively branched mycelium that lacks rhizoids and has a large central vacuole (Fig. 23-3). The hyphae of all water molds have large numbers of nuclei but no septa or cross walls, except occasional ones in older hyphae or where reproductive structures are delimited. Multinucleate mycelia lacking septa are said to be coenocytic and have coenocytic hyphae. A haustorium, which is a special, food-absorbing hyphal branch within a living cell of a host, is produced on the rhizoidless coenocytic mycelium of such parasitic oomycetes as *Peronospora* and *Albugo*. Zygomycetes also have a coenocytic vegetative mycelium that lacks rhizoids (Fig. 23-14). *Rhizopus,* a mucor (order Mucorales), is the best known member of this large and widespread group of terrestrial phycomycetes.

In *Allomyces* branching is dichotomous or forked (Fig. 15-6), but the vast majority of mycelial phycomycetes have hyphal systems with main axes and side branches, and they are said to have monopodial branching or to be monopodial.

Perhaps the most representative or characteristic type of vegetative thallus in phycomycetes is the coenocytic mycelium without rhizoids.

Asexual reproduction Many phycomycetes apparently have asexual life cycles only. Hyphal fragmentation is rare and not an important means of asexual reproduction of phycomycetes, but segmentation of hyphae into resting segments called gemmae and chlamydospores is fairly common.

Multiplication is accomplished primarily by asexual spores produced within sporangia, each of which is a sac (modified cell wall or sporangium wall) containing sporangiospores (the spores are cleaved or delimited endogenously from a common protoplast). The asexual sporangium is characteristic of phycomycetes and is not found in other true fungi. (The asci of ascomycetes and the basidia of basidiomycetes are interpreted as sexual sporangia).

The asexual spores of most Planomycetes are zoospores, which are unwalled and which effect spore dispersal actively by swimming and passively with water currents. Also, zoospores may be amoeboid, and a few have contractile vacuoles. Perhaps these are reflections of their protozoan or early-algal ancestry.

Fig. 23-6 Photomicrographs of living zoospores of *Allomyces*. F, flagellum; GM, giant mitochondrion (side body); L, lipid globules; M, mitochondria; N, nucleus; NC, nuclear cap; NO, nucleolus; V, vacuole.

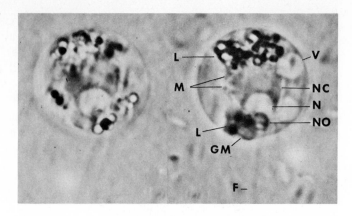

There are four basic types of planonts, based primarily on the differences in flagellation discussed in the introduction, but there are many interesting variants of these. For example, in the posteriorly uniflagellate Chytridiomycetes, some motile cells have many small mitochondria and their ribosomes are evenly dispersed in the cytoplasm, whereas others have their mitochondria united into a single giant one and their many ribosomes collected together and bounded by endoplasmic reticulum over a portion of the nucleus to form a nuclear cap (Fig. 23-6). And in the biflagellate Oomycetes, some motile cells have two morphologically and functionally distinct swimming stages (diplanetism) (Fig. 23-8), whereas others have but a single swimming stage (monoplanetism). The cytological features common to all phycomycete flagella, indeed to all eukaryote flagella, are described in the introduction to Project 22 under vegetative features (p. 165).

In simple unicellular forms like *Olpidium,* the whole mature vegetative cell is converted into a single sporangium (the fungus is said to be holocarpic). The other phycomycetes are eucarpic, with only part of the vegetative thallus used in reproduction. Here portions of the mature vegetative thallus are cut off by septa or cross walls. The entire contents of young multinucleate sporangia cleave into spores (Fig. 23-7), which have a single nucleus in Planomycetes and one to a few nuclei in Zygomycetes. Some chytrids (e.g., *Chytriomyces*) discharge their zoospores through a pore after the dehiscence of a lid or operculum (Fig. 23-2). The remaining Planomycetes have sporangial papillae that rupture at the time of zoospore liberation (Figs. 23-5, 23-7). The sudden release of zoospores in *Saprolegnia* is an exciting phenomenon to watch! Also, the fact that the primary zoospore encysts and later emerges as a secondary zoospore is an interesting and unusual phenomenon (called diplanetism) (Fig. 23-8).

In *Allomyces,* although asexual zoospores are produced in asexual zoosporangia only on the diploid sporophytic thallus, the female anisogametes produced by the gametophyte are known to be able to germinate parthenogenetically into new thalli (Fig. 15-1).

Certain "amphibious" Oomycetes, for example *Albugo,* live on the tissues of higher plants and release into the air entire sporangia that can either produce zoospores upon germination or produce a germ tube directly, depending on the environment (Fig. 23-9).

Terrestrial phycomycetes produce their sporangia elevated on hyphal branches, sporangiophores, which in rare cases (e.g., *Rhizopus*) are supported by rhizoid-

Fig. 23-7 Zoospore development in *Saprolegnia.* Right: Zoosporangium in the process of cleaving zoospores. Far right: Same sporangium after cleavage and shortly before zoospore release through the apical papilla. (*Photomicrographs courtesy Carolina Biological Supply Company.*)

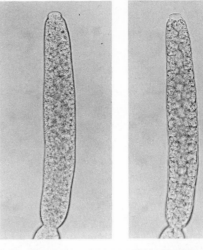

Fig. 23-8 (middle of page) Diplanetism in *Saprolegnia.* Left: Primary zoospore. Center: Encysted primary zoospore. Right: Secondary zoospore. (*Photomicrographs courtesy Carolina Biological Supply Company.*)

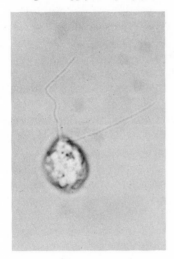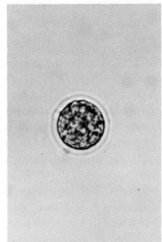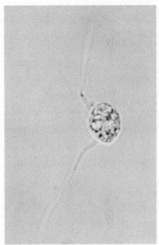

Fig. 23-9 (at right) *Albugo candida* (cause of white rust disease of cruciferous angiosperms). Stained section of the host (*Capsella*) showing multinucleate sporangiophores and sporangia (in rows) beneath the protruding epidermis of the host. (*Photomicrograph courtesy Carolina Biological Supply Company.*)

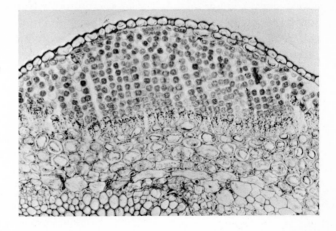

Fig. 23-10 Stained sporangia, sporangiophores, and supporting rhizoids of *Rhizopus*. *(Photomicrograph courtesy Carolina Biological Supply Company.)*

like hyphae (Fig. 23-10). *Rhizopus* and most other Zygomycetes have windblown, walled spores that are dispersed after the fragile sporangium wall fragments. *Pilobolus,* which grows in the dung of native animals, forcibly discharges its entire sporangium into the air.

In some terrestrial forms, for example *Entomophthora,* the sporangia are small, reduced, single-celled structures called conidiospores or conidia, which is the term used for the common asexual spores of ascomycetes and most imperfect fungi (Fig. 23-11).

The presence of conidiophores and conidia in the advanced members of the Zygomycetes indicates an evolutionary link with Ascomycetes.

Sexual reproduction   Sexual reproduction likewise is highly varied. Several *methods of sexual fusion (syngamy) and zygote behavior* are known. For example, some species of *Olpidium* liberate motile, flagellated isogametes (all the gametes look alike) that fuse in pairs and form swimming "zygotes" with both of the flagella and nuclei of the contributing gametes. These are not true zygotes because at this time only cytoplasmic fusion (plasmogamy), and not nuclear fusion (karyogamy), takes place. These swimming zygotes soon encyst, germinate, and form binucleate (dikaryotic) unicellular thalli. In *Allomyces* the gametes are different in size (called anisogametes, heterogametes that are similar in form but different in size) (Figs. 15-1, 15-9). A cell that produces gametes is called a

Fig. 23-11 Stained longitudinal section of a pustule of conidia and conidiophores of *Entomophthora musca,* parasitic on a housefly. *(Photomicrograph courtesy Ripon Microslides Laboratory.)*

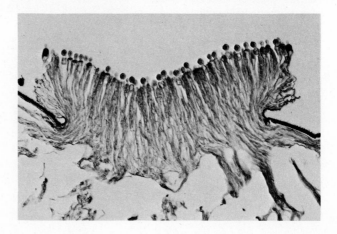

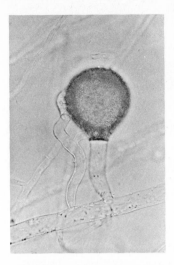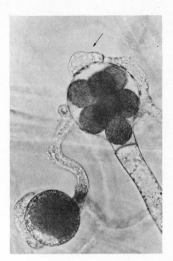

Fig. 23-12   Oogonial and antheridial development in
Saprolegnia. Left: Young oogonia with antheridial hyphae
attached. Center: Oogonium in egg origin (cleavage) stage.
Right: Mature oogonium with several cleaved eggs (arrow
points to an antheridium). *(Photomicrographs courtesy Carolina
Biological Supply Company.)*

gametangium, and in *Allomyces* the gametangia are anisogametangia. Female
gametes secrete a hormone, called sirenin, that causes male gametes to swim to
them. The swimming zygote of *Allomyces* is biflagellate and has a single diploid
nucleus: cytoplasmic fusion (plasmogamy) was followed immediately by nuclear
fusion (karyogamy). The zygote germinates immediately after encystment to
initiate a diploid sporophytic thallus. In *Monoblepharis* the heterogametes are
differentiated as nonmotile eggs and flagellated sperms. The female gametangium
is called an oogonium and the male gametangium an antheridium. The fertilized
egg secretes a thick wall and is thus converted into a zygospore called an oospore.
After a period of rest the oospore germinates by a tube and forms a hypha.

All the foregoing methods of sexual fusion are known as gametic fusion or
gametic plasmogamy because two differentiated gametes are involved in each
sexual fusion. However, in water molds of the *Saprolegnia* type, although the
contents of oogonia do differentiate one or more eggs, antheridia do not differentiate sperm cells. Instead, an antheridial hypha grows toward an oogonium and
makes contact, a chemotactic response caused by sex hormones (Fig 23-12).
After the antheridium is differentiated it sends in one or more tubes, and one
antheridial tube makes contact with each egg and discharges into the egg a single
male nucleus. This method is referred to as gametangial contact or gamete-
gametangial plasmogamy. The egg becomes an oospore, and after a period of
rest the oospore germinates by a tube and forms a hypha.

The final method is called gametangial fusion because no differentiated
gametes of any sort are produced. Instead, gametangia fuse and form a zygospore.
There are many variations on this method. The monocentric, aquatic *Chytriomyces*
forms its zygospore after the fusion of two rhizoidal tips of contributing thalli
(Figs. 23-13, 23-4). *Rhizopus*, like all Zygomycetes, differentiates its gametangia
at the tips of lateral, appressed hyphal tips called progametangia. The gametangia

179

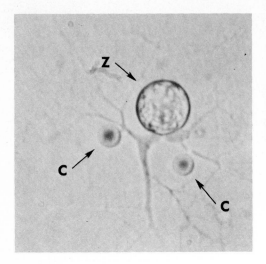

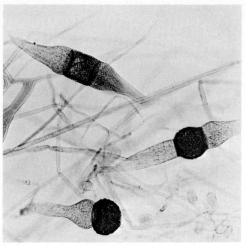

Fig. 23-13 Photomicrograph of zygospore formation in *Chytriomyces* growing on an agar culture medium. Z, young zygospore; C, the two contributing thalli.

Fig. 23-14 Stained young and mature zygospores of *Rhizopus*. Coenocytic vegetative mycelial hyphae are also seen. *(Photomicrograph courtesy Carolina Biological Supply Company.)*

are multinucleate and the zygote is a multinucleate coenozygote (Fig. 23-14). In *Chytriomyces, Rhizophydium,* and other chytrids having gametangial fusion, the zygospore liberates zoospores upon germination. The zygospore of *Rhizopus* and other Zygomycetes germinates with a tube and produces a sporangium at its tip.

The mucor *Endogone* is interesting because it forms large numbers of zygospores in a somewhat spherical mass of fungal tissue up to 3 cm in diameter. These hypogean (subterranean) sporocarps or fruit bodies, specifically called phycocarps, represent the sole case of tissue formation by phycomycetes and link them with the higher fungi, which regularly form sporocarps.

Although most phycomycetes require but a single thallus for sexual reproduction (they are homothallic or display homothallism), such species as *Achlya bisexualis* and *Rhizopus stolonifera* require two thalli of opposite mating type (they are heterothallic and display heterothallism). If male and female structures are differentiated, as in the water mold *Achlya,* a homothallic mycelium or strain is both male and female (⚥) and a heterothallic mycelium or strain is either male (♂) or female(♀). If maleness or femaleness does not express itself morphologically, as is the case in *Rhizopus,* a homothallic strain can only be called self-compatible or self-fertile (±) and a heterothallic strain called cross compatible and self-sterile (either + or −) (Fig. 23-15).

Interestingly, experiments have shown that sexual potential in heterothallic water molds like *Achlya* may be relative rather than fixed. A thallus has the potential for being either male or female. For example, a thallus that has a greater potential for maleness than femaleness (a "strong male") will develop antheridia and function as a male in the presence of another thallus that has a greater potential for femaleness than maleness (a "strong female"). Furthermore, because this strong female is also a weak male, it would develop antheridia instead of oogonia in the presence of an even stronger female.

180

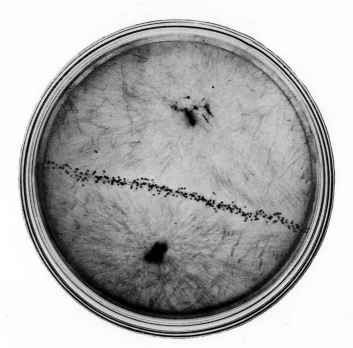

Fig. 23-15 Agar plate culture showing a line of zygospores between the opposite mating strains of a heterothallic species of the zygomycete *Phycomyces*. *(Courtesy Carolina Biological Supply Company.)*

Phycomycetes with *sexual life cycles* have the same basic kind; that is, most have a vegetative phase that alternates with a resting spore (zygospore).

The site of meiosis has not been established in many cases, so whether the vegetative phase is haploid (and the life cycle haplonic) or diploid (and the life cycle diplontic) is rarely known for sure. It is assumed that most phycomycetes have haplontic life cycles, with zygotic meiosis—meiosis occurring in the zygote or zygospore. There is some good genetic evidence for this in zygomycetes.

A few aquatic forms have sexual cycles involving an alternation of generations or phases, which is the sexual cycle typical of plants. For the most part *Allomyces* (subgenus *Euallomyces*) has isomorphic generations, which means that the haploid vegetative gametophyte or gametothallus has the same form and size as the diploid vegetative sporophyte or sporothallus. These species of *Allomyces* have a diplo-haplontic (= haplo-diplontic) type of life cycle. Meiosis occurs in the meiosporangium (sexual sporangium), which in *Allomyces* is also called a resistant sporangium because it can live in the dried condition. The zoospores produced by the meiosporangium are meiospores or, more specifically, meiozoospores (Figs. 15-1, 15-2).

Project

I. **Aquatic fungi with posteriorly uniflagellate reproductive cells** (Chytridiomycetes)

    A. *Allomyces, a chytridiomycete with a true mycelium in the order Blastocladiales*
        1. Refer to the drawings in Project 15, p. 84.
        2. Habit and form
            a. Observe the appearance of both the sporophytic and gametophytic

mycelia growing out from hemp seeds in water. Are the vegetative hyphae of the haploid and diploid phases identical in appearance (isomorphic)?

   b. Using low power, study agar plate cultures of the sporophyte and gametophyte. For these observations place the agar plate on the stage of the microscope. Note the dichotomous mode of branching. Are sporangia and gametangia terminal, intercalary, or both?

3. Gametophyte

   a. Gametangia. Are male gametangia above or below female gametangia? Are both gametangia pigmented? Is the pigment localized? If so, where is it located? By observing gametangia in various stages of development, note the changes that occur during maturation.

   b. Gamete discharge. Good material for the production of gametes can be had by scraping gametangia off the surface of a 1- to 2-week-old agar culture and mounting them in water. Gametes start emerging after about 1 hour. Observing a pair of male and female gametangia, determine whether or not female gametes start emerging before male gametes. Is this true for other pairs of gametangia?

   c. Syngamy. Find the clumping and fusion of the motile anisogametes. Try to determine if fusion begins at the anterior or posterior ends or if it is lateral. After plasmogamy try to observe the fusion of nuclei and nuclear caps. To see details of this sort, an optically excellent mount must be studied and you may need to use an oil immersion objective.

   d. Motile cell structure. (Refer to Project 11, p. 62.) Fix gametes and motile zygotes with the fumes of osmic acid and stain very lightly with crystal violet. (Warning: Osmic acid fumes are very dangerous. Do not inhale them.) Note flagellum, nucleolus, nucleus, nuclear cap, and an anterior and a posterior cluster of lipid globules. Note that the nuclear cap is at the opposite pole from the attachment of the flagellum. Only with an excellent optical system can you see all these details.

4. Sporophyte. In either a broth or hemp-seed culture, using low and high power (including oil immersion), find a branch showing asexual sporangia (zoosporangia) and meiosporangia (thick-walled resting sporangia). Observe that discharging zoosporangia have the features of discharging gametangia. Note that the resting sporangium is pigmented, has a pitted wall, and with oil immersion can be seen to have a very thin line or slit on one or more sides. It is along this preformed line that the resting sporangium ruptures in the germination process. Features of the wall are very hard to see.

5. Germination of meiosporangia (resting sporangia). Look for stages in the germination of the resting sporangia that have been dried on filter paper for several weeks, and then rewet for several hours. Note the relatively thin, colorless inner wall that protrudes through the slit in the thick, pitted, pigmented outer wall. Look for papillae on this thin wall.

6. Vegetative cytology. Using oil immersion on a very thin mount of actively growing hyphae, observe at the tip of a hypha lipid globules, nuclei, filamentous mitochondria, and vacuoles. Farther back on a hypha observe septa. Note that the septa are unevenly thickened. Find one that gives you an oblique view. Phase microscopy is best for studying these features.

7. Culture. Directions for culturing *Allomyces* are given in Project 3: V,

p. 27, and Project 15, p. 83. If materials and time are available, start your own cultures.

B. *Chytriomyces hyalinus, a monocentric chytrid (lacking a mycelium) of the order Chytridiales*

1. Study *Chytriomyces hyalinus*. From pollen and agar cultures observe as many of the following developmental stages as the material permits. Make mounts by removing material from pollen and agar cultures, placing it in a small drop of water on a slide, and adding a cover glass. If the resulting mount is too thick for use with oil immersion, draw it thinner with absorbent paper or gently mash the tiny block of agar. Oil immersion will be necessary for observation of details.

    a. Zoosporangial Thalli

    (1) Encysted zoospore with a single, conspicuous lipid globule.
    (2) Germling with the spore cyst and the incipient rhizoidal system.
    (3) Young thallus with one large nucleus and many conspicuous lipid globules.
    (4) Mature thallus with the sporangium showing a discharge plug and cleaved zoospores, each with a conspicuous lipid globule. Is there an apophysis?
    (5) Zoospore discharge with the zoospores emerging in a clump and surrounded by a discharge vesicle. Is an operculum present at discharge? What is the shape of the spore while swimming?

    b. Resting spore or resting sporangial thallus. The resting spore in this chytrid is formed by a sexual process involving the fusion of rhizoids of two different thalli. Look for stages in the formation and development of the young zygote and resting spore in agar culture.

2. Compare *Chytriomyces* with any other available chytrids, such as *Rhizophydium* and *Phlyctochytrium*. Look especially for differences in the number of discharge pores and in the method of zoospore discharge.

II. Aquatic fungi with biflagellate zoospores and coenocytic hyphae: *Saprolegnia* and *Achlya*, oomycetes of the water mold family Saprolegniaceae

A. *Zoosporangial development and zoospore discharge in Saprolegnia*

1. Zoospore discharge. Mount an entire hemp-seed culture (about 2 days old) in several drops of water on a slide, making certain that the hyphae are spread out. Do not add a cover glass. With low power look for a sporangium that will discharge its zoospores within about 5 minutes, one in which the zoospores are clearly cleaved and rocking back and forth just slightly. Patiently wait and then watch the exciting process of zoospore discharge. (Note: For zoospore structure, refer to Project 11, p. 62.)

2. Zoosporangial development
    a. Cut off the hyphae and discard the hemp seed. (If the seed is put back into water, new hyphae will grow out from it.) Follow sporangial development, from high power in an uncovered mount, starting with the spore-initial stage (zoospore cleavage) to the pre-emergence stage that leads to zoospore discharge. Prior to the emergence of zoospores, they rock back and forth slightly because of flagellar undulation.
    b. Between your intermittent observations of development, study with

183

oil immersion another mount of hyphae. Note as many cytological details as you can in the tips of both vegetative and zoosporangial hyphae.

B. *Test for cellulose.* After you have finished with one of your mounts, lift the cover glass, drain off most of the water, add 2 or 3 drops of chloriodide of zinc, add a few cotton fibers as a control, cover, and observe the purple coloration of structures containing cellulose.

C. *Oogonial, antheridial, and oospore (zygospore) development*

1. Find as many stages in the development of oogonia and antheridia as you can. You may need to observe the culture for several days, but hopefully this material has been timed so as to produce during this laboratory period the necessary stages (see Project 3: V, p. 28). The oil immersion lens may be needed for seeing the fertilization tube that leads from the antheridium through the oogonial wall to the egg (oosphere) or the zygospore (oospore).

2. Test a matured culture (containing oospores) for cellulose. Identify those structures that do not stain purple with chloroiodide of zinc.

D. *Culture.* Directions for culturing water molds for their reproductive stages are given in Project 3: V, p. 27, and directions for subculturing water molds are given in Project 3: III, p. 24. If materials and time are available, make your own cultures.

III. **Terrestrial fungi with coenocytic hyphae and nonflagellate spores:** mucors (order Mucorales) of the zygomycetes

You will be provided with prepared slides and with cultures that have been grown for 1–5 days at room temperature.

A. *Rhizopus stolonifer (= R. nigricans)*

1. Asexual stage (sporangium development)

a. Place a petri dish culture, containing *Rhizopus* growing on a piece of bread, on the stage of a dissecting microscope and locate the cottony growth. Identify vegetative hyphae, stolons, rhizoids, sporangiophores, and sporangia.

b. Mount some of this material in 7 per cent KOH (a wetting agent) or obtain prepared slides showing sporangia in various stages of development. Identify the structures listed above and in addition the sporangium wall, columella, and spores.

2. Sexual stage (zygospore development)

a. Examine an agar (e.g., cornmeal agar) plate culture that was inoculated with both plus (+) and minus (−) strains of this heterothallic fungus. Can you find a line of zygospores that have formed, or are forming, at the line of contact between the two strains of opposite mating type?

b. Mount some of this material in 7 per cent KOH or obtain prepared slides showing various stages in zygospore development. Identify vegetative hyphae, progametangia, gametangia, suspensors, zygotes or young zygospores, and mature zygospores.

3. Spore germination and the vegetative mycelium

a. Cut out small portions of agar containing *Rhizopus* at different stages of vegetative development, mount in water, add cover slips, and study from high power.

(1) Examine germinated spores (germlings) from an agar plate culture that is about 24 hours old. Identify old spore walls and hyphae. Note the mode of branching if any has occurred.

(2) Examine young mycelium from the edge of a colony. Note mode of branching and the coenocytic condition. Can you find cytoplasmic strands traversing the central vacuole?

(3) Examine older mycelium from near the center of a colony. Find septa in the older hyphae. Are they regularly spaced along the length of a hypha?

b. (Prepared slide) Study mycelium that has been stained to show nuclei.

Project 24   Ascomycetes or sac fungi

Contents

Introduction

Taxonomy   Ascomycetes or sac fungi are organisms of the group technically known as Ascomycetes, Ascomycophyta, or Ascomycota. There are about 1,800 genera and 25,000 species.

Ascomycetes comprise the largest group of fungi. There are over 20 orders and these are classified into larger groups primarily on the basis of whether or not they form reproductive fungal tissue, called fruiting bodies, sporocarps or ascocarps, and also on how the ascocarp develops. The primitive yeasts and related forms (Hemiascomycetes) do not form ascocarps, whereas the higher ascomycetes (Euascomycetes and Loculoascomycetes) do. The orders of Euasco-mycetes are grouped according to the development and form of the ascocarp— whether it is a cleistothecium (Plectomycetes), perithecium (Pyrenomycetes), or apothecium (Discomycetes).

Although some mycologists think that ascomycetes have their origin in red algal seaweeds, most consider their conidia, asci, and other features to link them with the higher phycomycetes. For example, the ascus of some filamentous Hemiascomycetes resembles the sporangium of some Zygomycetes, and the

Fig. 24-1 Three brown apothecia (fruiting structures) of morel (*Morchella*), a discomycetous euascomycete, growing from humus in a woods. *(Courtesy Carolina Biological Supply Company.)*

conidium of Ascomycetes resembles the uninucleate sporangium or conidium of Zygomycetes. Indeed, their habitat, thallus, and asexual and sexual reproduction indicate that Zygomycete-like fungi of the past probably evolved into Ascomycete-like fungi of the past, which in turn have evolved into the present-day forms. Ascomycetes are in a direct evolutionary line between Phycomycetes and Basidiomycetes.

Asexual fungi that have the vegetative and asexual features of known ascomycetes are given names of convenience, for identification purposes, and are classified in the form-group Deuteromycetes (imperfect fungi). Most of the imperfect fungi are either the asexual or imperfect stages of known ascomycetes or are thought to have evolved from ascomycetes and to have permanently lost their sexual or perfect stages.

Importance Ascomycetes are important decomposers of the dead organic matter in forest and other terrestrial ecosystems. *Neurospora* and *Sordaria* have unique qualities that make them invaluable biological tools in basic genetic research.

Fleshy forms are a source of food for insects and mammals, and man finds morels (Fig. 24-1) and truffles favorite edible fungi. Yeasts serve as a high-

Fig. 24-2 Two heads of rye (an angiosperm) infected with *Claviceps purpurea*, a pyrenomycetous euascomycete. Arrows point to three black sclerotia. *(Courtesy Carolina Biological Supply Company.)*

vitamin food source and are important in the alcoholic fermentation of beverages and in the leavening of bread and other bakery products.

Aspergillus can cause a serious lung disease, aspergillosis. *Penicillium* and *Aspergillus* give desirable flavors to certain cheeses, produce a high quality of citric and other organic acids, and are the source of such antibiotic drugs as penicillin. *Claviceps purpurea* is responsible for the plant disease of rye known as ergot (Fig. 24-2). Ergotism, an animal and human disease that can lead to death, is caused by eating rye infected with *Claviceps.* The ergot drug (alkaloid), which is derived from *Claviceps,* is used to induce uterine contractions. Ergotism may cause hallucinations, and LSD is also derived from ergot-diseased portions (sclerotia) of rye. Yeasts cause a human disease, thrush, and also cause serious inflammations of vaginal and mouth membranes.

Ascomycete molds are major spoilers of stored food, leather, cloth, painted surfaces, etc. Many ascomycetes are destructive parasites of plants important in nature's and man's economy, such as chestnut blight, Dutch elm disease, powdery mildews of a wide variety of ornamental and crop plants, oak wilt, sycamore blight, rye ergot, grape black rot, strawberry, pear, and banana leaf spots, apple canker, apple scab, cherry and peach brown rot, and peach leaf curl.

Occurrence   Yeasts are universally distributed from the tropics to the poles and are especially abundant in plant exudates rich in sugar. They are also in polluted waters and most aquatic and terrestrial habitats where there is a food source. The other ascomycetes are also ubiquitous saprobes or are parasites restricted by the host ranges of a wide variety of plants, some animals, and man. Most ascomycetes are terrestrial saprobes living in soil, dung, decaying logs, sticks, leaf mold, fallen fruit, chitinic insect exuviae, and keratinic feathers, hair, and horn. The fungal components of most lichens are ascomycetes, and these are mostly Discomycetes.

Vegetative features   Most ascomycetes have a well-developed, delicate, cobweb-like, branching, septate, haploid mycelium with cells having one to several nuclei, vacuoles, a few lipid globules and chitinous walls (Fig. 16-1). Some ascomycetes have uninucleate cells. Some parasitic forms develop haustoria. Ascomycete septa or cross walls have small, simple pores through which protoplasm may flow. The nuclear membrane is generally thought to persist throughout vegetative nuclear division (but to disappear during meiosis). A few ascomycetes, like the powdery mildew *Erysiphe* and the filamentous yeast *Dipodascus,* have mycelia with uninucleate cells. *Taphrina* has vegetative hyphae that are binucleate, with the two nuclei of a cell in heterothallic species being of opposite mating type and therefore dikaryotic. In ascomycetes, the haploid (n) mycelium, which is initiated from an ascospore, is called a primary mycelium. The dikaryotic ($n + n$) mycelium, the product of plasmogamy, is called a secondary mycelium. In the Hemiascomycetes, only *Taphrina* produces a secondary mycelium, and of all ascomycetes this is the only one with an $n + n$ trophic phase.

Many yeasts have small, ovoid, elongate, or globose unicellular and uninucleate thalli (Fig. 24-3). The cells may be haploid or diploid, and they can hang together, forming chains called pseudomycelia.

Vegetative plectenchyma (fungal tissue) may form in Euascomycetes. *Claviceps* forms a stroma which, as with all stromata, serves as a base or cushion on, or in which, reproductive structures develop (Fig. 24-6). A sclerotium is a hard body resistant to unfavorable conditions (Fig. 24-2).

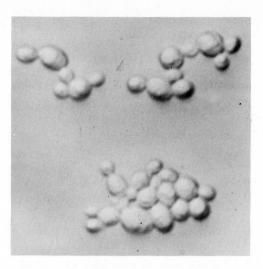

Fig. 24-3 *Saccharomyces,* a unicellular budding yeast. *(Photomicrograph courtesy Carolina Biological Supply Company.)*

Fig. 24-4 Stained conidiophores and conidia of *Penicillium. (Photomicrograph courtesy Carolina Biological Supply Company.)*

Hyphae commonly fuse with other hyphae, a process called anastomosis, and this makes possible a vegetative exchange of nuclei between genetically different strains of a species (Fig. 15-1E). After anastomosis, the nuclei of each strain may migrate throughout the mycelium of the other strain, passing from cell to cell through the tiny pore in each septum or cross wall; however, karyogamy and meiosis do not follow and this is not truly a sexual phenomenon. However, a haploid mycelium that has only one kind of nucleus genetically (a mycelium that was homokaryotic) may thus be converted into a heterokaryotic mycelium. This paves the way for a semisexual phenomenon, parasexuality, which will be discussed at the end of the section dealing with sexual reproduction

Asexual reproduction Although hyphal fragmentation is common, multiplication in most ascomycetes usually is accomplished through wind-disseminated asexual spores, conidia, borne on conidiophores. It is difficult to find any air, even at high altitudes, that does not have a lot of conidia in it.

The powdery mildews form uninucleate conidia in a chain and in a very simple manner on conidiophores that are simple, erect hyphae. *Penicillium* and *Aspergillus* have specialized, differentiated conidiophores bearing many chains of uninucleate conidia that develop in a more complicated way, by budding from a phialide (Figs. 24-4, 26-2). (Higher red algae and some ascomycetes form male reproductive cells, spermatia, in this manner.) There are many other variations on the conidium method of asexual reproduction. Some conidia are multinucleate and some are multicellular and have a variety of shapes. Those produced by the relatively few aquatic species have shapes that enhance flotation. Some ascomycetes have conidiophores massed together in elongate synnemata, others have them in cushion-shaped sporodochia or bedlike acervuli, and still others form conidia in hollow pycnidia.

Most unicellular yeasts reproduce asexually by budding (Fig. 24-3), but some have simple binary fission. Buds may be called blastospores. Budding is not a phenomenon restricted to ascomycetes. It occurs in certain Zygomycetes and

Basidiomycetes, sometimes when these fungi are under special environmental conditions.

Sexual reproduction   Ascomycetes are sexual and have sexual life cycles distinguished by the production of sexual sporangia called asci. Karyogamy and meiosis occur in the ascus (Figs. 16-3, 16-8).

The majority of ascomycetes (Euascomycetes) have a haplo-dikaryotic life cycle. Plasmogamy, but not karyogamy, occurs between either specialized or unspecialized cells. If cells are specialized as antheridia ($\male$) and ascogonia ($\female$), with or without receptive hairs called trichogynes, plasmogamy is said to be of the gametangial kind. If no special cells form, plasmogamy is said to be somatic— somatogamy has occurred. The former is more characteristic of Euascomycetes. Ascogonia, which may be either uninucleate or multinucleate and unicellular or multicellular, ordinarily develop in a tiny ball-like mass of haploid hyphae called a protoascocarp. Some Euascomycetes form tiny uninucleate male cells or gametangia called spermatia that can empty their contents into an ascogonium through its trichogyne, a process called spermatization. In some Euascomycetes ordinary conidia (macroconidia) serve as male cells. After plasmogamy in most Euascomycetes the paired nuclei replicate conjugately (together at the same time) and septa are laid down between daughter pairs, initiating a secondary ($n + n$) mycelium, referred to as ascogenous hyphae. The primary mycelium of the proto-ascocarp develops as tissue while the ascogenous hyphae are growing (Fig. 16-2). In time, the branching (n) and ($n + n$) hyphae develop into a mature ascocarp. Ordinarily, asci are initiated at the tips of ascogenous hyphae by a curious hook or crozier process, believed to be the forerunner of cell division by clamp formation in Basidiomycetes (Fig. 16-3b). Typically, the four nuclei produced by meiosis in an ascus undergo one mitotic division, resulting in eight nuclei around which eight ascospores are cleaved (Figs. 16-7, 16-8, 24-10, 24-11). But asci with as few as two and as many as hundreds of ascospores occur.

Three major types of ascocarps are recognized, but there are many variations in ascocarp development. For example, whereas the sexual stage of *Aspergillus* is a typical cleistothecium (Fig. 24-5) with scattered globose asci completely surrounded by a sporocarp wall (peridium) and with ascospores not forcibly ejected from the sporocarp, and whereas *Sordaria* forms a typical perithecium (Figs. 16-4, 24-6) with an internal basal layer or cluster (hymenium) of elongate asci surrounded by a peridium in which an apical pore develops through which the asci forcibly discharge their ascospores, powdery mildews (Erysiphales) have ascocarps with intermediate characteristics (Fig. 24-7). Also, whereas *Peziza* and *Urnula* form a typical cup-shaped apothecium (Figs. 24-8, 24-9) with a large number of asci and sterile hyphae, paraphyses, forming a smooth hymenium that covers the upper and inner surface (Fig. 24-10), *Morchella* has a massive hymenium covering numerous pits in a big, stiped, somewhat dome-shaped and spongelike portion (Fig. 24-1).

Most Hemiascomycetes, such as *Schizosaccharomyces octosporus,* are haploid and have haplontic life cycles. Two vegetative, haploid cells fuse (plasmogamy) and become a cell (young ascus) in which karyogamy, meiosis, and ascospore formation immediately follow (Fig 24-11). Some, like *Saccharomycodes ludwigii,* are diploid and have diplontic cycles, with meiosis taking place in a mature diploid vegetative cell (ascus), followed at once by ascospore formation. When asco-

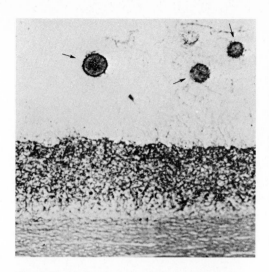

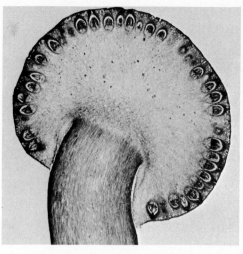

Fig. 24-5 Stained section of an orange peel showing *Aspergillus* mycelium on the surface and three globose cleistothecia (arrows).

Fig. 24-6 Stained longitudinal section of a stroma of *Claviceps purpurea* bearing many sunken perithecia. *(Photomicrograph courtesy Carolina Biological Supply Company.)*

spores germinate, they fuse immediately and reestablish the diploid condition. And other yeasts, like *Saccharomyces cerevisiae,* have both haploid and diploid growth phases and thus, like *Allomyces* and typical plants, a haplo-diplontic (or diplo-haplontic) life cycle. *Taphrina* is unique in having a dikaryo-haplontic cycle, like basidiomycetes.

Hyphal anastomosis can cause a vegetative (somatic) mycelium to become heterokaryotic, as discussed at the end of the section dealing with vegetative features. A heterokaryotic mycelium of *Aspergillus,* for example, can undergo a semisexual phenomenon, parasexuality, through which somatic gene recombination occurs. This is a very rare event; however, somatic nuclear fusion does occur occasionally, and these rare diploid nuclei, amongst large numbers of ordinary haploid nuclei, do occasionally have mitotic crossing over during division. When one of these scarce recombinant diploid nuclei becomes haploid (vegetative

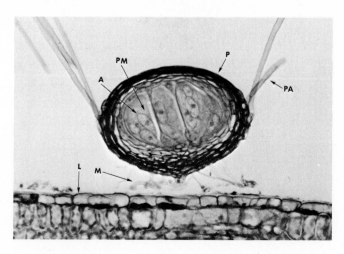

Fig. 24-7 Stained longitudinal section of the perithecium of the powdery mildew *Uncinula salicis* parasitic on a willow leaf. PA, perithecial appendage; P, peridium; PM, periplasm; A, ascospore; M, primary vegetative mycelium on the surface of the host; L, leaf in cross-sectional view. *(Photomicrograph courtesy Carolina Biological Supply Company.)*

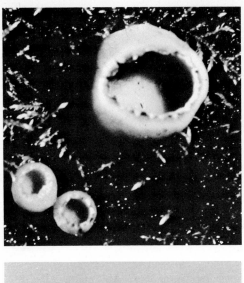

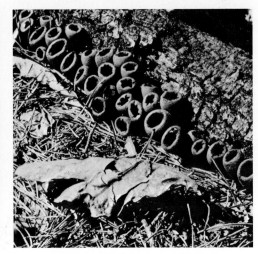

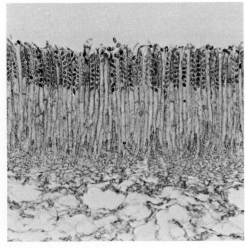

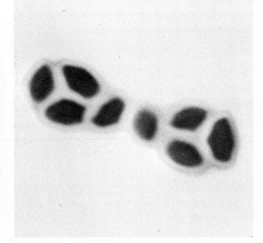

Fig. 24-8   Three orange-colored apothecia of *Peziza* growing in a bed of moss. *(Courtesy Carolina Biological Supply Company.)*

Fig. 24-10   Stained longitudinal section of the subhymenial and hymenial portions of an ascocarp of *Peziza*. Each ascus contains eight ascospores. *(Photomicrograph courtesy Carolina Biological Supply Company.)*

Fig. 24-9   Many dark-colored apothecia of *Urnula* growing on a decaying log in a forest. *(Courtesy Carolina Biological Supply Company.)*

Fig. 24-11   Stained, eight-spored ascus of *Schizosaccharomyces octosporus. (Photomicrograph courtesy Carolina Biological Supply Company.)*

or somatic haploidization), as generally happens, but in successive steps, the genetic events of sexual reproduction have been completed in the absence of true sexuality. A haploid nucleus with a genotype unlike those of either of the two original mycelia has come into being. When this nucleus is incorporated into a conidium and when the conidium produces a new mycelium, a new genetic strain has been established.

Project

I. **Ascomycetes without fruiting bodies (Hemiascomycetes):** yeasts of the order Endomycetales

    A. *Schizosaccharomyces octosporus, a fission yeast.* Using a flame-sterilized wire loop, mount a bit of a 6- to 8-day-old PDA or CMDP agar plate culture in a drop of water on a glass slide. Add a cover slip and study with your highest power lenses.

        1. Vegetative cells. Find stages of somatic cell division (fission).

        2. Find several stages (from gametangia to mature ascus) in ascus formation. Can you find periplasm, the cytoplasm not included within ascospores? Identify young gametangia (just prior to plasmogamy), zygote, mature ascus and ascospores.

    B. *Saccharomyces, a budding yeast*

        1. Budding. Observe with oil immersion stages in this special kind of cell division. Note that cross walls do form. Find a pseudomycelium.

        2. Sex. Observe a prepared slide (using oil immersion) showing stained asci and ascospores.

    C. Observe yeasts growing in various carbohydrate solutions and in distilled water. Each carbohydrate solution (glucose, fructose, maltose, sucrose, starch) is a 5 per cent solution and to each (and to the distilled water) has been added 0.1 per cent peptone (10 ml of a 1 per cent solution). Observe each fermentation tube and the CO_2 level in each tube.

II. **Euascomycetes with cleistothecia (Plectomycetes):** *Penicillium* and *Aspergillus* of the order Eurotiales

    A. *Mycelium and asexual reproduction.* Cut a thin sliver or cross-sectional piece of a molded, decaying orange or of an agar plate culture. Include the peripheral portion where the youngest hyphae and reproductive structures are. (You may need to add a wetting agent like 7 per cent KOH to see reproductive structures clearly.) Put on a cover slip and mash the mount.

        1. Thallus. Examine the mycelium. What is the mode of branching? Can you distinguish any organelles other than vacuoles and lipid granules? Are cross walls present in all the hyphae? From what part or parts of the cells do branch hyphae arise?

        2. Asexual reproduction. Study a reproductive branch (conidiophore) from low and high power. How do reproductive branches here differ from those of *Rhizopus* (Phycomycetes)? The spores on a conidiophore are called conidia. How are they arranged?

    B. *Sexual reproduction.* (Use prepared slides of sections of cleistothecial ascocarps.) Ultimate observations should be made from oil immersion. Note

193

that the spherical asci are scattered, arising from different levels within the cleistothecium. Note the outer sterile hyphae forming the cleistothecial wall (peridium), the ascus wall, the Yo-Yo–shaped ascospores, and the ground tissue (hyphae surrounding asci). Look for developmental stages.

III. Euascomycetes with perithecia (Pyrenomycetes)

A. *Powdery mildews or common leaf mildews (order Erysiphales)*
   1. Habit. Using the dissecting microscope, study a diseased leaf showing the extent of the mycelium. Are both surfaces infected? Also find fruiting bodies. Young ones are light; mature ones are black.
   2. Vegetative and conidial stages. (From prepared slide: cross section of leaf.) Conidia are produced during the early part of the growing season on the leaf surface, with short upright hyphae giving rise to chains of conidia.
      a. Identify mycelium of the parasite and the upper epidermis, mesophyll, and lower epidermis of the host.
      b. From high power and oil immersion observe details of a haustorium (lobed in this species) in an epidermal cell, mycelium or hyphae on the surface of the epidermis, conidiophore, and short chain of conidia. Find nuclei in haustoria and ordinary hyphal cells.
   3. Sexual stage
      a. Fruiting bodies (perithecia or "cleistothecia") are usually formed early in the season but do not mature, as a rule, until after the host's deciduous leaves fall. Perithecia are minute, black, spherical bodies smaller than a pinhead. Study with high power of the dissecting microscope. With water or 50 per cent alcohol moisten the surface of a leaf and scrape perithecia off. Mount the scraped material in water and find perithecial appendages. So that you can see asci and ascospores, crush perithecia under a cover glass. Asci will emerge. How many asci are there in each perithecium? How many ascospores are there in each ascus? Note periplasm around ascospores.
      b. Using prepared slides find perithecia cut in longitudinal section, study the development of perithecia, asci, and ascospores. Find (1) stage when ascus is uninucleate, (2) division stages, and (3) the mature condition. Identify, if possible, astral rays, ascospore, periplasm, ascus, peridium (perithecial wall), vegetative mycelium, and ascogenous hyphae. (If the slides you are studying are of *Erysiphe aggretata* infecting alder catkins, most of the material on the slide is host.)
   4. Variation in perithecial structure. Study as many genera as are available, noting differences in perithecial appendages and in the number of asci in each ascocarp. For example, you may have available the powdery mildews *Uncinula macrospora* and *Phyllactinia corylea* on the elms *Ulmus alata* or *U. americana* or the oak *Quercus alba*.
B. *A typical perithecial ascomycete (order Spheriales): Sordaria*
   1. Refer to the drawings in Project 16, p. 107.
   2. Examine an agar plate culture of *Sordaria*. Remove the lid and put the culture dish on the stage of your microscope. Find the numerous dark perithecia. Notice their characteristic shape, looking especially for the

neck. Discharged ascospores will probably be seen among the mycelial hyphae on the surface of the agar.

3. Remove a few perithecia from the agar culture and put them in a drop of water on a microscope slide. Put a cover slip on top and gently press down, without squashing the perithecia to bits, to release the cluster of asci from each perithecium. Identify peridium (perithecial wall), ascus, ascospore, and epiplasm. In the apex of the ascus find the pore through which ascospores are discharged.

4. Genetics. If your culture is *Sordaria fimicola* and is one in which a dark-spored strain and a tan- or gray-spored strain have been crossed or mated, you may have hybrid perithecia and hybrid asci in your mount. Such asci have spores of two colors in each ascus: Four dark spores and four tan or gray spores. For additional details refer to Experiment 2 in Project 16, p. 108, especially Figs. 16-4, 16-7, and 16-8.

IV. Euascomycetes with apothecia (Discomycetes)

A. *A cup fungus: Peziza*
   1. If fresh or preserved material is available, make a thin longitudinal section of an apothecium and make a microscopic examination of it.
   2. Examine with low power a prepared slide of a longitudinal section of an apothecium. Find: ectal excipulum, hypothecium, hymenium, asci, ascospores, paraphyses, and (if present) stalk.
B. *A large ascomycete fleshy fungus: Morchella esculenta, morel*
   1. Study an ascocarp, observing the stalk and the hymenium that covers the concave surfaces of the spongelike portion of the apothecium.
   2. With forceps pinch off a piece of the ascus-bearing surface (hymenium) and mount in water. Study a well-mashed piece under high power. How many ascospores are in a single ascus? Is the number in each ascus the same? Was all the cytoplasm of the young ascus used in ascospore formation? Look for the epiplasm in asci with young ascospores. Trace the ascus down to the hyphae subtending the asci. This region is called the trama.

Project **25** Basidiomycetes or club fungi

Contents

Introduction
Taxonomy; Importance; Occurrence;
Vegetative features; Asexual reproduction;
Sexual reproduction

Project

Introduction

Taxonomy   Basidiomycetes or club fungi are organisms of the group technically known as Basidiomycetes, Basidiomycophyta, or Basidiomycota. There are about 550 genera and 15,000 species.

Basidiomycetes are classified into larger groups primarily on variations in the meiosporangium, or basidium; on the absence or presence of reproductive structures composed of tissues, the basidiocarp; and on variations in the basidiocarp. The rust, smut, and jelly fungi groups (Heterobasidiomycetes) have septate or deeply divided basidia with basidiocarps either lacking, poorly developed, or well developed and crustlike or jelly-like. With the exception of *Exobasidium,* the other basidiomycetes (Homobasidiomycetes) develop basidiocarps and none have septate or deeply divided basidia. Leather fungi, coral fungi, pore fungi, tooth fungi, and gill fungi (Hymenomycetes) have their hymenia or layers of basidia exposed to the air before basidiospores mature and are forcibly discharged. Puffballs, earthstars, stinkhorns, and bird nest fungi (Gasteromycetes) have their basidiocarps remaining closed at least until the basidiospores are mature and passively separated from their basidia.

Basidiomycetes appear to have their origin in early euascomycetous fungi, although some mycologists think that similarities in life cycles relate the rust fungi either directly or indirectly to red algal seaweeds. It is clear that the basidiocarp evolved from the ascocarp, the basidium from the ascus, the dikaryotic secondary mycelium from ascogenous hyphae, and clamp connections apparently from croziers. The evidence further indicates that Heterobasidiomycetes are more primitive and Homobasidiomycetes are more advanced.

Basidiomycetes are the most advanced of the fungi. Some fungi formerly classed as Deuteromycetes have been shown to be the vegetative stages of known basidiomycetes, but other imperfect fungi are conjectured to be basidiomycetes that have permanently lost sexuality. Even with such Deuteromycetes, Basidiomycetes are still the most advanced of the fungi.

Importance   Basidiomycetes are the major wood decay organisms (Figs. 25-1, 17-1). Also, most trees have fungi living in a balanced relationship with their roots. Most of these endotrophic (living inside roots) and ectotrophic (outside covering the surface) mycorrhizal fungi are basidiomycetes. As both mycorrhizae and as saprobic wood decay organisms, basidiomycetes are extremely important in nature. They are of ecological importance as cellulose and lignin degrading agents, as mineral recyclers, and as parasites of a wide variety of terrestrial plants, mostly seed plants.

Cultivation of the mushroom *Agaricus* is a large industry today, and native edible mushrooms are an important part of man's diet in many countries. However, some mushrooms, like certain species of *Amanita,* are poisonous and cause either serious illness or death. Poisonous mushrooms look and taste just as edible as those which really are, so one must know the species well before he eats them.

Several mushrooms are hallucinogenic. *Psilocybe* is used by some Mexican Indians in religious rituals. Also, its hallucinogenic substance, psilocybin, has been experimented with in psychotherapy.

Species of the leather fungus *Stereum* causes heart rot of oak trees and other basidiomycetes parasitize other trees of importance to man. Rusts and smuts are parasitic on many of the cereal crops (Fig. 25-2), fruit and timber trees (Figs. 25-3, 25-4), and other vascular plants. They cause millions of dollars in crop loss annually. It is estimated that the annual wheat crop is reduced by one fourth because of the rust *Puccinia graminis.*

Occurrence   Basidiomycetes are common in woods and fields, growing saprobically in wood, leaf humus (Fig. 25-5), soil (Fig. 25-6), and lawns (Fig. 25-7). They are all terrestrial and are worldwide in distribution. Parasites are usually host specific and are limited by the ranges of their hosts, most of which are seed plants. Most fleshy basidiomycetes (those producing soft, fleshlike basidiocarps) give the erroneous impression that they are more abundant during warm, rainy, and humid seasons or periods. Actually, it is just that these environmental conditions favor the development of the conspicuous fruiting bodies of many species.

Vegetative features   Basidiomycetes have two trophic stages and both are branching mycelia that are regularly septate and with chitinous walls. However, a yeastlike, budding thallus is found in some genera.

The primary mycelium (Fig. 17-4) arises from haploid basidiospores, oidia, conidia, arthrospores, or buds. Its cells may be multinucleate but are usually uninucleate. The secondary mycelium is the dominant or major one and arises as

Fig. 25-1 Upper surfaces of basidiocarps of a bracket fungus growing out from a decaying log on a woods floor. *(Courtesy Carolina Biological Supply Company.)*

Fig. 25-3 Two apple leaves infected with cedar-apple rust (*Gymnosporangium juniperi-virginianae*). Lower surfaces of leaves showing clusters of aecial sori. *(Courtesy Carolina Biological Supply Company.)*

Fig. 25-2 *Ustilago nuda*, a smut basidiomycete causing the smut disease of barley. Infected head to left; uninfected head to right. *(Courtesy Carolina Biological Supply Company.)*

Fig. 25-4 Branch of cedar tree infected with cedar-apple rust (*Gymnosporangium juniperi-virginianae*). Many telial sori are expanding and elongating from the gall caused by the rust fungus. *(Courtesy Carolina Biological Supply Company.)*

Fig. 25-5 (top left)   Gelatinous basidiocarps of a dark jelly fungus (*Auricularia* or *Exidia*), which is decaying the humus of a forest floor. *(Courtesy Carolina Biological Supply Company.)*

Fig. 25-6 (top right)   Basidiocarps of the earthstar *Geaster* growing on soil. *(Courtesy Carolina Biological Supply Company.)*

Fig. 25-7 (left)   Basidiocarp of a stink horn gasteromycete (probably *Phallus*) growing in a grassy area. *(Courtesy Carolina Biological Supply Company.)*

a result of somatogamy (Fig. 17-5), or from dikaryotic oidia or arthrospores, or from uredospores in rusts. Some of the more advanced basidiomycetes with binucleate, dikaryotic basidiospores lack a primary mycelium.

Some parasitic rusts develop haustoria for obtaining food from their hosts. Rusts, like wheat-barberry and cedar-apple rusts, alternate between two hosts in the completion of their developmental cycles (they are called heteroecious rusts), and each rust has mycelia that are host specific for two hosts—a remarkable phenomenon.

Basidiomycete septa are typically of the dolipore type, which means that with the electron microscope the septum is seen to flare out in the middle portion and form a barrel-shaped structure with open ends around the septal pore. Also characteristic of basidiomycetes is the special method of cell division in secondary hyphae by clamp formation (Fig. 17-7), but clamps are not found on all secondary mycelia.

Secondary mycelial strands may grow together (and function in conduction) as white, yellow, or orange masses called rhizomorphs, so called because of their rootlike appearance. Another type of vegetative fungal tissue, the sclerotium, is less frequent. Secondary mycelium frequently is perennial in wood, leaf mold, and soil. If it grows at a uniform rate in all directions it may form fairy rings of mushrooms in lawns, fields, and forest floors.

Asexual reproduction   Reproduction by mycelial fragmentation is common, especially when the branching mycelium grows forward and the older portion dies and decays. Budding is common in smuts. Uredospores are the asexual spores of some rusts (Fig. 25-8) and bring about multiplication of the dikaryotic secondary mycelium. Other asexual spores are either haploid or dikaryotic oidia, conidia, and arthrospores (Fig. 17-10).

Sexual reproduction   Sexual reproduction (through basidiospores) accounts for the main means of multiplication and dissemination in the vast majority of basidiomycetes, a situation parallel to that of vascular plants, interestingly enough. Also, as in vascular plants, the major trophic phase or the dominant of the alternating generations is the genetically diploid phase: $(n + n)$ in basidiomycetes and $(2n)$ in vascular plants. The life cycle of almost all basidiomycetes is of the dikaryo-haplontic type.

Plasmogamy usually is somatic, happening between unmodified vegetative cells of the primary mycelium (Fig. 17-5); however, haploid oidia or conidia can fuse sexually with haploid hyphal cells. Also, in smuts plasmogamy may be between two basidiospores (giving these smuts a dikaryotic life cycle) or between a basidiospore and a haploid hyphal cell. And some higher basidiomycetes have a dikaryotic life cycle: their basidiospores are dikaryotic and they bypass the haploid mycelial stage. Rusts have a special type of plasmogamy, spermatization, which occurs between spermatia and receptive hyphae that emerge from spermogonia (Fig. 25-9) or stomates. One spermogonium develops both spermatia and receptive hyphae, but rusts are with few exceptions heterothallic, like the majority of basidiomycetes, and outbreeding is assured. As in all basidiomycetes, karyogamy and meiosis occur in the basidium. Segregation for mating or compatibility type takes place during meiosis, and rusts are bipolar heterothallic basidiomycetes, which means that two of the basidiospores of each basidium are of one mating type (+ or *A*) and the other two basidiospores of the opposite mating type (− or *a*). Most of the other bipolar basidiomycetes have multiple alleles at a single locus.

Of interest is the genetic control of mating by the so-called tetrapolar basidjomycetes. *Schizophyllum* is the best known mushroom of this type. Here there are two pairs of alleles controlling mating and each of the four basidiospores of a basidium may be of a different mating type, or two basidiospores may be of one type and two of another, depending on the type of segregation at meiosis.

The distinctive sexual structures of basidiomycetes are its sexual sporangia, the basidia, and the sexual tissues that bear them, the basidiocarps. The heterobasidium is one that is septate or deeply divided. There are several distinct types of heterobasidia. For example, some have vertical septa and others have transverse septa. Some have basidiospores borne on short, pointed extensions called sterigmata; others have sessile basidiospores. Each cell of a rust teliospore (Fig. 25-10) germinates in situ by a tube (young basidium). After karyogamy, meiosis takes place in the tube. Septa separate the four meiotic nuclei and these nuclei than pass through lateral sterigmata and squeeze out into developing basidiospores.

200

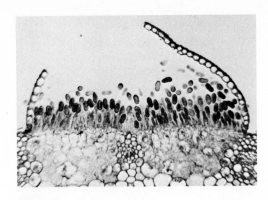

Fig. 25-8 Stained longitudinal section of a uredial sorus of wheat-barberry rust (*Puccinia graminis*) on a wheat stem. The expanding mass of unicellular, asexual uredospores has ruptured the epidermis of the host. *(Photomicrograph courtesy Ripon Microslides Laboratory.)*

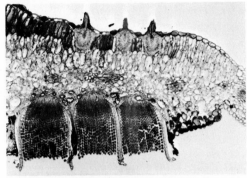

25-9 Stained longitudinal section of a portion of a barberry (*Berberis*) leaf showing longitudinal sections of three sunken spermogonia above and three sunken aecia below—wheat-barberry rust, *Puccinia graminis*. *(Photomicrograph courtesy Ripon Microslides Laboratory.)*

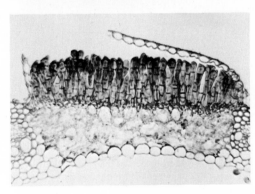

Fig. 25-10 Stained longitudinal section of a telial sorus of wheat-barberry rust (*Puccinia graminis*) on wheat. The expanding mass of two-celled teliospores and their stalks have ruptured the epidermis of the host. *(Photomicrograph courtesy Ripon Microslides Laboratory.)*

The homobasidium is globose to elongate and not septate. Typically, four basidiospores develop at the tips of four apical sterigmata (Figs. 17-9, 25-11) from which they are shot off by an interesting gas-bubble mechanism in the Hymenomycetes, but some homobasidia have sessile basidiospores, and some genera have as few as two and as many as a dozen or so basidiospores borne laterally as well as apically. Basidiospores of Gasteromycetes are not forcibly discharged; instead they are usually either blown out and away by wind or washed out and away by rain. Mushroom basidiospores seen in mass have various colors, and this variation aids in the identification of species.

Basidiocarps vary in size from tiny structures a few millimeters across to foot-high mushrooms and 1- to 2-foot-wide puffballs. There are many variations in form, some of which follow: crustlike or flat, as in some leather, pore, tooth, and gill fungi; bracketlike or shelflike, as in some of the same kinds of fungi; or with a

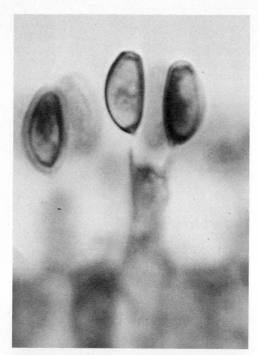

Fig. 25-11 Apical portions of stained homobasidia of *Coprinus*. Two sterigmata each with an apical basidium are clearly visible on one basidium. *(Photomicrograph courtesy Carolina Biological Supply Company.)*

Fig. 25-12 Basidiocarps of the gill mushroom *Amanita* growing in a grassy area.

Fig. 25-13 Basidiocarp of a large puffball, *Calvatia cyathiformis*, growing in a grassy area. *(Courtesy Carolina Biological Supply Company.)*

stalk (stipe) and cap (pileus), as in some of the pore, tooth, and gill fungi. One of the most distinctive features of some of the stipitate mushrooms, for example the edible *Agaricus,* is the presence of a ring or skirtlike veil on the upper part of the stipe. The poisonous *Amanita* (Fig. 25-12) not only has a veil on its stipe but also a bulb or cup at its base.

The wall of Gasteromycete basidiocarps is called the peridium, and the inner spore mass is called the gleba. Puffballs have ball-like basidiocarps (Fig. 25-13). Earthstars have two peridial layers with the outer one splitting open, giving the basidiocarp a starlike shape (Fig. 25-6). Stinkhorns have a sterile stalk with a bad-smelling, slimy gleba upon it (Fig. 25-7). The basidiocarp of a bird nest fungus looks like a tiny bird's nest with eggs in it. Each "egg," called a peridiole, is a glebal mass surrounded by sterile tissue.

It should be emphasized that although such a basidiocarp as a mushroom is relatively conspicuous, it is only the sexual structure of the fungus. The vegetative mycelium growing in its food source (e.g., soil) is analogous to the roots, stems, and leaves of a tree, and the mushroom (basidiocarp) is analogous to a flower produced on the tree.

Project

I. Gross morphology of the major kinds of basidiomycetes

Study the specimens on display and from them learn to recognize: smut fungi, rust fungi, jelly fungi, leather fungi, coral fungi, pore fungi, tooth fungi, gill fungi, puffballs, earthstars, stinkhorns, and bird nest fungi.

II. Gill fungi

A. Refer to the drawings in Project 17, p. 115.
B. *Morphology and cytology of a living mushroom*
    1. Secondary or dikaryotic mycelium. Mount the mycelium of *Coprinus, Schizophyllum,* or a similar mushroom growing in axenic culture. Mash the material to make the mount thin. Using high dry and oil immersion, find clamps or clamp connections between cells. Observe clamps in side, top, and oblique views. Determine which part of a hyphy is anterior and which posterior by noting the position of the cross wall in a clamp (see Fig. 17-7).
    2. Rhizomorph. Observe the demonstration material of rhizomorphs, which probably were collected from decaying logs or leaves.
    3. Basidiocarp development. If suitable material is available, make longitudinal sections of young stages of gill mushrooms. In the very youngest "buttons" of certain kinds (e.g., *Amanita*) you should be able to find prelamellar (pregill) cavities. As the buttons mature the parts found in the mature basidiocarp can be identified.
    4. Mature basidiocarp
        a. Identify stipe (stalk), pileus (cap), and lamellae (gills). Some species also have an annulus (ring or inner veil). Some have a volva or cup and scales on the cap. These are the remains of the universal veil or outer covering in the button stage of development.
        b. If sufficient material is available, make longitudinal and cross sections

of various portions of a basidiocarp. Study the different fungal tissues (plectenchyma).

    5. Basidia. With a razor blade make and mount a very thin cross section of several gills. Find the trama and hymenium. Find basidia in various stages of development. (You may have to mash the preparation to observe this, and you probably will have to use oil immersion. Time should be spent in searching for an entire basidium showing its connection to the trama. Is there a clamp connection at the base of the basidium in this species? Do all of the spores of a basidium mature at the same time in your material?

C. *Morphology and cytology of Coprinus from prepared slides*

    1. Using low power, study a cross section through pileus tissues and stipe.

    2. Using oil immersion, find the trama and hymenium and study the development of basidia and basidiospores. Look for stages of basidial development showing one, two, and four nuclei.

D. *Culture.* Directions for growing mushrooms are given in Project 3: VIII, p. 31. Detailed directions for culturing a bracket mushroom, *Schizophyllum*, are given in Project 17, p. 114. If time and materials are available, grow mushrooms.

III. Rust fungi

Study one of the following two rusts:

A. *Cedar-apple rust: Gymnosporangium juniperi-virginianae.* Cedar-apple rust causes a widespread, economically important disease of the apple known as apple rust or cedar-apple rust. The fungus attacks the leaves, fruit, and rarely the young twigs of the apple tree. Part of its life is passed upon the red cedar *(Juniperus virginiana),* where it causes the formation of galls, called cedar apples or cedar balls.

    1. Rust on red cedar trees. Aeciospores (from infected apple tree leaves) are set free during the summer and these spores bring about infection of trees of red cedar *(Juniperus virginiana).* During the following summer and fall, galls (cedar balls) mature on the cedar trees.

        a. Examine an infected cedar twig collected during the fall, winter, or early spring (early April) before telia have elongated. Note that the gall originates at one leaf. Note cedar twig, gall, and unexpanded telium.

        b. With a sharp razor blade make a thin section of a portion of a gall, mount, and examine several host cells with intercellular fungal hyphae. Look for haustoria. Can you determine the nature of the stored food in the cedar gall?

        c. Examine cedar galls collected in April during or following a rain. Find expanded telia, gall, and cedar leaf.

        d. The major portion of the body of the expanded telium is made up of the long stalks of the teliospores. Pinch off a bit of the telium, mount it in water, crush with a cover slip, and look for germinating teliospores. Find teliospores and their basidia in various stages of development, if the latter are present.

        e. Using prepared and stained slides of any rust, find other stages in basidiospore formation. Look for nuclei. Find teliospore stalk, teliospore crosswall, basidium, basidium crosswalls, sterigmata, and basidiospores. Where does meiosis occur? What host plant is infected by basidiospores?

2. Rust on apple trees
   a. With a dissecting microscope examine a diseased apple leaf showing spermogonia (pycnia) and aecia (cluster cups). On the upper surface of the leaf are the relatively small spermogonia that produce many spermatia and receptive hyphae. Notice that there are clusters or sori of spermogonia. Each sorus is either $+$ or $-$ with respect to sexual compatibility. Are aecia found only on the lower surface of the apple leaf?
   b. Examine prepared slides of cross sections of infected apple leaves taken from trees during August.
      (1) Using a dissecting microscope, find the spermogonia and aecia as viewed in cross section.
      (2) Using your compound microscope, study with low and high power. Look for spermatiophores and the manner in which spermatia are formed. Look for receptive hyphae. Can you see the large nucleus in a spermatium? Note the aeciospore mother cell and look for a smaller intercalary cell between two aeciospores. You can see the dikaryon (one $+$ nucleus and one $-$ nucleus) in each cell. (An oil immersion objective may be required for the observation of nuclei.)

B. *Wheat-barberry rust: Puccinia graminis*
   1. Rust on barberry shrubs
      a. Spermogonium. Study a prepared slide showing the flask-shaped spermogonia in the upper surface of a barberry leaf (cross section). Look for the spermatiophores, closely packed around the inner periphery, upon which are produced great numbers of spermatia. Look, too, for the receptive hyphae protruding from the ostiole at the top. What is the function of spermatia? Of receptive hyphae? Can spermatia accomplish plasmogamy with receptive hyphae from the same spermogonium? Are spermatia and receptive hyphae n, n plus n, or $2n$?
      b. Aecium. From the same slide observe aecia and aeciospores on the lower surface of the leaf. Study development of a chain of aeciospores. What is the chromosomal complement of the aeciospores? Where does this condition originate? What stage of this fungus results from infection by aeciospores? What plant do the aeciospores infect?
   2. Rust on wheat
      a. Uredium. From another prepared slide observe erumpent masses of hyphae on wheat stems that are forming uredospores (urediospores). These masses are uredia (uredinia). Note that the uredospores are borne singly on stalks. Are these spores one or two celled? Uninucleate or binucleate? What plant may these spores infect? Their infection gives rise to mycelium that may produce what types of spores?
      b. Telium. From another prepared slide observe telia, the cells of which have pushed through the host epidermis and are producing thick-walled teliospores. Are the teliospores one or two celled? Are the cells of this spore binucleate or uninucleate . . . are they first one and then the other? Are the nuclei haploid or diploid? What do teliospores develop into?

c. Basidium. Using prepared and stained slides of any rust, find stages in the development of basidia and basidiospores. Look for nuclei. Find teliospore stalk, teliospore cross wall, basidium, basidium cross walls, sterigmata, and basidiospores. Where does meiosis occur? What host plant is infected by the basidiospores?

Project 26   Imperfect fungi

Contents

Introduction

Taxonomy   Imperfects (imperfect fungi) are organisms of the form group (artificial group) technically known as Deuteromycetes, Deuteromycota, or Fungi Imperfecti. There are about 1,450 genera and 20,000 species.

Most imperfect fungi either are or resemble the vegetative and asexual stages of ascomycetes, but some are vegetative stages of basidiomycetes. Also, conidial rusts, smuts, phycomycetes, and actinomycetes are often included in this artificial group. A large number of the fungi important to man are found in the asexual (imperfect) condition only; therefore, names of convenience for identification purposes are given to them, and they are grouped together as a convenience to the person needing to identify them into the form group Deuteromycetes. Actually, these fungi are either the asexual or imperfect stages of known fungi or are thought to have evolved from sexual (perfect) fungi and permanently lost their sexual stages.

The vast majority of imperfect fungi either are or look like asexual ascomycetes. These are classified into three form orders: (1) Moniliales have conidia borne on vegetative hyphae, on single conidiophores (Figs. 24-4, 26-1, 26-2), or on clustered conidiophores often as elongate synnemata or cushion-shaped sporodochia. (2) Sphaeropsidales produce conidia within globose or flask-shaped

Fig. 26-1   Stained section of an orange peel showing mycelium, conidiophores, and conidia of *Penicillium. (Photomicrograph courtesy Carolina Biological Supply Company.)*

pycnidia. (3) Melanconiales form their conidia in an acervulus, a tuft or layer of short conidiophores arising from a disc of closely crowded hyphae.

Form genera are based on conidiophore type and on color, shape, and septation of conidia. Form species are based upon the kind of host or substratum and on size of conidia. A recent reclassification of imperfect fungi stresses variations in the way conidia develop.

It should be pointed out that ascomycetes with different kinds of ascocarps may have identical conidial or imperfect stages. Also, ascomycetes of the same group may have different conidial stages. Indeed, a single species of ascomycete may have more than one conidial stage. Thus, the imperfect fungi in one group may be totally unrelated, and those in different groups may be related.

Fig. 26-2   Stained conidiophore and conidia of *Aspergillus. (Photomicrograph courtesy Carolina Biological Supply Company.)*

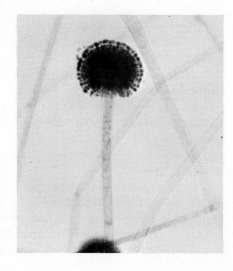

Other features For discussions of their importance, occurrence, vegetative features, and asexual reproduction, read the appropriate parts of previous projects, especially the one dealing with Ascomycetes. Imperfect fungi are mostly saprophytic on plant parts, and they are also parasitic on plants, insects, and man. Some, like *Dactylella,* are able to trap nematodes and parasitize them. A virulent new strain of *Helminthosporium maydis,* which causes corn blight, is a major threat to the corn crop and aspects of the economy of the United States. Some of the human diseases produced by deuteromycetes are Cryptococcal meningitis; various conidioses of the skin, nails, hair, mucous membranes, and lungs; ringworm; athlete's foot; blastomycosis of the lungs and alimentary tract; histoplasmosis; and others.

Project

I. **Spores not borne in any special structure** (Form order Moniliales)

  A. *Penicillium and Aspergillus.* You have already studied these in connection with their perfect or sexual stages, under the Plectomycetes in Project 24: II, p. 193. These genera have single-celled conidia.

  B. *Other genera with single-celled conidia.* Living or preserved specimens and slides of one or more of the following form genera may be available for your study: *Botrytis, Geotrichum, Verticillium, Hormodendrum, Tubercularia, Isaria,* and *Graphium.*

  C. *Form genera with two- to many-celled conidia.* Living or preserved specimens and slides of one or more of the following genera may be available for your study: *Trichothecium, Epidermophyton, Cladosporium, Helminthosporium, Alternaria, Stemphylium, Cercospora, Helicosporium,* and *Fusarium.*

II. **Spores borne in a pycnidium** (Form order Sphaeropsidales)

  A. *Form genera with single-celled conidia.* Living or preserved specimens and slides of one or more of the following genera may be available for your study: *Phyllosticta, Phoma, Phomopsis, Dendrophoma, Sphaeropsis,* and *Coniothyrium.*

  B. *Form genera with two- to many-celled conidia.* Living or preserved specimens and slides of one or more of the following genera may be available for your study: *Ascochyta, Diplodia,* and *Septoria.*

III. **Spores borne in an acervulus** (Form order Melanconiales)

  A. *Form genera with single-celled conidia.* Living or preserved specimens and slides of one or more of the following genera may be available for your study: *Gloeosporium, Colletotrichum,* and *Melanconium.*

  B. *Form genera with two- to many-celled conidia.* Living or preserved specimens and slides of one or more of the following genera may be available for your study: *Marssonina, Entomosporium, Pestalotia,* and *Cylindrosporium.*

Project **27**

Lichens or symbiotic fungus–alga plants

Contents

Introduction

Taxonomy   Lichens are ambiguous and perplexing plants. There are about 400 genera and 15,000 species. Each plant is two in one: there is a fungal partner, the mycobiont, and an algal partner, the phycobiont. Some botanists think that together they make a third plant, the lichen, which has its own characteristic structure and appearance. However, other botanists are of the opinion that lichens are not plants at all but only associations of two plants growing together. They say lichens are symbionts and nothing more.

Lichens, like deuteromycetes, are an artificial group. Their phycobionts are mostly green algae and some are blue-green algae. Their mycobionts are mostly ascomycetes and some are basidiomycetes and imperfect fungi. For this reason lichens usually are not classified formally as a separate group. Often they are grouped with fungi because the fungal component generally is the dominating partner, accounting for the characteristic form and appearance of the lichen. This is not completely satisfactory because it minimizes the importance of the algal partner and because there are lichens with dominating algal partners. In any case, species of lichens are given scientific binomials. Each has a generic and specific name.

Lichens are classified for convenience in identification according to their growth form—whether they are closely appressed to the substratum, with only

Fig. 27-1 Foliose and crustose lichens on a tree branch. F, foliose lichen; C, crustose lichen. *(Courtesy Carolina Biological Supply Company.)*

Fig. 27-3 *Cladonia gracilis* with a rough squamulose thallus from which arise podetia bearing terminal apothecia. This species is common and widespread on soil, humus, and mosses in open areas. *(Courtesy Carolina Biological Supply Company.)*

Fig. 27-2 *Peltigera*, a foliose lichen growing among mosses. Arrows point to margins of foliose lobes. *(Courtesy Carolina Biological Supply Company.)*

Fig. 27-4 *Usnea,* a fruticose lichen growing epiphytically on a tree limb. Arrows point to apothecia. *(Courtesy Carolina Biological Supply Company.)*

the upper side visible (crustose) (Figs. 27-1, 27-5), more loosely attached with the lower and upper surfaces visible (foliose) (Figs. 27-1, 27-2), intermediate between crustose and foliose (squamulose) (Fig. 27-3), or attached at one point and erect or pendant (fruticose) (Fig. 27-4). Other important features used for classification relate to color, details of form, asexual propagules (isidia and soredia), and the sexual structures of the fungal component.

Concerning the evolution of lichens, as symbionts of diverse algae and fungi they are polyphyletic in origin, but it is likely that some lichens have their own evolutionary pathways as symbionts.

Importance Rock-inhabiting lichens are important agents in initiating soil formation. They secrete acids that help break down rocks into a primitive type of soil. As the organic remains of the lichens accumulate, the soil is enriched and the way is paved for microbes and higher forms of vegetation and animals. Reindeer moss, a species of the lichen *Cladonia*, provides forage for caribou and reindeer. Lichens in forested areas can become very dry, thus aiding the spread of forest fires. Litmus, dyes, and medicines are obtained from lichens. Lichens are indicators of industrial air pollution when air toxins reach a level they cannot tolerate, causing them to die.

Occurrence Lichens are widely distributed from both poles to the equator and at various altitudes. They are predominantly terrestrial xerophytes able to withstand long periods of desiccation. Some are aquatic and a few of these are marine. Lichens are common on the bare surfaces of exposed rock, on tree trunks and limbs, on decaying wood, and on bare earth. They are a conspicuous terrestrial cover of arctic tundras.

Vegetative features The thallus of most lichens is distinctive in appearance and looks somewhat like that of liverworts and mosses; however, the lichen thallus is a composite structure made up of a fungus and alga living together symbiotically to their mutual advantage.

About 30 genera of symbiotic algae have been found in lichens. The commonest are green algae and the commonest of these is the small, globose, unicellular *Trebouxia*. Lichens with green algal phycobionts are usually mineral gray and have a firm consistency when moist. Lichens that are black or brown in color and gelatinous when wet contain blue-green algae, such as *Nostoc*. Individuals of the same lichen species may have different symbiotic algae, and different lichens may have the same alga. Although the algal cells or filaments may be scattered throughout the main body of the thallus (for example, *Nostoc* in the lichen *Collema*), in the majority of lichens the alga occupies a definite stratified zone just below the surface of the thallus (for example, *Trebouxia* in the lichen *Cladonia*). Most lichens occupy xeric ecological niches, and their algal components are protected by their fungal partners from excessive drought.

The fungal components of the great majority of lichens are ascomycetes, and probably related to the discomycetes and pyrenomycetes. Unlike the phycobionts, the mycobionts are not known to have an independent existence in nature, but some of them can grow in axenic culture free from their symbiotic algae. The fungal hyphae are septate and usually white or translucent, or infrequently black and carbonized or encrusted with orange or yellow pigments. The cell walls are relatively thin in the algal zone, but elsewhere in the thallus the walls are heavily gelatinized and very thick. This protects against excessive water evaporation. The lichen fungi are heterotrophic and obtain food from their symbiotic algae. Some lichen fungi have haustoria or appressoria that clasp the surface of the algal cells.

The four major growth forms of lichen thalli (crustose, foliose, squamulose, and fruticose) were described in the taxonomic section. The fungal hyphae in most cases determine the shape, appearance, and consistency of the lichen thallus; however, when the fungus is grown free from the alga in laboratory culture, its different growth pattern indicates that the alga probably does play a morphogenetic role.

The typical foliose thallus is differentiated internally into several strata. The thick-walled hyphae of the upper cortex are usually oriented in different directions and are so compressed as to appear cellular or plectenchymatous. Below this is the thin algal layer, composed of scattered clumps of algae and loosely interwoven thin-walled fungal hyphae. Under the algal layer is the medulla, a thick layer of loosely packed hyphae constituting up to two thirds of the thickness of the thallus. The lower cortex is anatomically similar to the upper cortex except it is thinner, often blackened, and frequently covered with rhizines or hairs. A rhizine is a bundle of hyphae. Water is absorbed in the capillary spaces among the component hyphae of rhizines.

Asexual reproduction   Lichen thalli are multiplied and dispersed in nature principally by asexual or vegetative means. Soil lichens are trampled by animals, effecting fragmentation of dry, brittle thalli. Many lichens produce soredia, which are small clusters of algal cells enmeshed by a few gelatinized fungal hyphae. Soredia come out through a crack or pore in the upper cortex and form conspicuous powdery masses called soralia. Isidia are minute coralloid outgrowths occurring over the whole surface of the thallus. Soredia occur in about 30 per cent and isidia in 15 per cent of lichens. They are easily detached and spread by wind. The same is true for the lobes or squamules of the squamulose thallus.

Sexual reproduction   The lichen as a symbiont does not reproduce sexually. However, the mycobiont frequently reproduces sexually through spermatization followed by the formation of perithecial or apothecial ascocarps.

A typical ascocarp is a perennial apothecium, a disc-shaped structure (Fig.

Fig. 27-5 Apothecia borne on the surface of *Caloplaca*, a lichen with a thallus that is closely appressed to the boulder it is growing on. *(Courtesy Carolina Biological Supply Company.)*

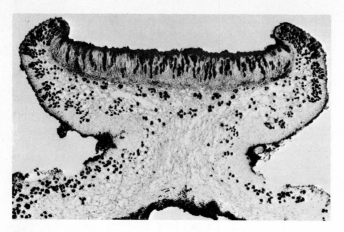

Fig. 27-6   Stained longitudinal section of a lichen thallus through an apothecium. *(Photomicrograph courtesy Carolina Biological Supply Company.)*

27-4, 27-5) on the surface of the thallus that forcibly discharges ascospores over many years. Apothecia are often adnate or even immersed on the thallus of crustose species, but they are conspicuously stalked in some foliose and fruticose species. The apothecium viewed in longitudinal section (Fig. 27-6) is seen to contain the following regions: epithecium, the surface layer composed of tips of paraphyses joined together; hymenium, composed of asci and the bases of paraphyses; and the hypothecium, a dense layer of hypae below the hymenium. In some lichens the hypothecium alone forms the apothecial wall. In others, the hypothecium is surrounded by thallus tissue containing algae. The conspicuous red tips of the match-stick lichen, *Cladonia cristatella,* contain asci and may be thought of as modified apothecia (Fig. 27-3). Color, size, and septation of ascospores are of as much importance in the taxonomy and identification of lichens as they are in the nonlichenized ascomycetes.

Project

I. Thallus

A. *Gross structure.* The thallus of a lichen may be classified as belonging to one of the three main types: (1) crustose, which grows closely appressed to the substratum with only the upper side visible; (2) foliose, which is more loosely attached, with the upper and lower surfaces visible; and (3) fruticose, which is attached at one point and is erect or pendant. Examine the lichens on demonstration and determine which type of thallus each has. You will find one or more specimens intermediate in structure between the foliose and crustose types. Species of *Cladonia* have this (4) squamulose type of thallus.

B. *Detailed structure.* With a razor blade make a very thin cross section through a foliose lichen such as *Parmelia.* Examine under the microscope. Identify upper cortex, algal layer, medulla, lower cortex, and rhizines. What is a lichen? Can you now account for the gray-green color of many lichens? What part does the alga play in the nutrition of the lichen? Do you think a lichen should be classed as a fungus, alga, or neither?

II. Asexual reproduction

Examine specimens for the presence of granular masses, soredia, on the surface of the thallus. A soredium contains one or more algal cells surrounded by closely adhered fungal hyphae. Soredia are disseminated by wind or rain; each is capable of growing into a new thallus. Mount soredia in dilute KOH (or any other wetting agent) and examine.

III. Sexual reproduction

Observe small cup-shaped apothecia on the surface of *Parmelia* and other genera. Cut a very thin section and examine under the microscope. What are the sac-like structures that contain spores? How are they arranged? Identify epithecium, hymenium (asci and paraphyses), hypothecium, and, if present, thallus tissue containing algae. How many spores are there in each ascus? Is it really the lichen that is reproducing sexually?

IV. Keeping specimens of lichens

If time is available, preserve some of the genera common in your area. Lichens keep well in the dried condition. Obtain a shallow cardboard box and fill it with a layer of cotton. Put the lichens on the cotton and put the genus name on a small piece of cardboard next to each lichen. Cover with clear sheet plastic.

Project **28**   Green algae

Contents

Introduction

Taxonomy   Green algae are plants of the group technically known as Chlorophyta, Chlorophycophyta, or Chlorophyceae. There are about 450 genera and 7,000 species.

Some botanists group green algae variously with other algae, fungi, protozoa, and prokaryotes into a larger group, Protista, and call them all protists, but this is an artificial or polyphyletic grouping of diverse organisms.

Although fossil green algae and other eukaryotic algae are not as old as fossil prokaryotes, their antiquity is clear (Table 18-2, p. 134). Fossil evidence indicates the early existence of diversity among eukaryotic algae and that all the major groups of algae had evolved by the beginning of the Paleozoic Era.

Green algae probably had their early origin in photosynthetic prokaryotes, and the evidence indicates that green algae represent the ancestral type from which all higher green plants evolved. The three main types of evidence indicating the green-algal ancestry of higher plants are (1) the structure, position and action of flagella of the motile cell (posteriorly directed whiplash flagella attached at the front end); (2) polysaccharide synthetic abilities and where food is stored (cellulosic cell walls and starch formation within plastids); and (3) pigmentation or the distribution and kinds of pigments involved in photosynthesis (grass-green chloroplasts containing both chlorophylls a and b). Indeed, green algae, stoneworts, and higher green plants appear to be more closely related to each other than

216

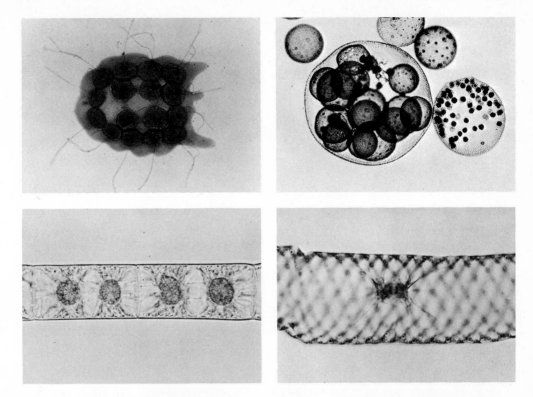

Fig. 28-1 Stained motile thallus (coenobium) of a volvocine genus, *Platydorina*, showing each cell bearing a pair of equal flagella. *(Photomicrograph courtesy Carolina Biological Supply Company.)*

Fig. 28-2 Several large, globose motile thalli (coenobia) of *Volvox*. Many daughter coenobia in various stages of development are seen within each large coenobium. *(Photomicrograph courtesy Carolina Biological Supply Company.)*

Fig. 28-3 Photomicrographs of uninucleate cells of filamentous tetrasporine green algae. Left: Living *Zygnema*. Right: Stained *Spirogyra* with its nucleus in mitosis. [*Left: courtesy Carolina Biological Supply Company; right: courtesy CCM: General Biological, Inc. Chicago.*]

they are to plants in the other groups. Green algae, stoneworts, and the higher plant groups comprise the green-plant line of evolution or the green-plant phyletic group.

Table 18-1, p. 132, indicates that green algae are not only plants but, like stoneworts, euglenoids, chrysophytes, dinoflagellates and relatives, brown algae, and red algae, in increasing order of specificity, they are eukaryotic plants, cryptogams, nonvascular plants, thallophytes, and eukaryotic algae.

Stoneworts, which are treated in Project 29, are classified with green algae by many of those who specialize in the study of algae (phycologists). Even though they are similar to green algae, their morphology, cytology, and reproduction are so distinct that it is useful to study them separately.

There are three main lines of evolution in green algae, and most of the 10–12 orders clearly fit into one of these evolutionary tendencies. Those green algae that have motile vegetative thalli and lack vegetative cell division are of the *volvocine evolutionary line* (Figs. 28-1, 28-2). Mitosis and cytokinesis occur only at the time

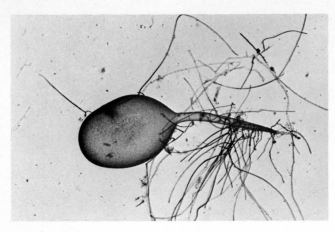

Fig. 28-4 *Derbesia (Halicystis),* a siphonaceous green alga. At left: Sac-like coenocytic *Halicystis* stage (haploid). Below: Filamentous coenocytic *Derbesia* stage (diploid). *(Photomicrographs courtesy Carolina Biological Supply Company.)*

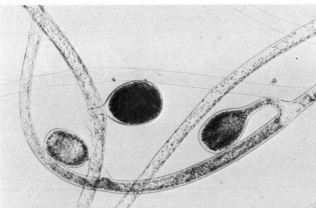

of reproduction. The other two evolutionary lines are composed of green algae with stationary or nonmotile vegetative thalli. The only swimming cells produced are reproductive ones. Stationary or nonmotile green algae with uninucleate cells, as in higher green plants, are of the *tetrasporine line or tendency* (Fig. 28-3). Finally, those stationary algae of the *siphonaceous line* have vegetative nuclear divisions but no cross-wall formation (Fig. 28-4). They have multinucleate, coenocytic thalli.

The major distinctive groups (orders) of green algae are further distinguished by combinations of such features as type of syngamy, type of life cycle, form and structure of the thallus or plant body, the nature of the chloroplast, and other cytological features. Great diversity exists among green algae.

Importance   Green algae play a prominent role as primary producers, occupying the lowest trophic level, in the complex food chains and webs of nature. They provide food for fish and many other animals. They produce significant amounts of oxygen during photosynthesis and help to oxygenate the part of top soil exposed to light, natural bodies of water, and sewage treatment plants.

A few green algae (especially sea lettuce, *Ulva*) are used in the preparation of soups and salads. Such unicellular green algae as *Chlorella* are used in studies investigating food sources and supplements for animals and man, both on earth and in space travel. Strains of *Chlorella* with very high proportions of proteins, carbohydrates and fats have been produced; there is a strain that is 88 per cent protein (dry weight), another one that is 37 per cent carbohydrate, and still another that is 85 per cent lipid or fat.

Green algae are important in basic biological research. Such unicellular genera as *Chlamydomonas* and *Chlorella* are major organisms being used for advancing our knowledge of the chemistry of photosynthesis, respiration, and other aspects of metabolism. Although not as widely used as the fungi *Neurospora, Sordaria*, and *Schizophyllum, Chlamydomonas* is becoming important in genetical research. A large number of morphological and biological mutant strains have been produced. Nonchromosomal, cytoplasmic inheritance, or the transmission of genetic information by means of cytoplasm, has been demonstrated; for example, resistance to the antibiotic streptomycin is inherited in this way. The genetic and hormonal control of sexual mating is being investigated in such green algae as *Chlamydomonas* and *Oedogonium*. The large cells of *Acetabularia* and *Valonia* (as well as the stonewort *Nitella*) make these organisms valuable for studies of such morphogenetic phenomena as the nuclear control of metabolism and structure and the effect of nuclear-cytoplasmic ratios on metabolism and development. They are also excellent for studying the important problem of ion exchange with the environment.

Occurrence   Green algae are universally distributed, and they are found in a wide variety of habitats. One species of *Chlamydomonas* even grows on snow. Green algae are found in all surface freshwater systems; in all marine systems, though in relatively less abundance; in and on moist soils; on rocks, dead wood, moist walls, and plant pots; epiphytically on larger algae, aquatic plants and trees; and epizoically on animals, as on turtle shells (Fig. 28-5). Some green algae occur

Fig. 28-5   Collecting *Stigeoclonium* attached to rocks in a flowing stream. Such a stream and forest provide many habitats for a variety of aquatic and terrestrial algae. *(Courtesy Carolina Biological Supply Company.)*

as endoparasites and commensals with higher plants, and others are mutualistic symbionts with fungi, forming lichens, and with such invertebrates as *Paramecium, Hydra,* and *Planaria.* Green algae have even been found in air.

Green algae are especially abundant in permanent and semipermanent fresh-water pools. Marine species may be attached to rocks, piling, and larger seaweeds or grow on the sandy bottoms of calm estuaries, often on shells. Plankton species occasionally have a population explosion, forming what is called an algal bloom.

Vegetative features   Green algae range in size from microscopic unicellular plants (Figs. 28-6, 28-7, 28-13) to macroscopic, well-differentiated seaweeds over 1 ft in length. Although some unicellular and colonial forms have swimming thalli, most green algae are stationary, like most other algae and like plants in general.

Most green algae are autotrophic, but some of the photosynthetic species are nutritionally auxotrophic (need an external supply of some organic substance) or mixotrophic (capable of utilizing organic compounds in the environment, which can also be called facultative heterotrophism, meaning that these green algae are not dependent on but do absorb and use any soluble organic substances in their environment.) A few green algae, such as *Polytoma,* lack chlorophyll and are heterotrophic; however, like bacteria and true fungi, they are lysotrophic and do not ingest solid food particles as do slime molds and some of the euglenophyte and chrysophyte algae. Heterotrophic green algae probably are derived from auto-trophic ones by the loss of chlorophyll and associated metabolic activities. This phenomenon has occurred in many groups of plants and is evidence for the algal origin of at least some fungi. Achlorophyllous green algae form species pairs with photosynthetic ones; for example, the lysotrophic *Polytoma* strongly resembles the *Chlamydomonas.*

The eukaryotic cells of green algae have a combination of features that distinguish them from the cells of other algal groups: their grass-green chloro-plasts contain chlorophylls *a* and *b* as well as carotenes and xanthophylls; their carbohydrate reserve food is stored as starch within chloroplasts and in association with proteinaceous centers called pyrenoids (Figs 28-3, Right; 28-6); their cell walls are composed of a firm inner cellulosic layer and an outer gelatinous layer of pectin-aceous material; and their motile cells typically have two apical flagella, and the

Fig. 28-6   Two of the unicellular green algae known as desmids. Left: *Closterium.* Right: *Micrasterias.* (*Photomicrographs courtesy Carolina Biological Supply Company.*)

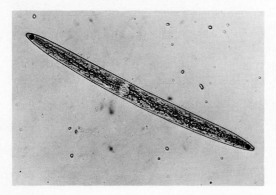
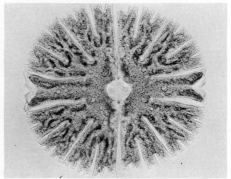

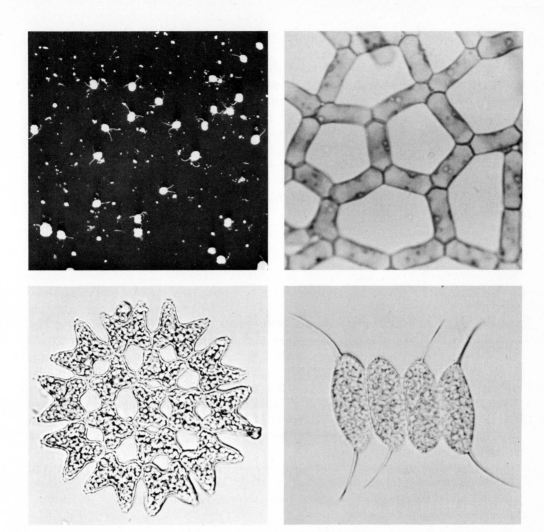

Fig. 28-7 (top left)   Darkfield view of many *Chlamydomonas* cells, each with two apical flagella of equal length. *(Photomicrograph courtesy CCM: General Biological, Inc. Chicago.)*

Fig. 28-8   Photomicrographs of three nonmotile colonies of green algae having cells with precise arrangements. Top right: Portion of a *Hydrodictyon* net-like coenobium. Below, left: *Pediastrum*. Below, right: *Scenedesmus*. [*Top right: courtesy Ripon Microslides, Inc.; others: courtesy Carolina Biological Supply Company.*]

flagella of a cell are always equal in length and of the whiplash type (Figs. 28-1, 28-7).

The cell wall of some marine green algae is impregnated with calcium carbonate, and a few green algae lack a rigid wall at all, but they are not amoeboid. Typical plant vacuoles are found in most green algal cells (Fig. 28-3, Right). Motile green algae and the motile reproductive cells of others may have contractile vacuoles near the apex of a cell and an eyespot within the chloroplast at one side. Chloroplasts of green algae are unusually varied. When many are present in a cell, they are usually small and discoid or lens shaped (Fig. 28-4, Lower). When there are only one or two chloroplasts, they may be axial or parietal and be shaped like a star, band, net, ring, half-filled cup, spiral ribbon, or be H shaped.

Thallus form is also highly varied. Many different shapes are found among unicellular forms. Colonies may be amorphous or composed of precisely arranged cells (Fig. 28-8). A colonial organism is generally considered to be one in which there is no division of labor, whereas a multicellular organism is one in which there is a division of labor, whether or not this is accompanied by morphological differences. Many green algae are filamentous, some are unbranched, and many are branched, in a variety of ways. The thallus of many attached forms has filaments that are prostrate on the substratum and filaments that are erect away from it. The relative extents and forms of the prostrate and erect systems characterize the thalli of different green algae. Some green algae have well-developed parenchymal tissue: it may be cordlike or rootlike in form and many cells in thickness, or it may be a sheet that is either one or two cells in thickness. Most green algae have uninucleate cells, but some have coenocytic thalli that give them the appearance of green Phycomycetes. On the other hand, some of the coenocytic green algae grow to over 1 ft in length and have a highly differentiated, even fernlike form. Remarkable, indeed!

As explained in the section on taxonomy, the green algal thallus is thought to have evolved along three main routes, and the many thallus variations for the most part are but different expressions of these volvocine, siphonaceous, and tetrasporine evolutionary tendencies.

Asexual reproduction   Many green algae have sexual life cycles with their sexual thalli also having some sort of asexual method of reproduction. Asexual spores may be haploid, as in *Ulothrix*, or diploid, as in *Ulva*. A few green algae have only asexual life cycles.

Asexual multiplication through fragmentation is accomplished in unicellular green algae by binary fission. Colony fragmentation is brought about by animals feeding upon the algae; the action of water currents; breaking at points where there are cells emptied of their specialized reproductive propagules, such as zoospores; and, as in the filamentous *Spirogyra*, autonomously breaking into individual cells or short series of a few cells each.

Zoospores account for the commonest method of asexual reproduction, and they effect not only multiplication of attached forms but also their dispersal or dissemination. Zoospore formation is often induced by environmental factors such as a change from light to dark, air to water, and running water to quiet water. When algae in laboratory culture are transferred to fresh culture media, they often liberate zoospores.

Zoospores usually are formed in vegetative cells morphologically similar to the others; thus, an incipient zoosporangium looks like an ordinary vegetative cell. The

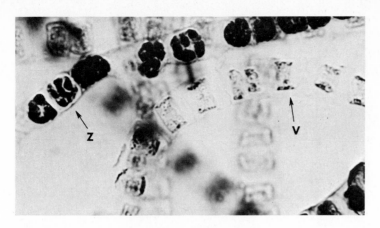

Fig. 28-9 Stained vegetative and zoosporangial filaments of *Ulothrix*. Z, zoosporangium; V, vegetative cell. *(Photomicrograph courtesy Carolina Biological Supply Company.)*

zoosporangia of *Oedogonium* and some others produce but a single zoospore, but the zoosporangia of *Chlamydomonas, Ulothrix,* and most green algae produce either 2 zoospores or multiples thereof, usually 4, 8, or 16 (Fig. 28-9). *Protosiphon* liberates hundreds to thousands of zoospores from a single zoosporangium.

Zoospores of green algae are generally liberated through a pore (discharge pore) in the parent cell wall (zoosporangium wall) and swim for variable lengths of time, but usually for about 1 or 2 hours. Swimming may be random or directed by environmental factors, especially light. Most zoospores have two or four flagella at their front ends; *Oedogonium* and *Derbesia* have an anterior whorl of many relatively short flagella. In all cases the flagella are of the whiplash type and are posteriorly directed during swimming. Zoospores come to rest, lose their flagella (in some cases they are known to retract their flagella), secrete a cell wall, and germinate. Germlings from asexual zoospores grow into plants like the ones that asexually produced the zoospores.

The zoospores, as well as motile gametes, of multicellular green algae look so much like swimming unicellular green algae that from an evolutionary or phylogenetic point of view, zoospores are interpreted as a temporary, ontogenetic reversion to the primitive, ancestral, flagellated condition. This is an example of the biogenetic law, which states that ontogeny recapitulates phylogeny.

Several other kinds of asexual spores may be produced by various green algae. Nonflagellated aplanospores have a cell wall, and it is distinct from the parent cell wall. Aplanospores are derived from potentially motile zoospores. Nonmotile asexual spores with greatly thickened walls are called hypnospores. An asexual spore with the same distinctive shape as the parent cell is called an autospore. An akinete has an abundance of food reserves and a thick wall that is fused with the wall of the parent cell.

Sexual reproduction   Unlike most phycomycetes and all other true fungi, the vast majority of green algae have motile flagellated gametes of some sort, but some green algae apparently cannot reproduce sexually in any environment. In green algae, gametangia are unicellular and usually are nothing more than vegetative cells that have changed to a reproductive function.

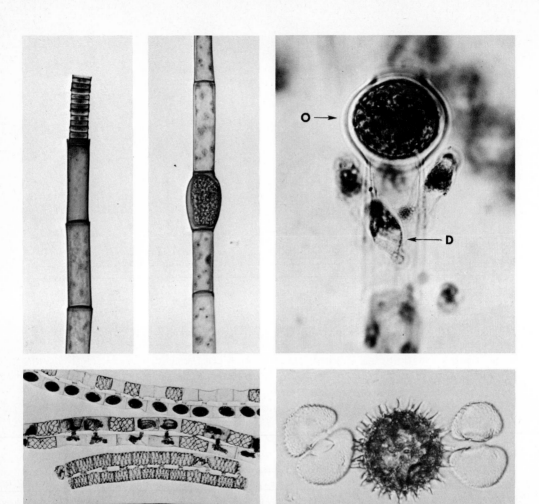

Fig. 28-10   Stained *Oedogonium* showing oogamy in a macrandrous species. Left: Male filament with several small antheridia. Right: Female filament with a single oogonium. *(Photomicrographs courtesy Carolina Biological Supply Company.)*

Fig. 28-11   Stained *Oedogonium* showing oogamy in a nannandrous species. O, oogonium: D, epiphytic dwarf male plant. *(Photomicrograph courtesy Carolina Biological Supply Company.)*

Fig. 28-12   Stained *Spirogyra* in all stages of scalariform conjugation (vegetative filament below). *(Photomicrograph courtesy Carolina Biological Supply Company.)*

Fig. 28-13   Zygospore of the unicellular desmid *Cosmarium* with the two empty isogametangia (former vegetative cells) to the left and right. *(Photomicrograph courtesy Carolina Biological Supply Company.)*

Isogamy is common, as in *Gonium, Ulothrix*, and species of *Ulva* and *Chlamydomonas*. Isogametes (all gametes look alike) are either + or −, and the cells that produce them are + and − isogametangia. Anisogamy is found in others, as in *Eudorina, Codium*, and other species of *Ulva* and *Chlamydomonas*. Anisogametes (heterogametes that are similar in form but different in size) are either ♀ or ♂, and the cells that produce them are ♀ and ♂ anisogametangia. After isogametes or anisogametes unite, the zygote may swim for several hours before encystment. Oogamy occurs in such green algae as *Volvox, Oedogonium, Coleochaete*, and a few species of *Chlamydomonas*. In oogamous species, sperms (antherzoids) are formed in antheridia, and eggs (oospheres) are formed in oogonia, one egg per oogonium. In oogamous species the egg is immobile and the zygote (oospore) begins wall formation immediately after syngamy (which in oogamous form is called fertilization) (Figs. 28-10, 28-11). *Spirogyra* and its relatives are different from other green algae in that syngamy is effected by two gametangia being in contact and forming a tube (Fig. 28-12) or pore (Fig. 28-13) through which nonflagellated isogametes move in an amoeboid fashion. The parthenogenetic development of gametes into new plants is known for a few green algae.

As with fungi, if the haploid or gametophytic thallus produces gametes of both mating types (±) or sexes (♂♀), the alga is homothallic, as in species of *Spirogyra, Oedogonium*, and *Chlamydomonas*. If two haploid or gametophytic thalli are required for syngamy to occur, one of them + or ♀ and the other − or ♂, the alga is heterothallic, as in *Ulothrix, Ulva*, and species of *Oedogonium* and *Chlamydomonas*.

Three types of sexual life cycles are found in green algae: haplontic, as in *Chlamydomonas, Ulothrix*, and *Oedogonium*; haplo-diplontic (diplo-haplontic), as in *Ulva, Cladophora*, and *Derbesia* (*Halicystis*); and diplontic, as in *Bryopsis, Codium*, and *Caulerpa*.

Most freshwater and terrestrial green algae are haplontic. The only diploid cell is the zygote, and this usually becomes a thick-walled, resistant zygospore. Meiosis is zygotic. After meiosis, most zygospores liberate sexual zoospoers, meiozoospores, which give rise to new haploid plants. The meiozoospores of most haplontic algae look just like their asexual zoospores. The formation of the dormant zygospore seems to be an adaptation to life in freshwater and terrestrial environments, which are highly unstable, changing, and fluctuating.

In contrast, most marine green algae either have a well-defined alternation of haploid and diploid generations or they have only a diploid vegetative phase. In *Ulva* and *Cladophora* the alternating generations look alike (are isomorphic), whereas in *Derbesia* (*Halicystis*) they look quite different (are heteromorphic). The coenocytic *Derbesia* has a sac-like *Halicystis* stage (*n*) alternating with a filamentous *Derbesia* stage (2*n*).

Green algae with alternating generations have sporulative meiosis, which leads to the formation of meiospores. Diplontic green algae have gametic meiosis — gametes are the only haploid cells. Very few marine green algae have dormant stages in their life cycles. This may be due to the fact that the ocean affords a relatively stable or unchanging environment, making dormant and resistant stages unnecessary for growth and development throughout the year.

Project

I. Volvocine evolutionary tendency (Volvocales)

A. *Chlamydomonas*

    1. Vegetative structure and asexual reproduction

        a. Motile phase. Mount a drop of water from a collection of *Chlamydomonas* and observe the mode of swimming of this unicellular alga. Study one of the largest motile cells that you can find. Cell structure can best be seen in a plant that has stopped moving for a while. Look carefully for the different parts of the plant. Stain for flagella. The simplest method is to kill, fix, and stain the cells in one operation by adding iodine solution. (Refer to Project 11, p. 62, if you want additional directions.) When you use the above stain (I_2KI), you stain starch, which is located mostly around the special structure within the chloroplast called the pyrenoid. Using oil immersion, look for the nucleus and the two contractile vacuoles in a cell (not stained). How many eyespots are there in each cell? Is an eyespot within a chloroplast? Can you distinguish between mature plants (individuals) and zoospores? Might zoospores be mistaken for gametes or vice versa? Could any significance be attached to this?

        b. Nonmotile or palmella phase. Look for a group of from two to eight or more cells that have remained together after division and have failed to grow flagella. Each group of cells surrounded by the wall or walls of the parents is a simple colony. Can you tell the difference between the palmella phase and nonmotile adults that are dividing to form zoospores?

    2. Sexual reproduction or syngamy in *Chlamydomonas reinhardi* (Refer to Project 4: IV, p. 35, for additional directions.)

        a. The fusion of the isogametes of *C. reinhardi* is easy to follow in this heterothallic species if the cultures of both the (+) and (−) strains have been correctly preconditioned. You will be provided with such preconditioned cultures (see Project 4: IV, A or C, p. 36).

        b. Place a small drop containing the (+) strain on a clean slide and beside it place a small drop containing the (−) strain. Do not mix the two drops yet! Take the slide to your working space, then mix the two strains by stirring the drops together with a very clean needle. Gently add a cover glass and observe immediately with your compound microscope.

            (1) Clumping should occur within 1 minute as a result of a chemotactic response or attraction between cells of the opposite mating types.

            (2) Turn to high power and observe cells that have become attached in pairs by their flagella (5 minutes).

            (3) Watch them fuse "head on" (10 minutes).

            (4) They later fuse laterally (20 minutes).

            (5) As the mount becomes thinner through evaporation of water, try to find zygotes with four flagella and two eyespots.

            (6) After several hours to days look for zygospores (encysted zygotes with thickened walls).

B. *Gonium, Pandorina, or Eudorina*. It is desirable to use *Gonium* and either *Pandorina* or *Eudorina* for the following study. Note especially that each cell is essentially like an entire *Chlamydomonas* plant. How many cells are there in each plant? Does *Gonium* have a posterior and an anterior end (show polarity)? Do *Pandorina* or *Eudorina*? Is each a colonial plant or a multicellular plant? Observe swimming under the darkfield microscope set up either by your instructor or by you if you have a microscope with a condenser and a strong-enough light source (see Project 9: V, p. 53). Additional directions for studying mode of swimming and action of flagella are given in Project 11, p. 62.)

Look for asexual reproduction by mounting plants from the bottom of the container.

C. *Volvox*
1. Living material. Is *Volvox* phototactic? Do you see any evidence that *Volvox* can be segregated into age groups according to phototactic response? Does *Volvox* have a posterior end and an anterior end (show polarity)? Is *Volvox* a colonial plant or a multicellular plant? Living material usually is actively reproducing asexually. Look for stages in daughter plant (coenobium) development: gonidia, their inversion, eversion, and finally liberation from the parent coenobium.
2. Prepared slides (perhaps supplemented with living or preserved material)
   a. Observe eggs within a coenobium. An egg and its surrounding wall make up an oogonium. (Young, asexually produced coenobia should also be seen inside the "mother plant.")
   b. Observe mature zygospores within a coenobium. Your slide may be a whole mount or it may have sections on it. Note the protoplast and thick, wavy wall of the zygospore. Also note vegetative cells.

II. **Tetrasporine evolutionary tendency** (representative orders: Tetrasporales, Zygnematales, Ulotrichales, Oedogoniales, Ulvales): Study from living or preserved material supplemented with prepared slides

A. *Tetraspora*. Observe a portion of a large, gelatinous colony. Note the massive gelatinous sheaths (outer walls) and notice the organization of the many cells into tetrads. To what extent does each cell resemble the unicellular *Chlamydomonas*?

B. *Spirogyra*
1. Study the structure of a vegetative cell. Find cross wall, spiral chloroplast, pyrenoids, nucleus, cytoplasmic strands, and large central vacuole.
2. Study stages in sexual reproduction (conjugation). Find young gametangia, male gametangium, female gametangium, conjugation tube, and zygote or zygospore. [Although the gametangia have the same form (isomorphic), they are functionally different, as you can observe.]

C. *Unicellular desmids*
1. *Closterium*. Study cell structure. Notice that each half is an "exact" duplicate of the other half. Note cell wall and wall striations, chloroplasts, pyrenoids, starch grains (use I_2KI test), nucleus (centrally located), and vacuoles (terminal and with tiny gypsum crystals showing brownian movement).

2. *Cosmarium*
   a. Study cell structure in a vegetative plant.
   b. Observe zygospores (zygotes with thick, and in this case spiny, walls). Refer to Project 4: IV, C, p. 36, for the availability of a *Cosmarium* mating kit.

D. *Ulothrix*. Study vegetative cell structure in this filamentous green alga. Try to find a holdfast at the base of a filament. Observe the parietal, ribbon-like chloroplast in each cell. Find zoosporangia and/or gametangia and observe the cluster of motile reproductive cells within each zoosporangium or gametangium.

E. *Oedogonium*
   1. Study the vegetative thallus. Look especially for (a) holdfasts and (b) groups of rings on the lateral wall of the filament. These rings are best seen where the filament abruptly decreases in diameter. How are these rings formed?
   2. Study sexual reproduction:
      a. Macrandrous. Note antheridia on male plants and oogonia on female plants if the material you are studying is dioecious or heterothallic. If your material is homothallic or monoecious, antheridia and oogonia will be on the same filament or plant. Find the pore in an oogonial wall used for entrance of the sperm.
      b. Nannandrous. Find dwarf male plants attached to the cell (suffultory cell) below the oogonium.
      c. Refer to Project 4: IV, C, p. 36, for the availability of an *Oedogonium* mating kit.

F. *Ulva, sea lettuce*
   1. Study the appearance of this seaweed. Recall that *Ulva* has alternating haploid and diploid plants that are similar in appearance (isomorphic). Find holdfast and blade.
   2. Study a mounted portion of a blade. Note the thick cell walls. How are these of adaptive value? How many cells in thickness is a blade?

III. **Siphonaceous evolutionary tendency** (representative orders: Chlorococcales and Siphonales)

A. *Unicellular or coenobial freshwater forms*
   1. *Chlorella* and *Chlorococcum*. Study vegetative stages of these small, unicellular green algae. Note the cytological details that can be seen with your microscope. Look for and hope to find reproductive stages.
   2. *Pediastrum* and *Hydrodictyon*. Study the coenobia of these green algae. Can you see why *Pediastrum* is commonly called "water star" and *Hydrodictyon* "water net"? Studying *Hydrodictyon*, look for daughter nets (coenobia) within parent cells. Are any cell divisions involved in the growth of a tiny young net into a large mature net?

B. *Seaweeds*
   1. From living or preserved material and from specimens mounted on herbarium sheets, study the gross vegetative structure of several species of *Caulerpa* and of *Codium*.
   2. Living material of *Derbesia (Halicystis), Bryopsis, Acetabularia,* and *Batophora* may be available for study.

Project 29   Stoneworts

Contents

Introduction

Taxonomy   Stoneworts are a small group of plants technically known as Charophyta or Charophyceae. There are six genera and about 250 species.

Although stoneworts can be thought of as green algae, it is probably best and certainly useful to treat them as a separate group because they are so different, in five main ways: (1) they have a unique thallus (Fig. 29-1), both in appearance and in structural details; (2) their female and male reproductive structures are unique and multicellular; (3) their sperms resemble those of bryophytes; (4) very early thallus development is unique but perhaps more like that of ferns and mosses than green algae, and (5) like embryo plants they never produce zoospores. On the other hand, like many green algae and unlike embryo plants, stoneworts have a haplontic life cycle with zygotic meiosis. Stoneworts are clearly in the green-plant line of evolution and probably have a common origin with green algae.

Stoneworts are highly specialized green plants that appear to represent a side branch in evolution. Stoneworts of past geological times apparently did not give rise to more advanced plants, and although stoneworts of today are flourishing plants, they are at the end of their evolutionary line.

Stoneworts are put in a single order, Charales. Many genera are known only as fossils, which date back to Silurian and Devonian times, but there are 6 living genera with about 250 species. Calcareous material on the plants aids in the preservation of stoneworts as fossils, and their reproductive structures are so distinctive, especially the female one, that the identity of these fossil plants is certain. The best known genera are *Chara* and *Nitella*.

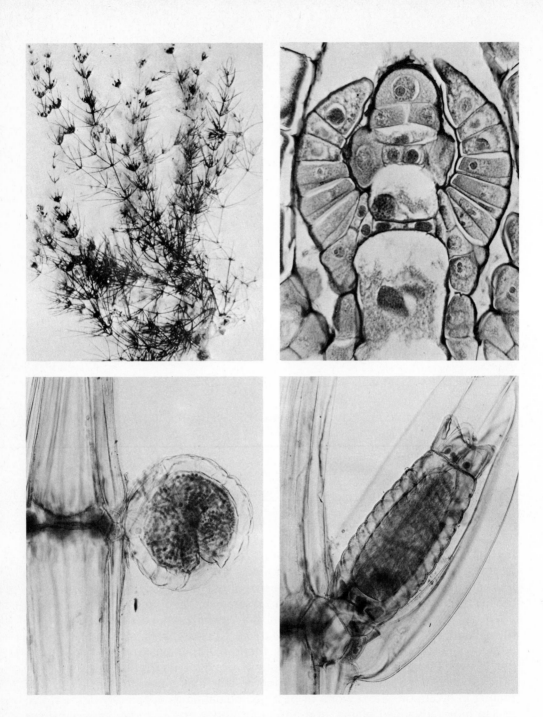

Fig. 29-1 Plant of *Chara deliculata* bearing reproductive structures. *(Courtesy CCM: General Biological, Inc., Chicago.)*

Fig. 29-2 Stained longitudinal section of a growing tip of *Chara* showing the apical cell. *(Photomicrograph courtesy Ripon Microslides Laboratory.)*

Fig. 29-3 Stained nodal region of *Chara* showing a male reproductive structure (globule). *(Photomicrograph courtesy Carolina Biological Supply Company.)*

Fig. 29-4 Stained nodal region of *Chara* showing a female reproductive structure (nucule). *(Photomicrograph courtesy Carolina Biological Supply Company.)*

Importance Stoneworts are not economically important, but they do make an attractive aquarium plant. Stoneworts are important organisms in research dealing with the active absorption of dissolved mineral salts. *Nitella*, for example, has the ability to actively absorb potassium and chloride ions when their concentrations within the cells are hundreds of times greater than in the water in which they are growing.

Occurrence Stoneworts grow submerged in freshwater ponds or lakes, especially in clear hard waters, where they may form extensive subaquatic meadows that can extend to a considerable depth. Stoneworts are so named because many, especially *Chara*, become encrusted with lime (calcium carbonate) and over a period of years may cause the formation of marl deposits upon the bottom of the pond or lake. A few stoneworts grow in brackish water.

Vegetative features Unlike most green algae, stoneworts have distinctive macroscopic features. Stoneworts are essentially filamentous and they are small plants that vary in height from less than 1 in. to 2 ft. They look superficially like the vascular plants *Equisetum* and *Ephedra*. Most genera have their walls impregnated with calcium carbonate. *Chara* especially has walls so heavily calcified as to make the plants rough to the touch and even brittle.

The geometric pattern of their green thalli originates by development from an apical cell that produces nodal and internodal cells (Fig. 29-2). Whorls of so-called leaves with limited growth arise from nodal cells, and so do branches. These distinctive plants are anchored to the substratum by branching filaments called rhizoids.

Each cell has a central vacuole, numerous peripheral disc-shaped chloroplasts arranged in spirally twisted rows, and actively and continuously streaming cytoplasm between the fixed chloroplasts and the vacuole. The long (up to 6 in.) internodal cell of *Nitella* affords a spectacular view of cyclosis. Internodal cells are coenocytic, but the internodal cells only are multinucleate. In some genera, like *Chara*, cortical filaments cover each internodal cell.

In other respects the vegetative cells of stoneworts have the basic cellular features found in green algae and embryo plants: cellulosic cell walls, grass-green chloroplasts containing chlorophylls *a* and *b* as well as carotenes and xanthophylls, carbohydrate reserve food stored as starch within chloroplasts, and the protoplasmic organelles common to all eukaryotic cells.

Reproduction Asexual reproduction occurs only by fragmentation of one sort or another. Rhizoids give rise to erect green shoots. Erect shoots themselves may break off and start new clones or beds of stoneworts elsewhere. Also, special growths may develop at nodes, break away from the parent plants, and develop into new individuals.

Sexual reproduction involves oogamous syngamy. Meiosis is zygotic; thus, stoneworts are haploid (only the zygote is diploid), and they have a haplontic life cycle with a resistant, resting zygospore that functions as an agent of dissemination. Most species are bisexual (monoecious or homothallic), but some are unisexual (dioecious or heterothallic).

The female and male sexual structures are unique and develop at nodes. They are structurally complex and each consists of an inner gamete-producing cell (the egg) or cells (sperms) and an outer cover or wall of sterile cells. They are often called nucules, or female fructifications, and globules, or male fructifications, rather than oogonia or archegonia and antheridia, because they are neither like the unicellular oogonia and antheridia of green algae nor the multicellular archegonia and antheridia of embryo plants.

The globule or male structure (Fig. 29-3) is orange red at maturity, spherical, and on a short stalk. From the inside of each of the outer sterile cells (shield cells) arises a generative cell (manubrium) that bears apically (farther inside) one or more capitulum cells. Arising from capitulum cells are coiled antheridial filaments each cell of which gives rise to a single, bryophyte-like sperm bearing two anteriorly attached and posteriorly directed whiplash flagella. Their mode of swimming is more like that of bryophyte sperms than green algal sperms.

The nucule or female structure (Fig. 29-4) is also on a short stalk and has a single, large, ovoid egg cell or oogonial cell surrounded by spiral, elongate sterile cells (tube cells) that have at their tips short crown cells, together forming a one-tiered (in *Chara*) or two-tiered (in *Nitella*) corona. At maturity the tube cells separate from each other immediately under the corona, thus providing an entrance to the egg for sperms.

After fertilization the zygote and inner walls of the spiral tube cells develop thickened walls, and this structure is abscised. After a period of dormancy, meiosis occurs, the zygote wall cracks, and one of the haploid cells divides. One of these two daughter cells grows into a colorless, filamentous initial rhizoid differentiated into nodes and internodes, and the other daughter cell grows into a green, filamentous protonema that is also differentiated into nodes and internodes. This juvenile stonewort plant gives rise to a young adult plant.

Project

I. *Nitella*

The Thallus or Plant
A. Observe with the unaided eye the characteristic pattern of growth or development. Between two whorls of "leaves," each originating from a node, is a single internodal cell.
B. Make a microscopic study of vegetative cell structure in living material. Notice that the chloroplasts of a cell are in a fixed position and spirally arranged. Observe (1) that the inner part of the protoplast is very actively streaming (cyclosis), and (2) that there is a large central vacuole.

II. *Chara* or *Nitella*

Sexual Reproduction
A. *Female structure (nucule or oogonium).* Using high power, find the basal stalk, the central cell containing the egg or the zygote, the spirally twisted tube cells that form a sheath around the central cell, and at the tips of the tube cells the crown cells or corona.
B. *Male structure (globule or antheridium).* Maturing and mature male structures are orange red. Dissect one, mount it, and with low and high power identify shield cells, manubrium and capitulum cells, and antheridial filaments. With good luck you will see the liberation of sperms (spermatozoids).
C. *Acetocarmine staining for a study of spermatogenesis.* If time and materials are available, follow the directions in Project 10: I,A,8, p. 57.

Project **30**   Euglenoids

Contents

Introduction

Taxonomy   Euglenoids are organisms of the small group technically known to botanists as Euglenophyta or Euglenophycophyta and to protozoologists as Euglenoidina. There are about 25 genera and 450 species.

Euglenoids are unicellular, mostly motile organisms with both green and non-pigmented members. They have a combination of features not found in any other organisms, and their type of flagellum (one-sided tinsel) and type of carbohydrate food reserve (paramylum) are unique. Euglenoids are not clearly related to any other organisms. In some ways they resemble unicellular plants and in other ways these interesting organisms are like flagellated protozoa. They are a specialized group of organisms that represent a separate evolutionary line. In a sense, then, englenoids are a "kingdom" unto themselves. Euglenoids of the past apparently did not give rise to other kinds of organisms and present-day englenoids probably will not either.

Euglenoids are distinguished primarily by three types of criteria: differences in morphology and habit (for example, *Euglena* changes its shape actively and swims, *Phacus* has a fixed shape and swims, and *Colacium* has a fixed shape but grows while it is attached to a substratum); differences in cell structure (for example, *Trachelomonas* has a wall-like lorica and *Euglena* does not); and differences in nutrition (for example, *Astasia* is heterotrophic and *Euglena* is autotrophic).

Euglena can be experimentally induced to become nonpigmented and thus nonphotosynthetic and saprobic. In this condition *Euglena* is similar in form to the colorless saprobe *Astasia*. Because of their morphological similarity, *Euglena* and *Astasia* (like the green algae *Chlamydomonas* and *Polytoma*) are called a species pair. (Species pairs of photosynthetic and nonphotosynthetic organisms occur in chrysophytes and blue-green algae as well as in green algae and euglenoids.) *Astasia*-like forms could have evolved from *Euglena*-like forms. This could have happened more than once and may be happening in the present geological time or epoch.

Importance Euglenoids are of little economic importance, but some have an absolute requirement for vitamin B_{12} and are used as assay organisms for determining unknown concentrations of this growth factor. This can be done because their growth rate is directly proportional to the concentration of vitamin B_{12} in the culture solution, and with precision one can know the concentration of the vitamin in solution by measuring the growth rate of the organism. *Euglena* is a very important experimental organism yielding basic information about cell structure and function.

Occurrence Although a few are marine, euglenoids are predominantly freshwater organisms and are abundant in places high in organic nitrogenous compounds such as wet barn yards, the margins of pools and pasture streams, and polluted streams. Like other tiny algae in freshwater pools, they may have periods of rapid population growth and cause water blooms. Phagotrophic forms are found where small plankton and debris are present. A few nonpigmented forms live within the bodies of invertebrates as obligate heterotrophs.

Vegetative features Euglenoids are highly differentiated, eukaryotic, unicellular organisms. Most are motile (Figs. 30-1, 30-2), but a few are attached to objects and sometimes colonial. Their more distinctive features are the lack of a cell wall; the unique presence of the one-sided tinsel type of flagellum (one which has a single longitudinal row of submicroscopic hairs or mastigonemes), with one to three of these flagella attached anteriorly; the unique presence of paramylum, a glucose-like polymer (β-1, 3-glucan polymer) stored as glistening granules of various shapes in the cytoplasm; and pigmented genera with grass-green chloroplasts containing chlorophylls *a* and *b*, carotene, and xanthophylls (chlorophyll *b* is found only in euglenoids, green algae, stoneworts, and embryo plants). Although a chloroplast may have a pyrenoid, starch is never produced.

Most euglenoids are nonpigmented and either lysotrophic or phagotrophic. Some of the autotrophic genera are auxotrophs (require an external source of some organic substance) or mixotrophs (facultative heterotrophs). The cells of pigmented euglenoids have numerous discoid to band-shaped chloroplasts. When *Euglena* is grown in darkness on a suitable organic substratum, its chloroplasts disappear, but they reappear when returned to light. Under exceptional environmental conditions, such as high temperature, treatment of *Euglena* with the antibiotic streptomycin, or ultraviolet light, may give rise to colorless (apochlorotic) strains or races whose cells are permanently colorless, even when grown in light.

The outer part of the protoplast is a firm, punctate or striate pellicle or periplast closely associated with the underlying protoplasm. There are numerous muciferous bodies or glands in the pellicle. They take up neutral red stain vitally. These bodies

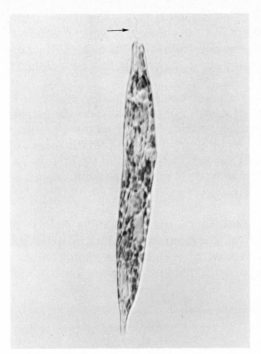

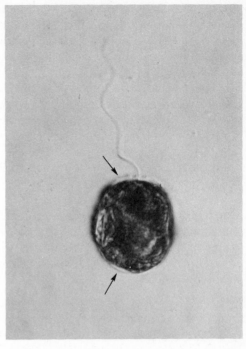

Fig. 30-1 A swimming *Euglena* showing part of its anterior flagellum (arrow). *(Photomicrograph courtesy Carolina Biological Supply Company.)*

Fig. 30-2 A swimming *Trachelomonas* showing its anterior flagellum projecting through its lorica (arrows). *(Photomicrograph courtesy Carolina Biological Supply Company.)*

may be scattered without a definite pattern or may be in spiral rows. The muciferous bodies slowly discharge or secrete their contents to the outside, apparently accounting for cyst formation. The secreted mucilage from muciferous bodies is largely, if not entirely, water-soluble mucopolysaccharide in nature.

In most genera, such as *Euglena* and *Astasia*, the pellicle is pliable or elastic, allowing cells to change shape in a characteristic manner known as euglenoid movement (metaboly or metabolic movement). In others, as in *Phacus*, the pellicle is rigid and the cell has a fixed shape. In a few forms, such as *Trachelomonas*, the protoplast is surrounded by, but stands free from, a firm lorica with only the flagellum projecting (Fig. 30-2). Loricas are yellowish red to brown when impregnated with iron compounds.

Euglenoid movements are probably due to forces similar to those which effect amoeboid movement, but the pellicle seems to impose certain restrictions on the change in form. In a frequent type of euglenoid movement, a cell shows a wide bandlike swelling that travels from posterior to anterior, and often back again. Also, a cell may become top shaped and rotate on its posterior tip. In species with less flexible pellicles, euglenoid movements may result in bending rather than lobing or bulging.

The anterior end of a euglenoid cell is invaginated to form a flask-shaped gullet, which may be involved in the ingestion of solid food particles by phago-trophic (colorless) genera and which is where flagella originate in all genera. In *Euglena* two flagella arise from the base of the reservoir (the lower portion of the gullet). One is short and is thought of as a rudimentary flagellum, and the other flagellum (a single flagellum) projects from the gullet. If flagellar action is helical or spiral and at an oblique angle, the cell rotates on its axis as it swims forward in a spiral path. If the flagellum stays out in front as pulses pass along it, the cell creeps or glides.

The reservoir is adjoined by one or more contractile vacuoles. In colorless genera, like *Peranema,* special ingestion structures (pharyngeal rods) lie parallel to the long axis of the gullet. Pigmented euglenoids have a reddish, granular eyespot or stigma located just below the membrane of the reservoir adjacent to one of the flagella in the gullet. The eyespot appears to function in the phototactic (phototaxic) responses of euglenoids. The eyespot is not within a chloroplast as it is in green algae.

Reproduction   Euglenoids reproduce asexually by the longitudinal division of motile flagellated cells or by the division of encysted cells, which may form a colonial (palmelloid) mass of cells embedded in a gelatinous matrix. Sexual reproduction is doubtful. It has been reported for only one genus and has not been confirmed.

Project

I. *Euglena*

    A. *How Euglena moves.* Can you see an individual cell of *Euglena* with the un-aided eye? With a hand lens? Is *Euglena* phototactic (phototaxic)? Mount a drop containing *Euglena* on a slide and observe with low power. Find en-cysted cells and find cells that change in shape as they move (metaboly, metabolic movement, or euglenoid movement). Observe both gliding and swimming types of movements. Observe swimming cells under the dark-field microscope set up either by your instructor or by you if you have a microscope with a condenser and a strong enough light source (see Project 9: V, p. 53).

    B. *Cell structure.* Does *Euglena* have a cell wall? How many eyespots are there? Where is the eyespot located? About how many chloroplasts and how many flagella does each organism have? (The simplest method for staining flagella is to kill, fix, and stain in one operation by adding iodine solution.) Is there any starch present in the cells? (Use the I_2KI test for starch.) *Euglena* stores food as carbohydrate in glistening granules of paramylum, a substance similar to starch (amylum). Where is the paramylum located? Complete your observations on the details of cell structure using an oil immersion objective lens. Look for as many cytological features as you can find in encysted cells (palmella stage).

    C. *Muciferous bodies or glands in the pellicle.* Make a thin mount of *Euglena.* Add a drop of 1 per cent neutral red to one edge of the cover slip and observe with the high dry and oil immersion lenses "diffusion front." The muci-ferous bodies in the pellicle are bright red in vitally stained cells—a beautiful sight!

II. *Trachelomonas*

Compare the movements and cellular components of *Trachelomonas* with those of *Euglena* and in addition find the lorica of *Trachelomonas*. What gives the lorica its color?

III. *Astasia, Peranema,* and *Distigma*

Compare the movements and cellular components of these large, colorless euglenoids with those of *Euglena*.

Project **31**

Xanthophytes, chrysophytes, and diatoms

Contents

Introduction to the three groups

Xanthophytes, chrysophytes, and diatoms comprise the group technically known as Chrysophycophyta or Chrysophyta. Some phycologists treat these as separate and distinct groups, but they do have certain features in common: (1) cárotenes and xanthophylls are the dominant pigments in their plastids and chlorophyll *b* is never present; (2) excess photosynthate is never stored as starch but instead as oil and as a polysaccharide called chrysolaminarin (laminarin-like) or leucosin; (3) cell walls are often silicified; and (4) motile cells usually have a tinsel flagellum, one which has two rows of mastigonemes.

Despite these similarities, each of the three algal groups is distinctive enough to be treated separately. Indeed, xanthophytes are so different from chrysophytes and diatoms that phycologists now are placing them in a separate group, Xanthophyta. Also, some phycologists consider diatoms to be different enough to be put in a separate group, Bacillariophyta.

Xanthophytes

Taxonomy   Xanthophytes are also commonly called yellow-green algae. There are about 75 genera and 400 species.

At one time xanthophytes were classified with green algae. Although they are less numerous and diverse than green algae, their body forms parallel those of green algae and their classification into major groups (six orders) is based on this. Thus, motile genera like *Chloromeson* (order Heterochloridales) are of a volvocine-like evolutionary line or tendency; filamentous cellular genera like *Tribonema* (order Tribonematales) are of a tetrasporine-like evolutionary tendency; and coenocytic genera like *Vaucheria* (order Heterosiphonales) are of a siphonaceous-like evolutionary tendency (Figs. 31-1, 31-3). The counterparts of these three orders in green algae are Volvocales, Ulotrichales, and Caulerpales. A genus like *Chorarachnion* (order Rhizochloridales) is amoeboid and exhibits a vegetative type not found in green algae. A striking example of parallelism in body form is the coenocytic xanthophyte *Botrydium* and the coenocytic chlorophyte *Protosiphon*. Their type of thallus is a simple sac (cell) with rhizoidal extensions like the thallus of such chytrid (phycomycete) genera as *Chytriomyces* and *Rhizophydium*.

Importance and occurrence   Xanthophytes are relatively unimportant. With few exceptions xanthophytes are freshwater forms. Most of these, like *Tribonema*, are aquatic and grow in soft waters. *Vaucheria* may be aquatic or terrestrial, forming feltlike mats on damp soil. Xanthophytes are the algal symbionts of some lichens.

Vegetative features   Xanthophytes are mostly uninucleate, but some are coenocytic. Their thallus may be a motile, flagellated cell; an amoeboid cell or colony of cells; a nonmotile, palmelloid colony of cells; short or long filaments that are either attached (by holdfasts) or free floating and usually unbranched; a sac with rhizoids (which grow into mud); or an extensively branched and tubular system of filaments.

The xanthophyte wall contains cellulose and pectins, and some have silicified

Fig. 31-1   *Ophiocytium,* a xanthophyte with multinucleate vegetative cells forming a dendroid colony. *(Photomicrograph courtesy Carolina Biological Supply Company.)*

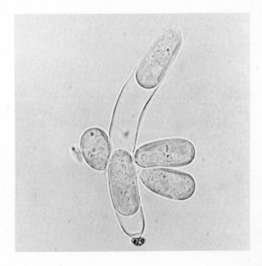

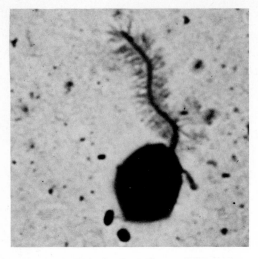

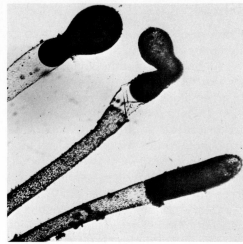

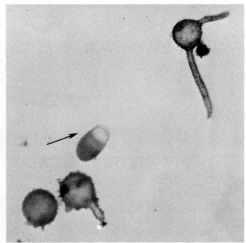

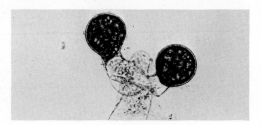

Fig. 31-2 Photomicrograph of a zoospore of *Botrydium* stained to show the two rows of tinsels (mastigonemes) on the anteriorly directed flagellum. (The whiplash tip broke off the shorter, posteriorly directed flagellum.)

Fig. 31-4 Photomicrograph of *Vaucheria sessilis*. Arrow points to a swimming compound zoospore. Below is an encysted zoospore and a germling with one germ tube. Above is a germling with two germ tubes.

Fig. 31-3 Photomicrograph of zoospore production in *Vaucheria geminata*. Below is a filament tip with a nearly mature asexual zoosporangium. Above are compound zoospores emerging from their sporangia. Note the numerous discoid chloroplasts in the coenocytic filaments.

Fig. 31-5 Photomicrographs of oogamy in *Vaucheria*. Upper: Vegetative filament of *V. aversa* developing laterally an oogonium and two short antheridial branches. The glistening bodies are lipid globules. Lower: An upright branch of *V. geminata* with two lateral oogonia containing thick-walled oospores and with a terminal, empty antheridium curved behind and out of view.

walls (with silicon dioxide). Some genera, like *Tribonema,* have walls composed of overlapping, H-shaped segments.

The distinctive yellow-green hue of xanthophytes is due to the abundance of carotene and xanthophylls in their lens- or disc-shaped chloroplasts, which also contain chlorophyll *a* and chlorophyll *e,* found only in this group of algae. Food is stored as oil and chrysolaminarin but never starch.

The two flagella of motile forms (and of the motile reproductive cell of non-motile forms) are unequal in length. The longer flagellum is of the two-sided tinsel type and the shorter one is a whiplash flagellum.

A contractile vacuole may be present in motile forms, but they lack an eyespot (stigma).

Asexual reproduction   Fragmentation is common in filamentous forms. Unicellular forms reproduce by binary fission. Motile unicells divide longitudinally while swimming. Nonmotile unicells may fail to separate after division and form extensive palmelloid masses. Many unicellular genera encyst, forming spores of survival, and some form a silicified cyst internally (e.g., statospores of chrysophytes).

Zoospores are a common means of asexual multiplication. The zoospore of *Botrydium* and *Tribonema* is typical: uninucleate and with two flagella at or near the front end, the longer one tinsel and the shorter one whiplash (Fig. 31-2). *Vaucheria* is unique in having a compound, coenocytic zoospore (Figs. 31-3, 31-4) with many peripheral nuclei and pairs of whiplash flagella (no tinsel flagella) that are almost equal in length. Because the sperm of *Vaucheria* has one of its two flagella of the tinsel type, one flagellum of each pair on the compound zoospore is probably derived evolutionarily from a tinsel flagellum and thus might be called tinsel-less rather than whiplash. Aplanospores, akinetes, and hypnospores may be formed.

Sexual reproduction   Sexual reproduction is not widespread among xanthophytes, although it is common in a few genera. Syngamy may be isogamous, as in *Tribonema* and species of *Botrydium,* anisogamous, as in other species of *Botridium,* or oogamous, as in *Vaucheria* (Fig. 31-5). The site of meiosis is not known with certainty, but apparently meiosis is zygotic and occurs on germination of the zygospore or oospore. Tentatively, then, xanthophytes are said to be haploid and have a haplontic sexual life cycle.

Chrysophytes

Taxonomy   Chrysophytes are also commonly called golden algae or golden-brown algae. There are about 75 genera and 300 species.

Chrysophytes are distinguished by a variety of cytological and morphological features. As with xanthophytes, the body forms of chrysophytes parallel those of green algae. For example, the common and predominant motile genera, like *Chromulina, Synura,* and *Dinobryon* (order Chrysomonadales), are of a volvocine-like evolutionary line or tendency.

Recent ultrastructural studies indicate that chrysophytes can be classified into subgroups (Chrysophyceae and Haptophyceae) based on two main characters: first, the nature of flagellation; second, the nature of scales on the cell surface.

Importance   Chrysophytes are an important component of plankton, and as such these algae play a significant role as primary producers. Both marine and freshwater species are providing cytologists with excellent material for investigating how the Golgi apparatus and other organelles function. Fossil coccolithophorid chrysophytes are important to geologists in stratigraphy.

Occurrence   Chrysophytes are predominantly freshwater algae, but a number of marine species are significant as marine nannoplankton (small plankton with dimensions less than 70–75 microns).

Vegetative features   Chrysophytes consist mainly of unicellular flagellated forms, like *Chrysochromulina* (Haptophyceae) and *Chromulina* (Chrysophyceae), but some, like *Synura* and *Dinobryon* are swimming colonies. Others are simple nonflagellated cells or amorphous palmelloid colonies. Some are amoeboid, some form gelatinous dendroid colonies, and some are filamentous and branching.

Most chrysophytes are either unwalled or have a cell surface covered by a layer of polysaccharide or proteinaceous scales or by siliceous scales, as in *Synura.* Encysted forms may have silicified or calcified walls. Genera like *Dinobryon* have protoplasts that are free from but surrounded by delicate shells, loricas.

Chrysophytes are various shades of brown depending on the abundance of carotene and xanthophylls (including fucoxanthin). Chlorophyll *a* is accompanied in many forms by chlorophyll *c*. Excess photosynthate is stored as oil and chrysolaminarin. Some of the autotrophic species apparently ingest particulate food and are therefore also phagotrophic. Colorless forms that are saprobic or phagotrophic are also known.

Flagellation is varied. Some have a single anterior, two-sided tinsel flagellum. Others, like *Synura* and *Dinobryon,* are anteriorly biflagellate with a longer tinsel flagellum and shorter whiplash flagellum. Still others have two anterior, whiplash flagella and a third filiform appendage, the haptonema, apparently used for temporary anchorage.

Asexual reproduction   Multiplication is accomplished by fragmentation: binary fission in unicellular forms and colony fragmentation in others. Nonmotile genera produce zoospores, usually singly within a cell. Statospore formation is common in chrysophytes and known only here and in some xanthophytes. A statospore is formed within a protoplast. The statospore wall is often ornamented; it is silicified, composed of two overlapping halves, and has a pore closed by a conspicuous plug.

Sexual reproduction   Sexual reproduction is rare. The fusion of biflagellate isogametes has been reported in some species. The zygote is a cystlike structure in which meiosis apparently occurs and four daughter cells are normally produced.

Diatoms

Taxonomy   Diatoms are also commonly called bacillariophytes. There are about 200 genera and 5,000 species.

Diatoms are distinctive because of their unique, silicified cell walls. They are divided into two groups (orders), the Centrales and the Pennales. This classification is based largely on cell shape and the symmetry and orientation of structural features of the wall. Centric diatoms have radial symmetry in valve (top or bottom) view, are nonmotile, are oogamous, and are more commonly planktonic and marine. The pennate diatoms (Fig. 31-6) have bilateral symmetry in valve view, many exhibit a gliding movement, are generally isogamous, and are usually freshwater forms, frequently occurring attached to aquatic plants and other objects and as components of the mud and soil flora. The more detailed classification of diatoms is based on the remarkable and elegant variation in structures or markings of the cell wall.

Centric diatoms appear to be more primitive. They appear as fossils first in the Jurassic Period. The earliest fossils of pennate diatoms are of the Tertiary Period.

Importance Diatoms are of great biological and economic importance. They are of major importance as primary producers in the food chains and webs of nature. Because oceans occupy most of the earth's surface, one half or more of the earth's photosynthesis occurs there (Map 18-1, p. 135), and the major primary producers in oceans are the phytoplankters. The most abundant marine phytoplankters are diatoms and dinoflagellates; they are, then, the first link in the food chains of animals of the open ocean.

Diatoms are useful indicators of varying ecological conditions in freshwater habitats. For example, rivers free from pollution have many species of diatoms, each in relatively small numbers; whereas, in polluted waters the number of diatom species is small.

Because of their fine markings, cleaned diatom walls are excellent for testing the resolving power of optical lenses. As diatoms of past geological ages died, their empty silicified walls accumulated in great numbers as diatomaceous ooze on the bottoms of seas. Raised above sea level by geologic activity, these vast

Fig. 31-6 Mixture of several kinds of freshwater pennate diatoms. *(Photomicrograph courtesy Carolina Biological Supply Company.)*

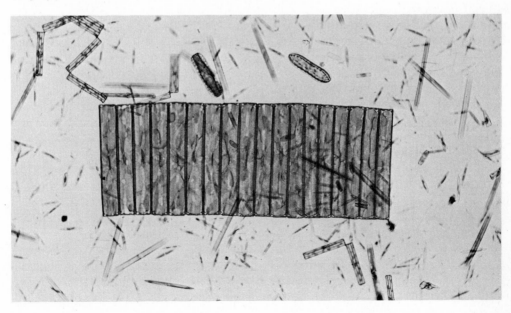

Part Four: Survey of the Major Groups of Plants

deposits became diatomaceous earth, which is now mined in various places. Diatomaceous earth is used in industrial and technical processes as an abrasive, as insulating material, in the filtration of liquids, and as a filler in paints and plastics.

Occurrence   Diatoms are extremely widespread and occur as the dominant organisms of many habitats. They are conspicuous components of the soil microflora and of both freshwater and marine phytoplankton. They may form extensive blooms in bodies of water. Diatoms, along with dinoflagellates, are the dominant marine plankton algae.

Marine diatoms also live on the surfaces of almost all solid substrates, on mud-flat surfaces, in salt marshes, and attached as epiphytes to other algae and marine seed plants. Freshwater diatoms are also common on the bottoms of lakes, ponds, and pools and on the surfaces of plants and other objects in freshwater bodies. In running water they often form a brown coating on submerged rocks, sticks, and vegetation.

Vegetative features   The vegetative cell of diatoms is characterized by three main features: The cell walls are silicified and have characteristic structural features. The photosynthetic pigments include chlorophylls *a* and *c* together with carotene and xanthophylls, including fucoxanthin. Food is stored as oils and chrysolaminarin. (In addition, the motile reproductive cell of diatoms has a single anterior two-sided tinsel flagellum.)

Diatom cells have a wide variety of shapes, such as essentially box shaped or boat shaped (e.g., *Pinnularia* and *Navicula*), somewhat club shaped (e.g., *Gomphonema*), and needlelike (e.g., *Asterionella* and *Fragilaria*). Many centric diatoms have a flat discoid form (e.g., *Coscinodiscus*). Others have a flattened triangular shape (e.g., *Triceratium*) or are short cylindric (e.g., *Melosira*). Diatoms may be unicellular or colonial, held together by mucilaginous secretions. Some colonies are dendroid (e.g., *Gomphonema*), stellate (e.g., *Asterionella*), ribbonlike or bandlike (e.g., *Fragilaria*), zigzag chains (e.g., *Tabellaria*), or filamentous (e.g., *Melosira*).

The diatom cell wall is made of an organic compound, called pectin, and is impregnated with large amounts of hydrated silica. It consists of overlapping parts fitting together like the halves of a petri dish. The halves are called frustules, the outer one (the "lid") is the epitheca and the inner one (the "bottom") is the hypotheca. Each half consists of a main surface, the valve, and the overlapping connecting bands; the two connecting bands constitute the girdle. When viewed from above or below, the diatom is seen in valve view. When viewed from the side, it is seen in girdle view.

The diatom cell wall is not of uniform thickness, and the variously arranged thicker and thinner areas provide the wall with complex "markings," striae, or sculpturing (Fig. 31-7). In centric diatoms the markings (pores and ridges) radiate from the center of the valve. In pennate diatoms the valve has an axial line or spine, and the finer markings are arranged pinnately as lateral branches. In the center of the valve of most pennate diatoms is an unsilicified groove called the raphe, which may be straight, wavy, or S shaped. At the center of the raphe is a wide area or central nodule, and at the ends of the raphe are polar nodules. The raphe seems to be associated with the jerky and gliding movements of many pennate diatoms.

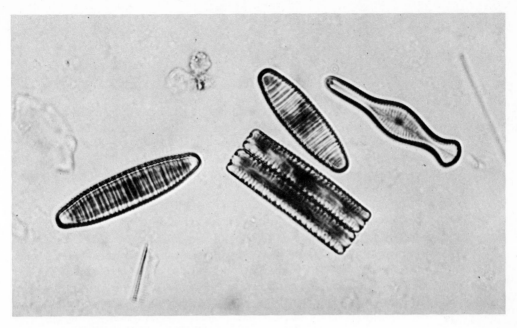

Fig. 31-7 Pennate diatoms showing characteristic markings of their silicified walls. *(Photomicrograph courtesy Carolina Biological Supply Company.)*

The diatom cell has a central vacuole and one, two, or many golden-brown chloroplasts. The cells are uninucleate and apparently diploid. They have a unique method of cell division, described below.

Asexual reproduction   Multiplication is effected primarily by fragmentation, either of colonies or by the separation of unicells after division. In the latter case, after mitosis and cytokinesis, the original wall contains two protoplasts. As they enlarge, each of the daughter protoplasts develops one new wall or frustule, using one old frustule of the parent cell as the epitheca. This means that the daughter cell using the hypotheca of the parent cell with be slightly smaller than the parent cell. If this continues, the population becomes progressively smaller. It may be restored through sexual reproduction.

Sexual reproduction   Sex is rare in diatoms. They are diploid and meiosis precedes and results in gamete formation; thus, diatoms have a diplontic sexual life cycle.

Diatom population size is restored and genetic diversity accomplished through special zygotes called auxospores. They are so called because they are naked protoplasts that increase greatly in size before they secrete their rigid silicified walls. In most pennate diatoms, as in many desmids of the green algae, protoplasts (isogametes) of two cells escape amoeboidly from their walls and fuse to form the zygote, called auxospore in diatoms. A parent cell, serving as a gametangium, may liberate one or two of the nonflagellated gametes. Most centric diatoms are oogamous. After meiosis, usually a single egg is formed in the female cell (oogonium) and 4–8 anteriorly uniflagellate sperms are produced by the male cell (antheridium).

Project

I. Xanthophytes (yellow-green algae)

A. *Tetrasporine-like evolutionary tendency*
   Tribonema
   1. Mount a group of filaments in water, add a cover slip, and study. Note the absence of branching, the several plastids and a single nucleus in each cell, and look for zoospore formation.
   2. H-Piece wall structure. Mount a group of filaments in 2 or 3 drops of 40 per cent chromic acid. Add a cover slip and observe with high dry. (Take care not to get chromic acid on lenses.)

B. *Siphonaceous-like evolutionary tendency*
   Vaucheria
   1. Vegetative structure. Note the lack of cross walls in these coenocytic, branching filaments. Find chloroplasts, lipid globules, and central vacuole.
   2. Reproduction
      a. Asexual. If material is available, study the unusual compound zoospores of *Vaucheria*. Compare them with the zoospores of green algae and water molds.
      b. Sexual. Find oogonia and antheridia on oogonial stalks and antheridial stalks, respectively. The oogonia in your material may be immature but they probably will have either eggs or zygotes in them, one per oogonium. If material of *Vaucheria sessilis* and *V. geminata* is available, note that these species demonstrate two types of orientation of sexual parts. How do they differ?

II. Chrysophytes (golden-brown algae)

A. *Volvocine-like evolutionary tendency*
   1. *Synura* and *Dinobryon*. Mount drops containing these colonial algae and observe their movements with low power. Does *Synura* have a posterior and anterior end (show polarity)? Observe swimming under the darkfield microscope set up either by your instructor or by you if you have a microscope with a condenser and a strong enough light source (see Project 9: V, p. 53). Add a cover slip and look for cellular details.
   2. *Chromulina* and *Chrysochromulina*. Mount drops containing these unicellular chrysophytes, and study as directed above.

B. *Tetrasporine-like evolutionary tendency*
   Apistonema and *Pleurochrysis*. If cultures of these or other chrysophytes known as coccolithophorids are available, study them.

III. Diatoms

A. *Pennate diatoms*. If living material of *Navicula* or better still a large *Pinnularia* is available, study its movement and structure. What is the mechanism of the gliding movement of pennate diatoms? Study valve and girdle views. Find striae of the wall or frustule, raphe of the wall, nodules of the wall, chromatophores, and lipid globules.

B. *Centric diatoms*. Study such centric diatoms as *Melosira, Stephanodiscus,* and *Coscinodiscus*. Compare them with *Navicula* and *Pinnularia* or any pennate diatoms, looking for differences in form and movement.

C. Study any other pennate and centric diatoms that are available. Study of a wide variety of diatoms will give you a good concept of specialization in vegetative cells.

D. Mount some diatomaceous earth and look for fossil diatom "shells." Note the details of ornamentation of these frustules and frustule fragments. (Incidentally, living diatoms are identified primarily on details of frustule ornamentation, which cannot be fully seen in most living specimens. Thus, the protoplasts of most diatoms must be removed by appropriate techniques, including incineration and treatment with strong acid, before the diatoms can be identified accurately. Fossil diatoms have their protoplasts removed, of course.)

Project **32**   Dinoflagellates and relatives

Contents

Introduction

Taxonomy Dinoflagellates and relatives (Dinophyceae and Desmophyceae) are organisms of the group technically known to botanists as Pyrrophyta or Pyrrophycophyta. They are commonly called pyrrophytes and there are about 125 genera and 1,000 species.

Pyrrophytes are characterized by three main features: a unique motile, flagellated cell; a unique type of nucleus and cell wall; and distinctive photosynthetic pigments. The few rare genera and species known as desmophytes, which are mostly marine, are not treated here. The discussion below deals with the major and important pyrrophytes, the dinophytes, of which most are dinoflagellates.

Although motile unicellular forms (dinoflagellates) are the major and most important dinophytes, there are nonmotile and multicellular members. Evolution appears to have paralleled that in green algae, xanthophytes, and chrysophytes; thus, the major groups (orders) of dinophytes parallel those in the algal groups just mentioned. For example, the dinophyte Dinotrichales is the counterpart of the green algal Ulotrichales, the xanthophyte Heterotrichales, and the chrysophyte Chrysotrichales.

As with euglenoids, pyrrophytes are a specialized group of organisms that represent a separate evolutionary line. Pyrrophytes of the past apparently did not give rise to other kinds of organisms and present-day pyrrophytes probably will not either.

There are two additional, distinctive, small groups of algae, predominantly flagellates, which are so incompletely known that they have undetermined

248

relationships and therefore are of uncertain taxonomic or systematic position: *Cryptomonads* (*Cryptophytes*) and *Chloromonads*. They are not pyrrophytes and are mentioned here only to make complete your awareness of all the known major kinds or groups of algae.

Importance   Dinoflagellates are important primary producers in both fresh and salt-water bodies. Dinoflagellates and diatoms are the most abundant marine phytoplankters and are the ultimate food source for fish and other animals of the open ocean.

Marine water blooms or population explosions of such genera as *Gonyaulax* can cause the red water and red tides and the widespread death of fish and many other marine animals.

Occurrence   Dinoflagellates occur in both freshwater and salt water where they often are an important component of the plankton. Most are found in the plankton of the ocean. Freshwater dinoflagellates are most abundant in water-filled ditches, pools, and small lakes. Nonmotile dinophytes are rare and are usually epiphytic on coarser algae. The several parasitic genera are found within and upon various animals.

Vegetative features   The vast majority of dinophytes are uniquely structured, flagellated unicells (dinoflagellates); however, there are some nonmotile unicellular and filamentous genera which produce motile cells that look like dinoflagellates.

Some dinoflagellates, such as *Gymnodinium*, are naked or unwalled and with a firm periplast. They are said to be unarmored. Most dinoflagellates are armored—they have cellulosic walls with definite patterns of sculpturing or with a number of discrete, sculptured plates held together tightly in a definite pattern. A common elaboration of the cell surface is the formation of spines and various processes (e.g., *Ceratium*, Fig. 32-1).

The most distinctive feature of dinoflagellates, and also the motile reproductive cells produced by palmelloid and filamentous dinophytes, is the presence of a transverse groove or furrow, the girdle, which divides the cell into two parts or semicells. The anterior and posterior semicells are approximately the same length in most dinophytes, but in *Amphidinium* the anterior semicell is shorter and in some species appears to be almost lacking. The anterior semicell is lacking in *Prorocentrum* (Fig. 32-2). Each cell is biflagellate: the two flagella come out from one place in the transverse groove; one flagellum is band shaped and simply undulates in the transverse groove, and the other flagellum is of the whiplash type and trails behind, at first in a short vertical groove or furrow, the sulcus.

The nucleus of pyrrophytes is unique. Each cell has a large nucleus with conspicuous beadlike chromatin (condensed chromosomes). Unlike the chromosomes of all other eukaryotic organisms except some fungi and like the nucleoplasm of blue-green algae and bacteria, the DNA of pyrrophytes is not complexed with histone. The DNA of the nuclei of other eukaryotic cells is combined with the special protein histone. The lack of histones in blue-green algae and pyrrophytes suggests that the counterpart of the nucleoplasm of a blue-green algal cell is the individual chromosome of a pyrrophyte nucleus rather than the entire nucleus, and it suggests that the nucleus of pyrrophytes is intermediate between the nucleoplasm of prokaryotes and the nucleus of other eukaryotes.

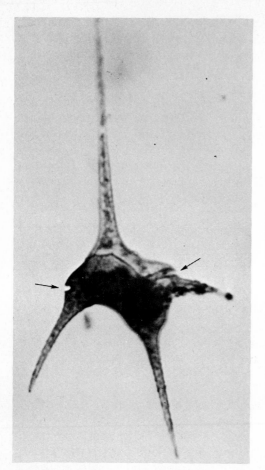

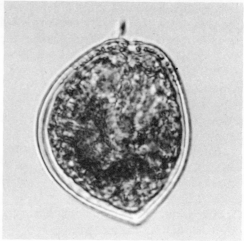

Fig. 32-1 (at left)   Stained specimen of *Ceratium*, an armored dinoflagellate. Arrows point to the transverse groove. *(Photomicrograph courtesy Carolina Biological Supply Company.)*

Fig. 32-2 (above)   *Prorocentrum*, a compressed, free-swimming marine dinoflagellate divided longitudinally into two equal halves (valves). *(Photomicrograph courtesy Carolina Biological Supply Company.)*

Pyrrophytes have both pigmented and colorless members. Pigmented dino-flagellates (e.g. *Glenodinium, Peridinium,* and *Ceratium*) are usually greenish brown or golden brown and may have a conspicuous red eyespot. Each cell has two or more small, discoid chloroplasts. The photosynthetic pigments include chlorophylls *a* and *c* as well as carotene and xanthophylls, some of which are unique to pyrrophytes. Carbohydrate food reserves are stored outside chloroplasts as starch, and food is also stored as oil.

At least some of the autotrophic dinophytes are auxotrophic, requiring an external source of vitamins. Colorless genera are saprobic or parasitic, and some are phagotrophic.

A number of marine dinoflagellates are dramatically luminescent, especially when seawater is disturbed at night, as in the wake of a ship.

Asexual reproduction   Multiplication is largely by cell division, frequently while cells are swimming. Nonmotile unicellular and filamentous forms produce unwalled, asexual zoospores ("gymnodinioid zoospores"). Either one or two to eight zoospores are formed in a cell. Most pyrrophytes have asexual life cycles only.

Sexual reproduction   Syngamy has been reported several times, but the process appears to be established only in *Ceratium* and *Glenodinium*. In both cases, the protoplasts (gametes) escape their walls and fuse. The vegetative cell is presumed to be haploid, with meiosis occurring at germination of the zygote. The few pyrrophytes that are sexual, then, are presumed to have haplontic life cycles.

Project

I. Look for dinoflagellates especially in plankton collections. You are most likely to find *Gymnodinium, Glenodinium, Peridinium,* and/or *Ceratium.* From high power and oil immersion find the girdle (transverse groove), sulcus (vertical groove), the transverse, girdling flagellum, the posterior, free flagellum, chromatophores, and cell wall, which is often composed of plates (not in *Gymnodinium*).

II. Add I_2KI solution to a preparation and examine cells for the presence of starch.

III. The following cultures of unicellular, motile pyrrophytes may be available for study:
   A. *Marine forms:*
      Amphidinium (unwalled dinophyte with shorter upper half)
      Glenodinium (walled dinophyte)
      Gymnodinium (unwalled dinophyte)
      Prorocentrum (desmophyte)
   B. *Freshwater form:*
      Peridinium (walled dinophyte)

Project **33**   Brown algae

Contents

Introduction

Taxonomy   Brown algae are plants of the group technically known as Phaeo-phyta or Phaeophycophyta. There are about 250 genera and 1,500 species.

Brown algae comprise the clearly defined group of algae characterized by six main features: (1) they are almost exclusively marine; (2) most have large and complex thalli; (3) their chloroplasts have an abundance of fucoxanthin and other carotenoids (carotenes and xanthophylls), which are more abundant than the chlorophylls (*a* and *c*), so the color of these plants is brownish; (4) food reserves are mainly laminarin and mannitol; (5) they have laterally biflagellate, almost pear-shaped motile cells, with the anteriorly directed tinsel flagellum usually longer than the posteriorly directed whiplash one; and (6) most brown algae have alternating sporophytic and gametophytic phases.

Although no unicellular brown algae are known, the relatively constant structure of the zoospores and gametes of all brown algae suggest their origin from free-living forms that looked much like the motile reproductive cells of present-

252

day brown algae. In addition, similarities in flagellation, pigmentation, and food reserve suggest a common origin for brown algae and chrysophytes.

The orders of brown algae are placed in evolutionary lines or groups based on type of life cycle, structural features of the thallus, and features relating to syngamy. The three major groups are distinguished by the three basic kinds of life cycles: isomorphic alternation of generations (Isogeneratae, with five orders, including Ectocarpales), heteromorphic alternation of generations (Heterogeneratae, with five orders, including kelps of the Laminariales), and diplontic life cycle with only a diploid vegetative stage (Cyclosporeae, with the single order Fucales, the rock weeds). Orders and genera are distinguished by such features as method of syngamy (isogamy, anisogamy, or oogamy); method of growth (diffuse, intercalary, or apical); and thallus organization (filamentous, pseudoparenchymatous, or parenchymatous).

Importance   Brown algae are important as primary producers in intertidal and subtidal coastal regions, and they are important as a protective cover for young fish and smaller invertebrates. Some animals browse directly on the tissues of larger brown algae and others feed on the detritus originating from beds and subtidal forests of decaying brown algae. Although no unicellular brown algae are known, the motile reproductive cells of larger brown algae can contribute significantly to the phytoplankton. For example, in dense beds of the large kelp *Nerecystis* (Fig. 33-2) an estimated 3,000,000 zoospores per liter per day are produced from June to September.

Larger brown algae are of direct importance to man. Kelps like *Laminaria* (Fig. 33-1) and *Alaria* are prepared and eaten in the Orient as a food called kombu; indeed, *Laminaria* is now cultivated in marine bays much like a crop plant.

Algin or alginic acid, a polyuronic acid, is a cell wall constituent, and is used by man in many ways. About 10 per cent of the wet weight of kelps is algin. The greatest production of algin is from the kelp *Macrocystis* in California, where dense beds are harvested by mowers on barges. Algin is colloidal and can absorb ten to twenty times its weight of water, but when dried it becomes extremely hard. The salts of alginic acid have a wide variety of uses. For example, sodium alginate is used as a stabilizer in ice cream, calcium alginate is used in plastics and as a laundry starch substitute, and ammonium alginate is used in sizing and fireproofing fabrics. Alginates are also used industrially as a clarifier in the manufacture

Fig. 33-1   View of a seashore with the kelp *Laminaria* in a windrow on the beach. *(Courtesy Carolina Biological Supply Company.)*

of beer, as a binder in printer's ink, in molding artificial limbs and buttons, and as components of soaps, shampoos, photographic film coatings, paints, varnishes, leather finishes, insecticides, toothpastes, shaving creams, lipsticks, and medicines.

Brown algae used to be of economic importance for the iodine that can be obtained from them, but cheaper sources are now available. Brown algae are of some value as a source of agricultural fertilizer. Their relative proportions of nitrogen, phosphorus, and potassium make this fertilizer particularly good for such crops as beets and potatoes.

Occurrence   Brown algae are primarily marine organisms of cold water. Some occur in brackish water and salt marshes. Both perennial and annual genera are known. There are only three rare freshwater brown algae.

Brown algae flourish in colder ocean waters and on rocky coasts. Most grow attached in the relatively shallow water of the intertidal and subtidal zones. *Ectocarpus* (Fig. 33-4), for example, commonly grows attached to stones and shells or epiphytically on larger marine algae.

There is a distinct vertical zonation. Some species grow in the subtidal zone. For example, certain giant kelps found along the Pacific Coast of this country grow attached to rocky reefs 10–20 meters below the surface of the ocean. Arising from their holdfast is a long slender axis whose upper part is expanded into blades that float on the surface of the water. Subtidal brown algae are continuously submerged and may be attached at depths of up to 110 meters, depending primarily, it seems, on the degree of light penetration into the water and also on other physical and chemical factors. In the North Pacific large kelps such as *Nereocystis* (Fig. 33-2) and *Macrocystis* grow attached in water 35 or more meters deep and form dense subtidal forests.

Many brown algae grow only in the intertidal region where they are exposed to pounding wave action and to the atmosphere with its increased oxygen availability and its dessicating and often freezing qualities. Even in the intertidal zone there is a definite vertical distribution. For example, kelps (Laminariales) are restricted to the lower portion of the intertidal zone, and rockweeds (e.g. *Fucus*, Fig. 33-3) to the upper intertidal belt. Species of the rockweed *Ascophyllum* are common in the middle of the intertidal zone.

Some species, such as *Sargassum* (Fig. 33-5), occur free floating in the Sargasso Sea of the North Atlantic. In tropical and semitropical waters many species of *Sargassum* form large dense beds that serve as grazing and breeding areas for marine animals.

Fucales have the largest number of their genera and species in the southern hemisphere and appear to have a center of distribution in southern Australia and New Zealand. Laminariales have more genera and species in the North Pacific and have an apparent distribution center in the northwestern part of the Pacific. Both of these most conspicuous groups of brown algae do have representatives in both the southern and northern hemispheres (e.g. *Macrocystis*); however, *Fucus* occurs in the northern hemisphere only and *Durvillea* (Fucales) only in the southern. *Hormosira* (Fucales) of the southern hemisphere occupies the same ecological niche that *Fucus* does in the northern hemisphere.

Vegetative features   Brown algae are the largest and vegetatively the most complex algae. All have diploid sporophytic thalli, and it is those of the giant kelps (order Laminariales) that attain the greatest height (up to about 50 meters) and the

Fig. 33-2 (left)   Entire plant of *Nereocystis* collected and placed in a tank of seawater. *(Courtesy Carolina Biological Supply Company.)*

Fig. 33-3 (right)   View of a *Fucus* plant attached to a rock, which has been taken out of the ocean. Note the enlarged fertile tips (receptacles) of many of the branches. *(Courtesy Carolina Biological Supply Company.)*

most advanced anatomical features. There are no motile brown algae, but they do produce motile reproductive cells.

Brown algal cell walls have an inner cellulosic layer and an outer mucilaginous layer of pectin and large amounts of the characteristic alginic acid and fucinic acid. The colloidal substances of the outer wall prevent excessive drying of intertidal brown algae when exposed during low tide. Unlike the cellulose of higher green plants, which consists solely of glucose subunits, brown algal "cellulose" resembles that of all red algae, except *Porphyra*, and the seaweed green algae *Ulva* and *Entomorpha* in consisting of both glucose (or glucan) and xylose (or xylan) subunits.

The cells of most brown algae contain many small discoid parietal chloroplasts (rarely encountered are stellate, platelike, and ribbon-like chloroplasts) (Fig. 33-4), one vacuole to numerous small vacuoles, and a prominent membrane-bounded nucleus that contains one to a few nucleoli and divides mitotically. The dividing nuclei of brown algae show centrosomes clearer than other algae. The cytoplasm also has many highly refractive fucosan vesicles, which are found in abundance at sites having high metabolic activity, such as dividing cells. It is not known if fucosan is a waste by-product of metabolism or a food reserve.

The brownish color of brown algae reflects the abundance in the chloroplasts of the xanthophyll fucoxanthin, which is dominant over the other xanthophylls, carotene, and chlorophyll *a* and *c*. Excess photosynthate accumulates outside chloroplasts as the polysaccharide laminarin, as the sugar alcohol mannitol, and less frequently as lipid droplets.

All brown algae but the Fucales have gametophytes as well as sporophytes, and depending on the genus, both may be minute with only a few cells or they may be quite large. The brown algal thallus may be filamentous and amorphous or it may

255

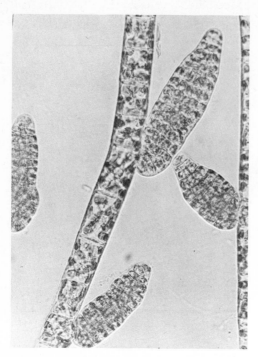

Fig. 33-4   Uniseriate filaments of the branching thallus of *Ectocarpus* bearing plurilocular sporangia. *(Photomicrograph courtesy Carolina Biological Supply Company.)*

Fig. 33-5   Portion of a free-floating thallus of *Sargassum. (Courtesy CCM: General Biological, Inc., Chicago.)*

be filamentous, pseudoparenchymatous (with closely appressed filaments), or parenchymatous and with a definite form, in which case it is usually differentiated into a prostrate portion, the holdfast, and an erect portion.

Genera like *Ectocarpus* (Fig. 33-4) are branching filamentous plants in which a branching erect system of filaments is attached to the substratum by a branching prostrate system, much as in the green alga *Stigeoclonium*. The growing apex is a branched uniseriate filament with intercalary or diffuse cell divisions.

Growth of many parenchymatous brown algae is initiated by a single apical cell or a marginal row of apical cells at the apex of each branch.

The gametophytes of kelps are filamentous and microscopic, but the sporophytes are parenchymatous, mostly very large, with apical growth, and with a complexity of form externally comparable to that of vascular plants: from the anchoring rootlike holdfast arises a simple or branched stemlike stipe that bears one to many leaflike blades (Figs. 33-1, 33-2). Growth of kelp sporophytes is unique in that it is not apical but is initiated by a meristem at the juncture of the stipe and blade or at the base of the stipe.

The kelps *Macrocystis, Nereocystis,* and *Pelagophycus* are especially noteworthy because their stipes contain sieve tubes, and these are similar to the sieve tubes of vascular plants. Flotation of the blades of *Macrocystis* and *Nereocystis* is aided by air bladders (pneumatocysts) (Fig. 33-2). The rockweeds *Fucus* and *Sargassum* are diploid parenchymatous plants that also have air bladders, and *Sargassum* has a high degree of morphological differentiation (Fig. 33-5).

Asexual reproduction   Asexual reproduction in *Sargassum* and several other brown algae is brought about by detachment of fragments of the thallus that float away and develop into new plants. It is the only known method of reproduction in *Sargassum natans*; however, fragmentation as a means of multiplication in brown algae is rare. A special fragmenting reproductive branch, called the propagule, is formed by *Sphacelaria*.

All brown algae except Fucales produce either asexual zoospores or aplanospores. Asexual zoospores, like the meiozoospores and flagellated gametes of brown algae, are pear, pip, or slipper shaped and have two laterally attached flagella. The flagella are unequal in length. The longer usually is the anteriorly directed, two-sided tinsel flagellum, and the shorter whiplash flagellum is posteriorly directed during swimming. The flagellated cell usually contains a chloroplast and an eyespot.

Asexual zoospores are diploid and produced only on sporophytic thalli and in special multicellular branches called many-chambered or plurilocular sporangia (Fig. 33-4). These asexual zoosporangia are made up of cuboidal cells and are many cells in height and several cells broad. Plurilocular sporangia lack a jacket of sterile wall cells—all are zoospore producing.

Gametes that fail to undergo syngamy sometimes develop into gametophytic plants, like those which produced them; thus, they multiply the gametophytic phase asexually or parthenogenetically.

Sexual reproduction   With respect to syngamy, brown algae with isogamy, anisogamy, and oogamy occur. The Fucales have a diplontic life cycle, but all other brown algae have an alternation of free-living multicellular gametophytic and sporophytic generations. In some, like *Ectocarpus* and *Dictyota*, the haploid and diploid phases have identical forms—are isomorphic. Most others are heteromorphic, with large parenchymatous sporophytes and microscopic filamentous gametophytes.

Ectocarpus and many of its relatives are isogamous. Relatively few brown algae are anisogamous. Isogametes and anisogametes are produced on gametophytic thalli in plurilocular gametangia. Plurilocular gametangia and gametes look like the asexual plurilocular sporangia (Fig. 33-4) and zoospores produced by sporophytes. The only way to tell them apart is to follow development of the liberated motile cells. Motile gametes have the same structure as diploid zoospores (described under asexual reproduction). A zygote germinates directly and forms a diploid sporophytic thallus. Gametophytes may be homothallic or heterothallic. *Ectocarpus*, like the green alga *Ulva*, is heterothallic and has an alternation of isomorphic gametophytic and sporophytic thalli. Thus, there are three different plants that look alike: the + gametophyte, the − gametophyte, and the sporophyte.

The diploid sporophytic plants of *Ectocarpus* produce, in addition to asexual plurilocular zoosporangia, single-celled or unilocular sporangia in which meiosis occurs. Unilocular sporangia, then, are sexual sporangia or meiosporangia. Following meiosis are several mitotic divisions and then cleavage into usually 32 or 64 uninucleate zoospores (meiozoospores). These zoospores encyst and develop directly into gametophytic plants.

The kelp *Laminaria* is oogamous and has an alternation of a large diploid sporophytic plant with tiny filamentous male and female plants. *Laminaria*, then, has an alternation of heteromorphic generations, much as in seed plants. Each

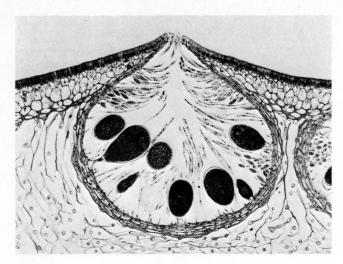

Fig. 33-6 Stained longitudinal section of *Fucus* showing a conceptacle containing both oogonia (large) and antheridia (small). Note ostiole of conceptacle. *(Photomicrograph courtesy Ripon Microslides Laboratory.)*

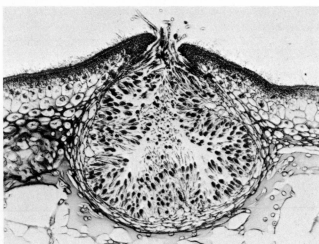

Fig. 33-7 Stained longitudinal section of *Fucus* showing a male conceptacle containing antheridia. *(Photomicrograph courtesy Ripon Microslides Laboratory.)*

antheridium of the male gametophyte liberates a minute biflagellate sperm. Each oogonium of the female gametophyte liberates a single egg that remains attached at the oogonial opening where it is fertilized, and the zygote then develops directly into a sporophytic thallus.

The rockweed *Fucus* is oogamous and has only a diploid plant. Eggs and sperms are produced after meioses in oogonia and antheridia within cavities (conceptacles) localized at the tips of branches in enlarged fertile areas called receptacles (Fig. 33-3). Conceptacles open to the surrounding water through narrow ostioles. Depending on the species, antheridia and oogonia may be in the same conceptacle (Fig. 33-6) or in different conceptacles on different plants (Fig. 33-7). Gametes are liberated into the water where great numbers of sperms swarm around the large, spherical, nonmotile eggs. After an egg is fertilized by a sperm, the zygote secretes a thin wall and develops directly into a *Fucus* plant.

All brown algae but *Fucus* and other members of the Fucales have life cycles involving an alternation of free-living, multicellular gametophytic and sporophytic generations. The *Fucus* plant is diploid, and because *Fucus* lacks a free-living multicellular gametophyte, it may be said to have a diplontic life cycle, like that of the seaweed *Caulerpa* and other siphonaceous green algae. However, *Fucus* does have alternating diploid and haploid phases. The haploid phase is reduced to single cells, which themselves become gametes. Meiosis occurs at gamete formation, and the gametangia are comparable to the unilocular meiosporangia of other brown algae. Indeed, the oogonium of *Fucus* can be called a female sporangium (also called megasporangium) that produces four female spores (megaspores) by meiosis and then eight eggs by one mitotic division. Similarly, the antheridium can be called a male sporangium that produces four male spores by meiosis and then sixty-four sperms by four mitotic divisions. From this point of view, *Fucus* may be said to have a diplo-haplontic life cycle with a highly reduced gametophytic phase, somewhat as in angiosperms.

Project

I. Macroscopic study of representative brown algae

A. The kelp *Laminaria* (observe holdfast, stipe, and blade).
B. The kelp *Nereocystis* (observe holdfast, stipe, air bladder, and blade).
C. The gulfweed or rockweed *Sargassum* (observe air bladders, stipe, blades, and holdfast if present).
D. The rockweed *Fucus* (observe air bladders and holdfast if present).
E. *Ectocarpus,* growing epiphytically on large seaweeds.

II. Brown algae with isomorphic alternation of generations

Ectocarpus
A. *Thallus.* Using low power, study the pattern of branching in *Ectocarpus.* Are the tips of the filaments all alike in structure? If you are studying preserved material, search for filaments well enough preserved to show cellular details (reticulate chloroplast and nucleus).
B. *Reproduction.* In "fruiting" material find either or both of the two forms of sporangia (prepared slides may be used to supplement the observations):
1. Unilocular sporangia (meiosporangia), produced by a sporophytic plant and occurring as single cells, solitary, sessile, or on short stalks in some species and in chains in others. Many of the cells have been plasmolyzed by the preserving solution. Each meiosporangium develops a large number of biflagellate zoospores.
2. Plurilocular sporangia (asexual zoosporangia), produced by a sporo-phytic plant, or plurilocular gametangia (isogametangia), produced by a gametophytic plant. These reproductive organs are indistinguishable from each other as far as structure is concerned. They are branches composed of a very large number of small cubical cells, each of which produces one or perhaps two or three biflagellate elements similar to zoospores, but which are known to be gametes in some forms. Conjugation occurs in pairs as in *Ulothrix.*
3. Should zoospores or gametes be discharged from living material, study their movements and then stain with iodine. Note their kidney or pear form and the pair of flagella inserted laterally.

III. Brown algae with heteromorphic alternation of generations

Laminaria and Other Kelps

Anatomy. Make cross sections or use prepared cross sections of the stipes and perhaps blades of such kelps as *Laminaria, Nereocystis,* and *Postelsia.* Identify the outer, photosynthetic, cortical cells; the larger storage cells of the cortex; and the loosely organized cells of the medulla. If material of *Pelagophycus, Macrocystis,* or *Nereocystis* is available, study sections of the stipes showing sieve tubes.

IV. Brown algae with no alternation of generations (Fucales)

Fucus, rockweed

From prepared slides and using low power, study a cross section of a receptacle showing a longitudinal section through a conceptacle. Note a conceptacle with its pore (ostiole) through which sterile filaments (paraphyses) may be protruding. Note the large oogonia containing eight eggs when mature. Using high power, look for antheridia, which are smaller and slightly tapering cells borne in groups on short branching filaments. Can you see the mass of sperms in an antheridium? Note the fertile sheet, a layer two or three cells in thickness lining the conceptacle from which oogonia and/or antheridia develop. Is the species you are studying monoecious or dioecious?

V. Living materials commercially available

The following living materials are available from Carolina Biological Supply Co.:

A. *Ectocarpus* with plurilocular sporangia
B. *Dictyota,* both male and female
C. *Sphacelaria,* both male and female
D. Mixture of *Ascophyllum* and *Fucus. Fucus* is sexual from about August until January. *Ascophyllum* is sexual from December through May.

Note: *Ectocarpus, Dictyota,* and *Sphacelaria* have alternating isomorphic generations. *Ascophyllum* and *Fucus* are diploid plants.

VI. Preserving large brown algae

If living kelps and rockweeds are available for collecting and you wish to preserve them permanently as dry specimens that will be flexible and lifelike, you can do so by soaking them in the following solution:

30 per cent glycerine
30 per cent ethyl alcohol (95 per cent)
10 per cent carbolic acid (phenol). (Danger, phenol is poisonous!) (Phenol is expensive, and 5 per cent is sufficient ordinarily.)
30 per cent water

Use a strong, well-covered bucket for soaking. Do not use plastic. Soak the large thalli until they are completely penetrated. The time varies with the specimen—usually months. After soaking, the specimens are dried. They will retain their flexibility and natural color for a long time. They can be handled without fear of their breaking.

Project **34** Red algae

Contents

Introduction

Taxonomy   Red algae are plants of the group technically known as Rhodophyta or Rhodophycophyta. There are about 600 genera and 4,000 species.

Red algae comprise a clearly defined group characterized by six main features: (1) they have a highly specialized and characteristic sexual process; (2) flagellated cells are never produced; (3) their photosynthetic pigments include characteristic biliproteins (R-phycoerythrin and R-phycocyanin); (4) their photosynthetic pigments include, among other carotinoids, a unique one (taraxanthin) and in addition to chlorophyll a, in some species chlorophyll d; (5) food storage products include floridean starch and a galactoside of glycerol called floridoside; and (6) polysulphate esters are components of the cell wall.

The origin of red algae and their relationships with other groups is uncertain. The absence of flagella, the presence of biliprotein photosynthetic pigments, and the presence of unassociated or unstacked photosynthetic lamellae indicate a relationship between the eukaryotic red algae and the prokaryotic blue-green algae. However, the relationship is not very close: the biliproteins are not identical in the two groups; a small, poorly known group of phytoflagellates called crytomonads or cryptophytes also have biliprotein pigments; and double-membrane structures such as mitochondria, chloroplasts, etc., which are found in red algal cells, are not found in blue-green algae, and this indicates a fundamental organizational difference in metabolic pathways in these two algal groups. Of course, this last difference exists between all eukaryotic groups and the two prokaryotic groups.

The theory that ascomycetes evolved from red algae like the present-day *Liagora* by the loss of photosynthetic pigments is based on similarities in the thallus (filamentous and with a pit or pore in each cross wall) and similarities in sexual reproduction and life cycle: the ascomycete perithecium would have evolved from the red algal cystocarp; ascogonia with trichogynes from carpogonia with trichogynes; ascogenous hyphae from gonimoblast filaments; and the ascus with ascospores from the carposporangium with carpospores. Antithetically, although there is no direct evidence for it, one can conjecture that red algae may have evolved from early ascomycetes through the incorporation of a symbiotic blue-green alga, with these early ascomycete–blue-green algal symbionts evolving into present-day red algae.

Red algae are classified into two groups: the more primitive Bangiophycidae (bangiophycids), for example *Porphyridium* and *Porphyra*, and the more advanced Florideophycidae (florideophycids), for example *Nemalion* (Fig. 34-1) and *Polysiphonia* (Fig. 34-2). Most red algae belong to the latter group. Characteristically, Bangiophycidae have a simpler thallus, diffuse or intercalary rather than apical growth, cells with a single axial stellate chloroplast rather than with many parietal chloroplasts, direct rather than indirect carpospore formation from the zygote, and a less frequent occurrence of pit connections between cells than in Florideophycidae. Orders and genera of Bangiophycidae are based primarily on differences in vegetative structure. Orders and genera of Florideophycidae are based primarily on differences in life cycle and details of development.

Importance Red algae are primary producers in intertidal and subtidal coastal regions. In freshwater habitats they are relatively rare and thus of minor importance as primary producers. Calcareous red algae contribute to coral-reef formation (Fig. 34-3). In the southern hemisphere some red algae are more important in reef formation than coral animals.

Marine red algae are of direct importance to man. *Porphyra* and *Rhodymenia* are eaten as food supplements in the Orient; indeed, *Porphyra* is cultivated and harvested as a crop. It is used in soups and on cookies and crackers in the Orient. *Rhodymenia palmata* grows on the rocky shores on both sides of the Atlantic Ocean—in Nova Scotia, for example—where it is dried, packaged, and sold under the name "dulse" or sometimes "sea kale." Dulse is chewed as well as used as a seasoning. Colloidal extracts of marine red algae have long been used as foods and in prepared foods. Carrageenin is extracted from *Chondrus crispus* (Irish moss) (Fig. 34-4) and is used in preparing puddings, as a thickening agent in the preparation of other foods, and in the many weight-reducing liquid meals on the market.

Agar as well as carrageenin is extracted in large quantities annually. Both are colloidal cell wall components. They are widely used as thickening, binding, and water-retaining media in foods (fruit cakes, pie fillings, icings, frosting, mayonnaise, salad dressings); in tooth pastes, shaving creams, and cosmetics as a base for greaseless creams; to hold the chocolate in suspension in chocolate milk; as cloth sizing agents; and they have a wide variety of medicinal applications. For

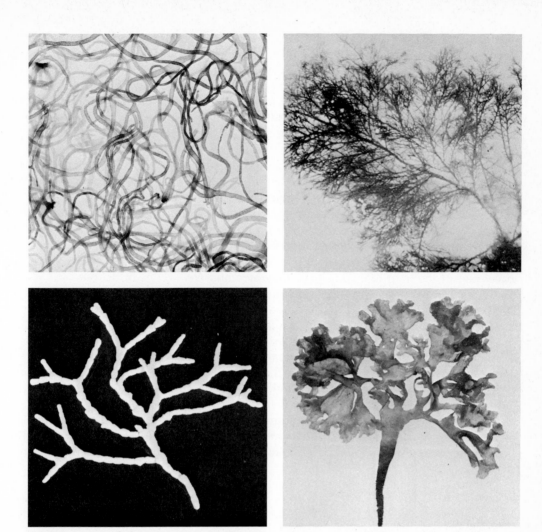

Fig. 34-1 Many thalli of *Nemalion* collected and placed in a bowl containing seawater. *(Courtesy Carolina Biological Supply Company.)*

Fig. 34-2 Portion of a thallus of *Polysiphonia nigrescens. (Courtesy CCM: General Biological, Inc., Chicago.)*

Fig. 34-3 *Corallina*, a calcareous red alga coated with deposits of calcium carbonate. *(Courtesy Carolina Biological Supply Company.)*

Fig. 34-4 Thallus of *Chondrus crispus*. *(Courtesy Carolina Biological Supply Company.)*

example, agar is used as a laxative. The baking, confectionery, meat-packing, and dairy industries make use of agar and carrageenin as emulsifying and stabilizing agents. Each of these two colloids has its own special characteristics.

Agar, which is extracted from many red algae (e.g. *Gelidium*), is the major solidifying agent in culture media used for growing a wide variety of organisms. The discovery at the end of the nineteenth century of this use for agar in growing microbes was a major breakthrough in microbiological and medical technique, because most microorganisms do not break down or liquify agar as they do gelatin, which was used previously.

Occurrence   Most red algae are marine and are more abundant in warmer marine waters. They are common on rocky and other seashores and in estuaries. *Polysiphonia*, for example, is common along the coast as a reddish-brown or somewhat purple, feathery or tufted frond (Fig. 34-2) attached to larger algae or to rocks, wharves, and piers below tide level. Most red algae grow in the middle to lower part of the intertidal zone (e.g. *Porphyra* and *Nemalion*) or deeper.

As with brown algae, there is a definite vertical stratification of red algae in the intertidal zone. For example, at Monterey, California, *Porphyra* is found in the middle and *Gigartina* in the bottom of the intertidal zone.

Although the majority of marine red algae grow attached to rocks or other inanimate objects, some grow epiphytically on larger red, brown, and green algae, and some are even parasitic on other red algae, usually on a closely related genus. Like brown and green algae, red algae may grow in clearer ocean waters attached at a depth of up to 100–200 meters.

Some red algae live in such freshwater habitats as streams, lakes and springs, and many of these, like *Batrachospermum* (Fig. 34-5), grow in cold, swiftly flowing streams. *Porphyridium* is a terrestrial red alga and grows on damp soil or walls.

Fig. 34-5   Portion of a thallus of *Batrachospermum* consisting of a main axis with whorls of branches. *(Photomicrograph courtesy Ripon Microslides Laboratory.)*

Vegetative features The vast majority of red algae are macroscopic and relatively small, up to about 10–15 cm in height (Fig. 34-2), but a few have thalli that are 1 meter or more long. Red algae, then, are in the size range of green algae and are generally smaller than brown algae. There are no motile red algae.

Red algal cell walls usually have an inner cellulosic layer and an outer mucilaginous layer of pectic material together with polysulfate esters. The colloidal polysaccharides agar and carrageenin are found in the cell walls of many florideophycids. The colloidal substances of the outer wall prevent excessive drying of intertidal red algae when exposed during low tide. In such genera as the coralline red algae, the outer wall is heavily calcified or encrusted with calcium carbonate (Fig. 34-3).

Adjacent cells typically are connected by large central pits or pit connections. Initially formed pits are called primary pit connections; those developed later are called secondary pit connections. Pits are less frequent in bangiophycids than florideophycids. Also, cells of the former group usually are uninucleate and have a single, axial stellate chloroplast, with or wothout a pyrenoid-like structure. Cells of the latter group are usually multinucleate and generally have many parietal chloroplasts. Electron microscopy reveals that the red algal chloroplast has unassociated lamellae, not in stacks or grana.

Most red algae are autotrophic. The characteristic reddish-purple color of red algae is due to the presence of their accessory, biliprotein chloroplast pigments, *r*-phycoerythrin (red) and *r*-phycocyanin (blue). The other photosynthetic pigments are carotenes, xanthophylls, the universal chlorophyll *a* and, in some, chlorophyll *d*.

The reddish color of most marine red algae distinguishes them from almost all other seaweeds, but they range in color from dull green or black to brown, purplish red, or rosy red. Those from greater depths in the sea are usually a bright rosy red, with phycoerythrin masking the other pigments. This is correlated with the fact that the blue portion of the light spectrum penetrates deepest into water. Here phycocyanin absorbs most of the light. Elegant experiments have shown that, as in blue-green algae, light energy absorbed by the biliproteins participates in photosynthesis.

Excess photosynthate is stored as food in cytoplasmic granules of a carbohydrate called floridean starch, which is similar to but not identical with the starch of green algae and higher green plants. Soluble food reserves include the galactoside of glycerol known as floridoside. One or more vacuoles are present in the cytoplasm.

Bangiophycids, even with only 15 genera, show a wide range in thallus morphology. For example, *Porphyridium* is unicellular. Other genera are filamentous and with uniseriate unbranched or branched thalli. The mature filaments of *Bangia* are frequently more than one cell in diameter. The parenchymatous thalli of *Porphyra* have smooth to convoluted blades that are membranous sheets one or two cells in thickness. Multicellular thalli are anchored by delicate to relatively massive holdfasts. Cell divisions and growth in bangiophycids is diffuse or intercalary.

Almost all florideophycids have apical growth with cell division initiated by an apical cell and restricted to the apical cells of a filament. Florideophycid algae are filamentous and have no members with unicellular or truly parenchymatous thalli. The branched uniseriate filaments may be loosely branched (Fig. 34-6) or have branches that are fused laterally, forming pseudoparenchymatous thalli (Fig. 34-4). The axis of a filament may consist of a single row of large cells (uniaxial), as in *Polysiphonia*, or of a number of rows of cells (multiaxial), as in *Nemalion*. Cells

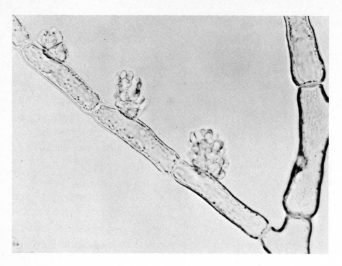

Fig. 34-6 *Callithamnion*, a red alga with branching uniseriate filaments and with all filaments free. Note the three clusters of spermatia on one branch. *(Photomicrograph courtesy Carolina Biological Supply Company.)*

formed by division of the apical cell divide tangentially and form pericentral cells lateral to the main axis. The degree to which and the manner in which the thallus becomes elaborated is determined by further development of these cells. Some of these red algae are intricately branched and lacy in appearance.

Asexual reproduction   No red algae ever produce zoospores. In this feature red algae are like blue-green algae, stoneworts, higher green plants, and higher fungi. Red algae seldom reproduce asexually by thallus fragmentation.

The two unicellular red algae multiply asexually by vegetative division of a cell into two cells (binary fission). Multicellular genera produce asexual spores, one in a cell, which are either produced in cells indistinguishable from vegetative cells or in cells of a different size and shape than vegetative cells. The former are called neutral spores and the latter monospores, or both can be called monospores. A monospore may come out of its monosporangium amoeboidly; if so, it then secretes a wall. Monospores are dispersed by wave action and water currents and develop directly into a thallus like the one that produced it. Asexual reproduction in almost all bangiophycids and gametophytes of florideophycids is accomplished by monospores. Monospores are haploid asexual spores produced by gametophytic thalli.

Sexual reproduction   No flagellated gametes are ever produced by any red algae. Plasmogamy is a specialized or highly evolved kind of oogamy called spermatization. It is found elsewhere in many of the higher ascomycetes, lichens, and rust fungi. Mycologists refer to spermatization as a specialized kind of gametangial plasmogamy. In red algae, nonflagellated walled male cells (spermatia) (Figs 34-6, 34-7), produced often by a budding process from cells called spermatangia (spermogonia), are dispersed by water currents and make contact with receptive hairlike extensions (trichogynes) of female gametangia (carpogonia). The carpogonial protoplast does not differentiate as an egg. The male nucleus of a spermatium, attached to a trichogyne, enters the trichogyne through a tiny hole and

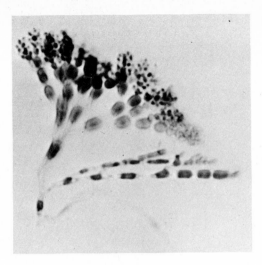

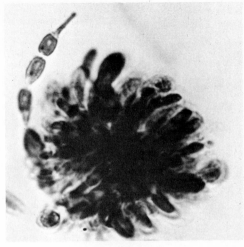

Fig. 34-7 Stained portion of a *Nemalion* thallus bearing clusters of spermatia. *(Photomicrograph courtesy Carolina Biological Supply Company.)*

Fig. 34-8 Stained portion of a *Nemalion* thallus bearing a fascicle of gonimoblast filaments, which produce carpospores at their tips. *(Photomicrograph courtesy Carolina Biological Supply Company.)*

migrates to and fuses with the female nucleus that is in the basal part of the carpogonium. Thus, syngamy is completed. Subsequent development varies.

Bangiophycids have a simple method of sexual reproduction. They have a haplontic life cycle and have direct carpospore formation from the zygote or fertilized carpogonium. As represented by *Porphyra*, which is heterothallic, proto- plasts of cells of male plants each cleave into a number of spermatia, which are released in the seawater around them. Female plants, which look like male plants, produce carpogonia that are only slightly modified vegetative cells. The male cell is carried by the water to the trichogyne, here but a short protuberance. The male nucleus enters through the trichogyne and fuses with the female nucleus of· the carpogonium. After meiosis, the contents of the zygote (fertilized carpogonium) divide to form a number of haploid carpospores, which are released into and dispersed by the water. Carpospores germinate and develop into new male and female *Porphyra* plants attached to rocks in the intertidal zone.

Florideophycids have more complex life cycles, all involving indirect carpospore formation and most involving an alternation of haploid and diploid multicellular phases. The simplest type of sexual development in florideophycids is represented by *Nemalion*, which is a haploid plant and has a haplontic life cycle. The nucleus of the fertilized carpogonium is diploid and undergoes meiosis. Then, short branches (haploid gonimoblast filaments) grow out from the carpogonium and form at their tips a cluster of haploid carpospores that are released, dispersed, and then germinate into new *Nemalion* plants. Thus, the haploid or gametophytic generation is biphasic or has two stages: the wormlike *Nemalion* plant itself (Fig. 34-1) attached to a rock in the middle of the intertidal zone, and the tiny tufts or fascicles of gonimoblast filaments (Fig. 34-8) parasitic on the wormlike thallus.

Other types of life cycles in higher red algae involve an alternation of multi- cellular haploid and diploid generations, and most florideophycids do have a diplo-haplontic life cycle. In some, for example *Liagora*, the sporophyte is simply a

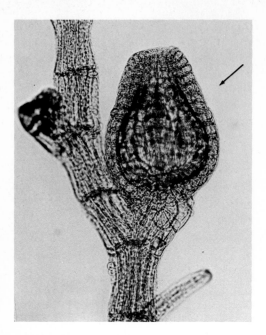

Fig. 34-9 Portion of a female plant of *Polysiphonia* showing a mature cystocarp (arrow). *(Photomicrograph courtesy Carolina Biological Supply Company.)*

tiny cluster of diploid gonimoblast filaments, called the carposporophyte, that is parasitic on the haploid thallus. This parallels the life cycle of higher ascomycetes, where dikaryotic ascogenous hyphae are parasitic on the haploid primary mycelium. In *Liagora* meiosis occurs in carposporangia at the tips of the diploid filaments.

The most complex type of life cycle in higher red algae is like that of *Polysiphonia*, which has an alternation of generations complicated by the fact that there are two diploid phases: one is an independent diploid plant (tetrasporophyte) and the other is a tiny carposporophyte that is parasitic on a haploid female plant and surrounded by a haploid, urnlike pericarp, open at its upper end. The pericarp and carposporophyte together comprise the structure called a cystocarp (Fig. 34-9). In *Polysiphonia* meiosis does not occur in the carposporangium. A mature carposporangium liberates a single carpospore. The carpospore germinates and develops directly into a free-living tetrasporophytic plant morphologically identical to the male and female gametophytic plants. Tetrasporangia (meiosporangia) develop in the vegetative axes of the sporophytic plant. After meiosis, each tetrasporangium produces and liberates four tetraspores. Two develop into male gametophytes and two into female gametophytes. *Polysiphonia*, then, has three kinds of independent thalli or plants, and they look essentially alike: male gametophyte, female gametophyte, and sporophyte (tetrasporophyte). In addition, there is the tiny parasitic diploid stage, the carposporophyte.

Project

I. Thallus with intercalary growth and division of the zygote into carpospores (Bangiophycidae)

A. *Porphyridium, of the order Porphyridiales*
 1. Observe *Porphyridium* growing in culture or on moist soil.

2. Mount some material in a drop of water on a slide and add a cover glass.
   a. Observe with low and high power.
   b. Add a small drop of India ink to one edge of the cover glass and observe the sheaths around the cells.
   c. Using oil immersion, in each cell find the central, stellate chloroplast with its pyrenoid and look for the nucleus and cytoplasmic granules.

B. *Porphyra, of the order Bangiales.* Observe living or preserved material and herbarium specimens of *Porphyra*. Mount some material and observe cellular organization. Study reproductive material if it is available.

II. Thallus with terminal growth and carpospores formed indirectly from the zygote (Florideophycidae)

A. *Nemalion, of the order Nemalionales*
   1. Study living or preserved material and herbarium specimens of *Nemalion*. Observe the general form and type of branching.
   2. Crush short segments of the thallus on a glass slide, add water, add a cover glass, and observe filament organization. The thallus is composed of a mass of photosynthetic filaments at right angles to a colorless central axis, all supported in a gelatinous matrix.
   3. Using high power, look for a large stellate plastid, containing a pyrenoid, and a nucleus in each cell. Can you find pit connections between cells?
   4. Look for dense clusters of spermatia at the tips of photosynthetic filaments.
   5. Look for carpogonial branches, carpogonia with trichogynes in younger material, and carposporangia on gonimoblast filaments in older material.

B. *Polysiphonia, of the order Ceramiales*
   1. Study living or preserved material and herbarium specimens of *Polysiphonia*. Compare the gametophyte and sporophyte, noting what differences or similarities in these two plants are apparent to the unaided eye or by use of a hand lens. Is *Polysiphonia* really isomorphic in its alternating generations? Note that the thallus is no way as elaborate or complex in structure as in rockweeds or kelps. Mount a bit of material and observe the method of branching. Using high power, study a portion of the thallus showing the tiers of cells and by careful focusing determine the arrangement and number of the cortical and central cells. Note the presence of protoplasmic strands (pit connections) that connect the cells. Note the dome-shaped apical cell.
   2. *Tetrasporic (meiosporic) plants.* Using high power, study a portion showing the tetrasporangium with its tetrad of tetraspores. Figure out the number and position of the tetraspores.
   3. Male plants. The male and female gametangia are developed on different plants. Mount a bit of a male gametophytic plant. Under low power note the cluster of fertile trichoblasts (filaments) near the thallus apex. Study one of these under high power. Spermatangia with their terminal spermatia are produced on the fertile axis. If necessary, crush out the material so that detail of structure can be seen.
   4. Cystocarpic (female) plants. Each cystocarp has as its outer layer an urnlike structure open at its upper end. This is tissue of the gametophyte and is called the pericarp. Large tear-shaped carpospores (in carpo-

sporangia) are seen within mature cystocarps. Very young cystocarps may still show evidence of the carpogonia.

III. Red algae cultures

Cultures of red algae that may be available (Carolina Biological Supply Co.) provide the following interesting features:

Porphyridium—single-celled construction
Bangia—primitive thallus
Antithamnion—gland cells
Callithamnion—good male (spermatium) producer
Acrochaetium—spore production
Spermothamnion—large cells
Rhodymenia—flattened blade

Project **35**   Liverworts

Contents

Introduction

Taxonomy   Liverworts are plants of the group technically known as Hepaticae or Hepatophyta. There are about 250 genera and 9,000 species. Liverworts are also commonly called hepatics.

Hornworts, which are treated in the next project, superficially resemble thallose liverworts and are called liverworts by some hepaticologists; however, they are significantly different in a number of ways and it is useful to study them as a separate group.

Table 18-1 (p. 132) indicates that liverworts are not only eukaryotic plants but, like hornworts and mosses, they are bryophytes, cryptogams, nonvascular plants, and embryophytes.

Liverworts and the other groups of embryo plants (embryophytes) may be called land plants or green land plants, much as zygomycetes, ascomycetes, and basidiomycetes may be called land fungi. They are morphologically and physiologically adapted for terrestrial life. Green algae, stoneworts, liverworts, and other embryophytes comprise the green-plant line of evolution or the green-plant phyletic group. They have in common the following cellular features: (1) They have chlorophylls *a* and *b* as well as many similar carotenoids, and all members of the green-plant group have these pigments in approximately the same proportions, which results in the grass-green color of these plants. (2) They have "true" starch as a stored food. Starch grains have a mixture of two kinds of glucose polymers or macromolecules, amylose and amylopectin. (3) Starch is formed within plastids, chloroplasts in green cells, and leucoplasts in colorless cells. (4) They have motile cells with only the whiplash type of flagellum, and each motile cell has two, four, or many (depending on the genus) posteriorly directed flagella attached at or near the front end. (5) They have cellulosic cell walls, characteristically with a pectic outer wall layer that contains galacturonic acid. These five features characterize or distinguish the green-plant phyletic group. All liverworts and other embryo plants are parenchymatous, oogamous, and have an alternation of generations. Although all liverworts have these features, only some green algae are parenchymatous, oogamous, or have alternating haploid and diploid phases or generations.

Because the dominant terrestrial plants (embryophytes) have an alternation of generations, we can say that this is the type of plant life that had special survival value as land became occupied by plants in geological times long past. Liverworts and other bryophytes are today's representatives of those early invaders of land which, so to speak, experimented with gametophytic dominance of plant life on land. Although the bryophyte way of life was and is of limited success on land, liverworts, hornworts, and mosses do have morphological and physiological adaptations that permit existence and survival in a drying atmosphere (air). These adaptations are unique and give bryophytes a characteristic ecology.

The progenitors of liverworts, hornworts, and mosses have not been identified in the fossil record. Each group seems to represent an independent evolutionary line, and there is no evidence that early members of any group gave rise to early members of any other group. Liverworts and other bryophytes probably either had a common origin with early green algae of past geological ages, or they evolved from green algal ancestors of the tetrasporine evolutionary tendency.

How far back in time liverworts and other bryophytes differentiated, diverged, or evolved is a matter of conjecture; however, the earliest bryophyte is a liverwort from the Upper Devonian Period (Table 18-2, p. 134), and paleontologists are of the opinion that bryophytes probably originated well before then. A number of bryophyte fossils, which are relatively scarce, are known from later Paleozoic periods. The fossil record indicates that liverworts are probably older than mosses and that the principal orders of liverworts (Jungermanniales and Marchantiales), as well as mosses (Bryales and Sphagnales), evolved by the end of the Paleozoic Era.

As with other bryophytes, liverworts appear to represent a side branch in evolution. Liverworts of past geological times apparently did not give rise to more advanced plants, nor are present-day liverworts or other bryophytes expected to. The closest relatives of liverworts are hornworts and mosses, and the closest relatives to all these bryophytes appear to be primitive vascular plants, even though there is no evidence that the latter evolved from the former. Bryophytes appear to be more closely related to vascular plants than to algae.

Liverworts can be classified into main groups (orders) on the basis of reproductive features and thallus structure. For example, Marchantiales, such as *Riccia* (Fig. 35-4), *Marchantia* (Figs. 35-1, 35-5), and *Conocephalum,* are thallose (have flat, strap-shaped or bladelike thalli) with a rather high degree of internal differentiation. Jungermanniales, the leafy liverworts, such as *Porella* (Fig. 35-2) and *Frullania,* are also dorsiventral, but their thalli are composed of axes ("stems") with two or three rows of "leaves." Although leafy liverworts are complex in external form, they are internally simple in structure. Leafy liverworts far outnumber thallose liverworts. (Thallose liverworts appear from the scanty fossil

Fig. 35-1 Closeup view of the thallose liverwort *Marchantia*. Arrow points to a gemma cup containing asexual structures, gemmae. *(Courtesy Carolina Biological Supply Company.)*

Fig. 35-2 Closeup view of the leafy liverwort *Porella. (Courtesy Carolina Biological Supply Company.)*

record to have arisen evolutionarily before foliose ones.) Other main groups are Metzgeriales, Sphaerocarpales, and Calobryales. Members of the last order differ from other liverworts in having an erect habit of growth, thereby resembling some mosses.

Importance   Liverworts are not economically important, and although they are not major contributors to the earth's primary productivity (Map 18-1, p. 135), they are important primary producers in their habitats. Some play a role in the early stages of converting bare rock surfaces to soil and cleared lands back to their normal vegetational cover. They are, then, among the pioneer plants in certain kinds of plant succession.

Fig. 35-3   Closeup view of male and female plants of *Sphaerocarpus*. White arrow points to a male plant (above). Black arrow points to a female plant (below). IN, female involucre surrounding an archegonium. *(Courtesy Carolina Biological Supply Company)*

Liverworts are used in research that investigates genetic and environmental controls of development or morphogenesis. *Sphaerocarpos* (Fig. 35-3) was the first plant in which sex chromosomes were discovered. The nuclei of male plants have a very small, special male-determining Y chromosome and those of female plants a very large female-determining X chromosome. The other seven chromosomes of a cell are called autosomes ($n = 8$).

It is said that in ancient and medieval medicine, because the surface of the thallus of certain species is marked in polygonal areas, looking like a cross section of the liver of an animal, these plants were believed to be good medicine for sickness attributed to liver malfunctioning; thus, the plants were called liverworts. Presently, liverworts and other bryophytes are not credited with medicinal value.

Occurrence Liverworts grow close to their substrata and are predominatly restricted to moist, shaded, humid environments, which indicates that, as a group, liverworts are not as well adapted to life on land as vascular plants. Such forms as *Marchantia, Conocephalum, Pellia, Riccia,* and *Sphaerocarpos* are common on moist soil. Common terrestrial habitats are shaded creek and ravine banks, faces of moist cliffs, rotting logs in wooded areas, epiphytically on the base of tree trunks, shaded, moist soil of old or undisturbed fields, and swamps and bogs. The few aquatic species, like *Riccia fluitans* (Fig. 35-4), are said to be secondarily aquatic because they probably evolved from terrestrial species. Some liverworts, for example species of *Porella* and *Frullania,* can grow in arid, xeric sites on soil, rocks, and tree bark where they withstand dessication for months, as do lichens in similar habitats.

More genera of liverworts occur in the tropics than elsewhere, especially tropical America and the East Indies. Some species are cosmopolitan and found throughout the world where conditions are favorable for growth. Other species are endemic, with restricted geographical distributions.

Vegetative features Liverwort plants are gametophytes and they are small plants. Thalli of *Frullania* and *Sphaerocarpos* may even be difficult to see without a hand lens, but bigger forms like *Porella* and *Marchantia* may form large clumps (Fig. 35-5) and mats up to several feet across. There are no motile liverworts, nor

Fig. 35-4 Clump of the aquatic *Riccia fluitans.* In the foreground is a piece broken off and showing dichotomous branching. *(Courtesy Carolina Biological Supply Company.)*

Fig. 35-5 Clump of female *Marchantia* thalli
with elongate archegoniophores bearing
sporophytes. *(Courtesy CCM: General
Biological, Inc., Chicago.)*

are any embryophytes motile; however, like all nonseed embryophytes and like
cycads and *Ginkgo,* liverworts do produce motile sperms.

Liverworts are parenchymatous and have the important cellular features listed
in the section dealing with taxonomy. In addition, their cells contain a single
nucleus and a large central vacuole, and green cells have many discoid chloroplasts
lacking pyrenoids. The cells are typical parenchymatous plant cells.

Liverworts also have a multicellular diploid sporophytic phase, but this is
relatively small, short lived, and attached to the gametophyte. The sporophyte is
parasitic on the gametophyte in the sense that it lives on and at least partially
within the gametophyte and obtains at least some of its nutriments from it. That
the sporophyte is not totally dependent on the gametophyte for food is indicated
by the presence of chloroplasts in young sporophytes.

Vegetative growth is terminal and initiated by a single apical cell. Leafy forms
have apical budlike regions. The liverwort thallus typically is dorsiventrally flattened
(Figs. 35-1, 35-5), dichotomously branched (Fig. 35-4), and attached to the
substratum by means of unicellular rhizoids. It may be annual or perennial. The
thallus is either thallose (with a branching bladelike or strap-shaped thallus) or
leafy (with two or three rows of "leaves"). "Leaves" are a single cell in thickness
and lack a midrib region (Fig. 35-2), unlike those of many mosses. The structures
in liverworts and mosses that are called leaves and stems are not true leaves and
stems because they lack vascular tissue and they are not homologous with the
leaves and stems of vascular plants. For this reason, leaves of liverworts and
mosses are also called phyllidia or phyllids and stems are also called caulidia
or caulids.

In leafy liverworts, larger leaves are arranged in two lateral rows, and there
is a third row of small leaves (amphigastria) located ventrally on the stem. The
two lateral rows of larger leaves are frequently notched at the tip, or even deeply
and complexly lobed so as to appear as two, as in *Porella* and *Frullania,* with one
lobe folded over and against the other (complicate bilobed).

Thallose liverworts are never this complex externally. The small, more or less
circular, thallose *Sphaerocarpos* is simply constructed. It has a multicellular midrib
region, lateral wings one cell in thickness, and smooth-walled unicellular rhizoids
extending from the ventral surface.

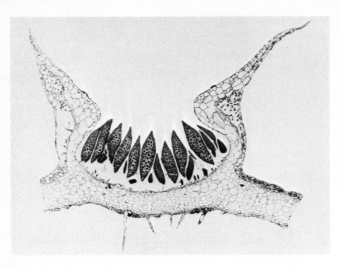

Fig. 35-6 Stained section of a gemma cup of *Marchantia*. *(Photomicrograph courtesy Carolina Biological Supply Company.)*

Thallose liverworts like *Marchantia* and to a lesser extent *Riccia* have considerable internal differentiation. On the ventral surface of the thallus of *Marchantia* are several rows of multicellular scales and many unicellular, filamentous rhizoids. The lower portion of the thallus is made up of closely packed parenchyma cells with little chlorophyll. This appears to be a storage region. The upper portion of the thallus is composed of a layer of air chambers surrounded by chlorenchyma (chloroplast-containing cells) and containing many, branched filaments of cells. Each air chamber has a large pore surrounded by tiers of cells arranged in a somewhat barrel or chimney shape.

Asexual reproduction   No liverworts ever produce zoospores. In this feature they are like all other embryophytes, as well as stoneworts, red algae, blue-green algae, zygomycetes, ascomycetes, and basidiomycetes. Reproduction by thallus fragmentation is common, especially when a branching thallus grows forward and its older portion dies and decays. Many leafy liverworts produce specialized clusters of unicellular or bicellular, thick-walled gemmae on the margin of leaves or the stem apex. *Marchantia* forms unusually large, multicellular gemmae in special cups on the upper surface of the thallus (Figs. 35-1, 35-6). A few liverworts can develop special parenchymatous structures, called tubers, that are rich in food reserves and that perpetuate the thallus through inclement environmental conditions.

Sexual reproduction   Massive multiplication and dissemination in liverworts, as well as other bryophytes, is accomplished through spores produced in tetrads within capsules. These are really sexual spores because they are produced directly after meiosis. They are, then, meiospores, and the capsule is a meiosporangium.

Liverworts and other bryophytes are oogamous in the sense that a relatively large nonmotile egg is fertilized by a flagellated sperm; however, they are distinct from oogamous fungi and algae in being archegoniate plants. An oogonium is unicellular, whereas an archegonium is multicellular and with a jacket of sterile

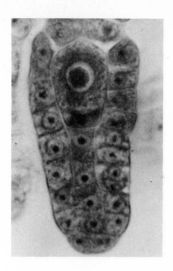 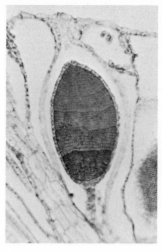

Fig. 35-7 (far left)   Stained longitudinal section of a mature archegonium of *Marchantia.* *(Photomicrograph courtesy Ripon Microslides, Inc.)*

Fig. 35-8 (left)   Stained longitudinal section of a nearly mature antheridium of *Marchantia. (Photomicrograph courtesy Ripon Microslides, Inc.)*

cells. The bryophyte egg is produced and fertilized in a distinctive, multicellular, flask-shaped archegonium that has a neck composed of wall and canal cells and a larger basal venter composed of wall cells and a ventral cell anterior to a single egg (Fig. 35-7).

Gametangia (archegonia and antheridia), which have short stalks, often are protected by tissue of the gametophyte. In *Riccia* gametangia are embedded in the palisade upper portion of the thallus. In others they may be surrounded by special sheathlike involucres. In *Sphaerocarpos* the dorsal surface of the thallus is densely crowded with ovoid (female) or flask-shaped (male) involucres and they are the most conspicuous parts of the female and male thalli (Fig. 35-3). Each involucre surrounds a single gametangium. Gametangia must be covered with a film of water for sperms to be released and swim to archegonia. Rain drops can splash sperms for significant distances.

Sperms are produced in globose or oblong multicellular antheridia consisting of a single layer of wall or jacket cells and a large number of cubical spermatogenous cells (Fig. 35-8). Each spermatogenous cell gives rise to a stonewort-like, thin, loosely spiral sperm bearing two long anteriorly attached and posteriorly directed whiplash flagella. All bryophyte sperms have about the same appearance and a characteristic mode of swimming. They are chemotactically attracted to the opened apex of the archegonial neck, whose canal cells have disintegrated and provide a fluid pathway for a motile sperm to swim through in its journey to the egg.

The zygote is retained within the archegonium, where it divides and develops into a multicellular embryo and on into a mature sporophyte. As this parasitic sporophyte is developing, cells of the archegonium also divide, making room for and protecting the growing sporophyte. The expanded archegonium is called a calyptra (Fig. 35-9).

The embryo is usually differentiated into two parts: a lower portion that develops mainly into the anchoring and absorbing foot and an upper portion that develops into the spore-bearing capsule (meiosporangium) and at least a portion of the stalk (seta) supporting the capsule (Fig. 35-10). *Riccia* is an interesting exception. Its entire sporophytic phase at maturity is but a single sporangium (Fig. 35-11) and the embryo is not differentiated into parts.

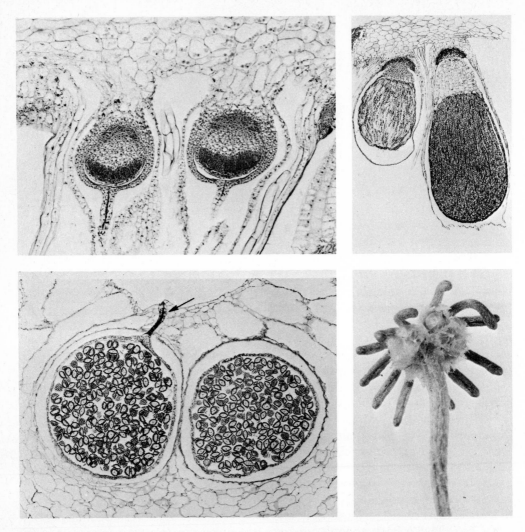

Fig. 35-9 *Marchantia*. Stained longitudinal sections of two young sporophytes (each within a calyptra) in an early stage of differentiation of tissues. *(Photomicrograph courtesy Ripon Microslides, Inc.)*

Fig. 35-10 Stained longitudinal section of a mature sporophyte (right) of *Marchantia* showing foot, seta, and capsule with spores and elaters. *(Photomicrograph courtesy Carolina Biological Supply Company.)*

Fig. 35-11 Stained longitudinal section of an upper portion of a thallus of *Riccia* with two sunken sporophytes (sporangia). In the one to the left, the old archegonial neck (arrow) can be seen. *(Photomicrograph courtesy Ripon Microslides Laboratory.)*

Fig. 35-12 *Marchantia*. Closeup of the underside of an elongated archegoniophore tilted to show protruding capsules, one of which is clearly visible. *(Courtesy Carolina Biological Supply Company.)*

When the sporophyte is mature, the colorless seta usually elongates, ruptures the calyptra, and elevates the spherical or oblong, dark sporangium well above the gametophytic thallus. In some forms, like *Marchantia,* archegonia hang down on the undersides of specialized structures called archegoniophores. Furthermore, after fertilization and during sporophyte development, archegoniophore stalks elongate well above the strap-shaped gametophytic thallus (Fig. 35-5). At maturity, then, the capsule of *Marchantia* projects downward (Fig. 35-12).

The mature capsule has an outer, sterile wall, and in most liverworts it splits longitudinally into four parts or valves that open back, exposing the many spores (meiospores), often along with many elongate, hygroscopic cells called elaters. Elaters have spirally thickened walls and can function in spore liberation. Spores of a liverwort are of similar size and thus may be called homosporous; however, with respect to genetic control of sexuality, in such genera as *Marchantia* and *Sphaerocarpos* two kinds of spores exist, male and female. Such genera, then, are heterothallic. Most bryophytes are homothallic.

Spores are dispersed mainly by wind, germinate in a suitable environment, and develop into free-living thallose or leafy gametophytes that bear gametangia at maturity.

Liverworts, like all the groups of embryophytes or land plants, have an alternation of multicellular, heteromorphic generations or phases in their life cycle. The major phase in liverworts and other bryophytes is gametophytic, and they may be said to have a haplo-diplontic life cycle.

Project

I. Thallose liverworts

  A. *Riccia*
  1. Note the dichotomous type of branching of a *Riccia* thallus.
  2. Study a longitudinal section (prepared slide) of a thallus showing a mature sporophyte (sporangium). Identify thallus of the gametophyte, calyptra (old archegonium that has enlarged), and the sporophyte, which consists of sporangium wall and spores.
  3. Dissect living or preserved material and find antheridia, archegonia, and young and old sporophytes. Note the differences between the sex organs of this and the other bryophytes and those observed in algae and fungi.
  B. *Marchantia*
  1. Cross-sectional view of the thallus. Make a cross section of living material (*Conocephalum* may be used if *Marchantia* is not available). (Also, in prepared slides to be looked at subsequently you will see good sectional views of the thallus.) Identify air pore, chlorenchyma, colorless region, and rhizoid. Are rhizoids unicellular or multicellular?
  2. Gemma cups (cupules)
    a. Observe a cupule with a hand lens or a dissecting microscope. Take out a single gemma and examine it.
    b. Study a longitudinal section (prepared slide) of a cupule.
    c. The gemmae of *Marchantia* (and *Lunularia*) germinate easily and quickly in water. Try it!

3. Female plant
   a. Using a hand lens or dissecting microscope, study an entire plant, noting especially the archegoniophore.
   b. Study a longitudinal section (prepared slide) of an archegonium. Identify the neck, consisting of the neck wall cells and neck canal cells, and the venter, consisting of the ventral canal cell, egg, and venter wall cells.
4. Male plant
   a. Using a hand lens or dissecting microscope, study an entire plant, noting especially the antheridiophore.
   b. Study a longitudinal section (prepared slide) of an antheridium. Identify the jacket or wall cells, spermatogenous cells, and stalk cells.
5. Sporophyte
   a. Study a longitudinal section (prepared slide) of a sporophyte. Identify the foot, seta, and capsule or sporangium. The sporangium consists of wall cells, spores (or spore mother cells in young sporangia), and elaters. Also identify the special gametophytic tissues calyptra and involucre (protective sheath).
   b. If living material is available, make sections of developing sporophytes. Stain sections with Safranin and fast green to show the differentiation between the potentially sporogenous and sterile regions very early in the development of the sporophyte.
   c. Dissect whole mature sporophytes and find the calyptra and involucre, as well as the foot, seta, and capsule. Break the capsule and notice the great quantity of spores and elaters.

II. Leafy liverworts

A. Using a hand lens or a dissecting microscope, study specimens of these mosslike liverworts (e.g., *Porella* and *Frullania*). Observe the pattern of branching. How many rows of "leaves" (phyllidia) do you see?
B. Mount two branches of each specimen in water, one with its dorsal side up and the other with its ventral side up. Add a cover slip and study. Do leaves have a midrib? How many cells in thickness is a leaf? Can you find three rows of leaves? As seen from below, the lateral two rows of leaves of such genera as *Porella* and *Frullania* are bilobed (complicate bilobed). Can you observe this?
C. Study available leafy liverworts with sex organs and sporophytes. These reproductive structures often are easier to see and study in leafy liverworts than in other liverworts.

Project 36   Hornworts

Contents

Introduction

Taxonomy   Hornworts or anthocerotes are plants of the group technically known as Anthocerotae or Anthocerotales. There are 5 genera and 100 or more species.

Hornworts superficially resemble thallose liverworts, but they differ significantly in the following ways: (1) Hornworts are the only embryophytes (land plants) to have cells with but a single chloroplast (although not all hornworts do) and to have chloroplasts with pyrenoids. (2) The sporophyte is unique in several ways, most noteworthy of which are the meristem, which permits indefinite or indeterminate growth, at the base of the photosynthetic capsule or sporangium, and the stomata with guard cells in the epidermis. A person looking for hornworts growing on soil in nature might overlook them because the gametophytes might be taken for liverworts or fern prothalli and the sporophytes for thin, delicate blades of grass (Fig. 36-1).

Fossil spores thought to be those of *Anthoceros* are known from the Tertiary Period. One can conjecture that like liverworts and mosses, hornworts probably became a separate or distinct phylogenetic line at least by Carboniferous times and probably before the Devonian Period (Table 18-2, p. 134).

For reasons stated in the introduction to liverworts (p. 271), hornworts probably evolved from parenchymatous green algae. They may have evolved from early green algae with isomorphic haploid and diploid thalli, or it is possible that they evolved from oogamous, haplontic green algae. If the latter is true, the

Fig. 36-1 Thallose gametophyte of *Anthoceros* bearing four slender, erect sporophytes. *(Courtesy Carolina Biological Supply Company.)*

parenchymatous sporophyte developed de novo from the algal zygote as hornworts evolved on land. If the former is true, which may be more likely, the green sporophytic thallus became attached to and dependent upon the gametophyte and became quite different from it. It is likely that hornworts and primitive vascular plants had their origins from the same ancestral group of plants. As will be discussed in the section dealing with sexual reproduction, there is evidence that the columella of the sporophyte of hornworts is comparable to the protostele of primitive vascular plants. The sporophyte of hornworts has a higher degree of complexity and has greater longevity than the sporophyte of other bryophytes.

Hornworts of past geological times apparently did not give rise to any other groups of plants. Although hornworts have come closer than liverworts and mosses to getting away from a mode of life requiring the sporophyte to grow on and be dependent on the gametophyte, there is no indication that hornworts evolved into primitive vascular plants—no evidence that the sporophyte developed vascular tissue and an independent absorbing structure rooted directly in soil, providing for anchorage and support as well as for water and nutrient absorption.

There are only five genera of hornworts: *Anthoceros, Phaeoceros, Dendroceros, Megaceros,* and *Notothylas. Anthoceros* and *Phaeoceros* are best known.

Importance Like liverworts, hornworts are not economically important and they contribute relatively little, even less than liverworts, as primary producers in nature. Even so, they are important as primary producers in their habitats. Botanists find hornworts noteworthy especially because in some of their features they are more like primitive vascular plants than are other bryophytes.

Occurrence   All hornworts are terrestrial and they are distributed throughout the world, except in polar regions. They most commonly occur on damp, shaded soil, on creek banks, shaded roadside cuts, and unplowed fields. Some species of *Anthoceros* are perennial and other species are winter annuals, like species of the liverworts, *Riccia* and *Sphaerocarpos,* and the urn moss, *Physcomitrium.* It is common to find all these growing together in the same habitat, as on the moist soil of a shaded margin of an old field. In the southern part of the United States, the thalli of winter annual species of *Anthoceros* appear in the fall. They produce their gametangia in the winter and produce spores during the spring.

Some hornworts in tropical regions grow epiphytically on the trunks of trees.

Vegetative features   The gametophytic thallus of hornworts is dorsiventrally flattened and often with a wavy margin (Fig. 36-1). It may occur as a simple, orbicular structure only a few millimeters across and superficially resembling a fern prothallus, or it may form a rosette of lobes, many inches across, in which the dichotomous branching is not obvious. The thallus is not differentiated into different tissues and there is little cell differentiation. Unicellular, smooth-walled rhizoids extend into the substratum, usually soil, from the lower surface of the thallus.

New cells are initiated by an apical cell. The lower surface of a mature thallus may have stomate-like pores surrounded by guardlike cells and leading into cavities or chambers that are often filled with mucilage or slime and frequently with filamentous blue-green algae, often *Nostoc.* The nitrogen-fixing ability of *Nostoc* presumably benefits hornworts in the same way that nitrogen-fixing bacteria *(Rhizobium)* in the roots of leguminous flowering plants benefit them. However, the normal growth and development of hornworts in axenic culture (without any other organisms) shows that blue-green algal symbionts are not essential. Guard cells do not regulate pore size and pores remain open at all times.

Each green cell of most hornworts (e.g., *Anthoceros*) has a single chloroplast with a single pyrenoid, and, among embryo plants, the presence of a pyrenoid as a center for starch synthesis is unique to hornworts. A few hornworts lack pyrenoids, and some have two to many pyrenoids within the chloroplast. Also, some hornworts have more than one and as many as six chloroplasts in a cell.

Asexual reproduction   The gametophytic thallus of some hornworts can reproduce itself asexually by the fragmentation of marginal lobes or masses of cells called gemmae. These structures are not resistant to inclement environmental conditions; however, a few species do form special parenchymatous structures, called tubers, that perpetuate the thallus through unfavorable periods.

Sexual reproduction   Hornworts may be either unisexual or, more commonly, bisexual, and they develop their gametangia dorsally, below the upper surface, from cells derived from marginal apical cells. Gametangia, then, are embedded in gametophytic thallus tissue.

In temperate regions gametangia develop in the fall, winter, and spring when the day length is short and water is relatively plentiful. It has been shown experimentally that certain hornworts are short-day plants with respect to antheridial formation.

Antheridia, which structurally are similar to those of liverworts, develop in chambers (one to several per chamber) in the upper portion of the thallus. At maturity antheridia are exposed by a rupturing of the cover cells of the vegetative thallus. Mature antheridia are yellowish orange, owing to the transformation of the chloroplasts in the wall or jacket cells to chromoplasts—much like the autumn coloration of leaves and the ripening of tomato fruits. Hornwort sperms, which look and swim essentially like liverwort and moss sperms, are liberated when water accumulates in the open antheridial chamber, during a rain or as dew collects.

The archegonium, which is not formed in a chamber, is completely submerged and protected by cells near the upper surface of the thallus; thus, the archegonium is essentially only several neck canal cells, a ventral canal cell, and an egg. Over the submerged archegonium is a single layer of cover cells of the gametophytic thallus. The cover cells part when the archegonium is mature and ready for fertilization. As in liverworts, the canal cells of a ripe archegonium decompose and provide an attractant for sperms and a medium through which sperms swim to eggs.

The zygote divides immediately and an embryo is soon established. The lower part of the embryo develops into an anchoring and absorbing, haustorium-like foot. The upper part of the embryo develops into an incipient capsule, the lower part of which is meristematic and produces continuously, from the base, the long terminal capsule or meiosporangium, which projects up from the top of the gametophytic thallus (Fig. 36-1). The meristem, then, is intercalary, and the mature sporophyte, which is photosynthetic as well as parasitic, consists of a foot embedded in the gametophyte and a green, long, slender, needle-like capsule. There is no seta. During early development the growing sporophyte is protected by a cylinder of gametophytic tissue, the involucre. Because of its intercalary meristem, the sporophyte can continue to grow and produce more spores as long as the environment is favorable.

The epidermis of a capsule is covered by a waxy cuticle. The epidermis is penetrated by air pores or stomata, each of which is surrounded by a pair of guard cells. Stomata lead to a system of intercellular spaces among the chlorenchyma cells of the photosynthetic region. This tissue resembles the mesophyll of some leaves, but in hornworts it is located between the epidermis and the cylindrical sporogenous region. The center of the capsule is occupied by a column of sterile cells, the columella (Fig. 36-2).

Walls with incomplete spiral thickenings occur in the outer columella cells of *Dendroceros*. Also, there is evidence that the hornwort columella can conduct solutions. These features suggest that the columella of hornworts is comparable to the protostele of primitive vascular plants.

In maturing regions of the capsule, a cylinder of cells between the columella and the photosynthetic region becomes the sporogenous zone. These cells have small chloroplasts. Many of these diploid cells are sporocytes (spore mother cells). They separate, become spherical, divide meiotically, and after cleavage form a tetrad of haploid spores (meiospores) (Fig. 36-2). The other cells in this cylindrical sporogenous zone remain sterile, divide, elongate, and become elaters, sometimes called pseudoelaters (Fig. 36-3).

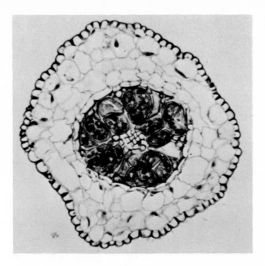

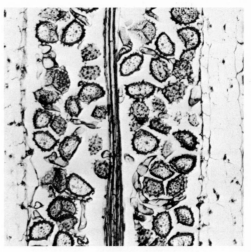

Fig. 36-2 Stained cross section of a capsule of *Anthoceros*. *(Photomicrograph courtesy Ripon Microslides Laboratory.)*

Fig. 36-3 Stained longitudinal section of part of a mature capsule of *Anthoceros*. *(Photomicrograph courtesy Carolina Biological Supply Company.)*

As the apical portion of the sporophyte matures, the sporangium wall (epidermis and chlorenchyma) darkens, dries, and splits into two parts or valves, exposing mature spores, elaters, and the columella. The valves are hygroscopic and exhibit twisting movements that aid in spore liberation.

Mature spores have thickened walls and are resistant to drying (Fig. 36-3). They may be disseminated by wind, runoff water during rains, or the feet of terrestrial animals. A spore germinates and first produces a clump of green cells and a rhizoid. This young gametophytic thallus continues development and growth until the thallus reaches reproductive maturity, if the environment remains suitable.

In summary, hornworts, like liverworts and mosses, reproduce sexually through two phases. They have an alternation of heteromorphic generations—a haplo-diplontic life cycle—and the gametophyte is dominant and independent, whereas the sporophyte is attached to the gametophyte. It is interesting to note that injured sporophytes of *Anthoceros* can develop directly into gametophytic thalli without forming meiospores—a condition known as apospory.

Project

I. *Anthoceros* gametophyte

A. Using a hand lens or a dissecting microscope, examine whole plants, noting their general form, dark-green color, texture, and lack of air chambers. (Note: The plants you examine may be entirely vegetative or they may have sex organs or emergent sporophytes.) Find rhizoids.

B. Mount a thin section of gametophytic tissue in water, stain with iodine solution, and crush flat by pressing down on the cover slip. Observing a single cell using high power, find the cell wall and chloroplast containing a pyrenoid and starch grains. Note: Look for endophytic blue-green algae in the thallus. Do you remember the genus?

II. *Anthoceros* sporophyte

A. Using a hand lens or a dissecting microscope, study a gametophytic thallus with emergent sporophytes ("horns"). You should be able to find both young and old sporophytes.
B. Dissect out the entire sporophyte to observe the foot.
C. Cut thin paradermal sections of the sporophyte, mount in water, add a cover slip, and study. Among the epidermal cells find guard cells surrounding a stoma.
D. Study longitudinal sections (prepared slides) of the sporophyte showing its attachment to the gametophyte and its production of spores. (You will probably need two slides for seeing all of this: one labeled "l.s. foot" and the other labeled "sporocarp l.s.") Identify gametophyte, involucre, and sporophyte [including foot, basal meristem, columella, spore, elater, and jacket (sporangium wall).]
E. Study a cross section of the capsule of a mature sporophyte (prepared slide). Find columella, spore, elater, and jacket or sporangium wall, composed of chlorenchyma and epidermis.

Project **37**   Mosses

Contents

Introduction
Taxonomy; Importance; Occurrence;
Vegetative features; Asexual reproduction;
Sexual reproduction

Project

Introduction

Taxonomy   Mosses are plants of the group technically known as Musci. There are approximately 600 genera and 14,000 species of mosses. Not all plants commonly called mosses are really mosses. Spanish moss *(Tillandsia)* is an epiphytic flowering plant; club mosses *(Selaginella* and *Lycopodium)* are vascular plants; reindeer moss *(Cladonia)* is a lichen; Irish moss *(Chondrus crispus)* is a marine alga; and the green film, which is often called moss, on the sides of trees is a mass of microscopic green algal cells *(Protococcus).*

Mosses are distinct from liverworts and hornworts in several ways: (1) All mosses have leafy gametophytes (have phyllidia and caulidia). Moss rhizoids are multicellular filaments. The leafy gametophytes of mosses differ from those of leafy liverworts not only because the rhizoids are multicellular but also because the leaves are often spirally arranged and rarely notched or lobed. In addition, the leaves of most mosses have midrib-like regions (costae). (2) The leafy gametophytes usually arise from a branching, filamentous system (protonema). (3) The young sporophyte is green and photosynthetic. The seta elongates during early development of the sporophyte, and the ruptured calyptra usually is on top of the elongating sporophyte, where it at least partially surrounds the developing and maturing capsule. (4) The capsule often has stomata and a central, sterile columella. Usually the capsule opens by the breaking off of a small cap (operculum), and the opening (peristome) is usually ringed by teeth (peristome teeth).

Fig. 37-1 Closeup view of an upright plant of
*Sphagnum. (Courtesy Carolina Biological Supply
Company.)*

Fig. 37-2 Upright plants of a typical moss,
*Polytrichum. (Courtesy Carolina Biological Supply
Company.)*

The oldest known fossil moss, a gametophytic fragment, comes from the Upper Carboniferous Period (Table 18-2, p. 134). The first fully preserved gametophytes of mosses are in Permian rocks. Because the first fossil liverwort is older (from the Devonian Period), mosses appear to have evolved, differentiated, or diverged more recently than liverworts. Many of the Tertiary and Quaternary mosses are identical to modern genera and even species.

Like liverworts and hornworts, mosses appear to represent a side branch in evolution and probably evolved from early green algae of the tetrasporine evolutionary tendency. Mosses, liverworts, and hornworts are enough alike to suggest that they have a common ancestry among ancient green algae. They are today's representatives of those early invaders of land that attempted gametophytic dominance of plant life on land. That sporophytic dominance was more successful is attested by the fossil record and by the present dominance of vascular plants.

Mosses can be divided into three major groups: (1) The peat mosses (variously called Sphagnobrya, Sphagnidae, Sphagnopsida, or Sphagnales) are in a single genus. *Sphagnum* has a thalloid protonema, a unique upright gametophytic plant, and a unique kind of sporophyte elevated on a special gametophytic stalk, a pseudopodium (Fig. 37-1). (2) The granite mosses (Andreaeobrya, Andreaeidae,

Fig. 37-3 Peat bog with a background of mature spruce trees. The bog in the foreground is in the shrub stage and with young spruce trees. *(Courtesy Carolina Biological Supply Company.)*

Andreaeopsida, or Andreaeales) are in three genera. *Andreaea,* the most common genus, has a mature gametophyte like that of "true" mosses, but in other respects it is much like *Sphagnum,* although *Andreaea* does have a unique capsule. (3) The typical or "true" mosses (Eubrya, Bryidae, Mnionopsida, or Bryales) have filamentous protonemata and ordinary leafy moss plants (mature gametophytes) and sporophytes (Fig 37-2). These will be described later. Some bryologists elevate the four main subgroups of "true" mosses to equal rank with granite mosses and peat mosses, making six major groups of mosses, and they believe them to be separate evolutionary lines.

Among mosses there is great morphological diversity in both the gametophyte and sporophyte, and moss classification and identification rests heavily on features of the sporophyte as well as the gametophyte. In contrast, within the liverworts and within the hornworts there is relatively little variation in sporophyte structure.

Importance   Mosses are significant members of diverse terrestrial plant communities and are important as primary producers. They provide microhabitats in which other tiny organisms live. Pioneer mosses on freshly exposed soil may quickly carpet the soil with their branching, filamentous protonemata and help prevent soil erosion.

In nature, peat or bog moss *(Sphagnum)* fills in bogs, hollows, ponds, and even small lakes, playing a major role in the natural conversion of these aquatic habitats to terrestrial habitats in the glaciated part of the northern hemisphere (Fig. 37-3). *Sphagnum* increases the acidity of these bodies of water and apparently produces antiseptic substances; thus, these bodies of water are relatively free of decay organisms, and much organic matter accumulates. *Sphagnum* grows into small ponds from the margin and can fill them entirely and form quaking bogs, which occur in glaciated portions of North America.

Economically, *Sphagnum* is of far more value than all other mosses. Peat is the partially decomposed deposit of dead swamp mosses and other plant remains.

Peat moss and peat are used by man as soil conditioners because they increase the water-holding capacity and aeration of soil. Peat will hold 80–90 per cent of its own weight of water. *Sphagnum* moss itself has special water-holding cells and will hold water up to 200 times its own dry weight. Both peat and *Sphagnum,* then, are excellent additives to garden soil, and they decompose very slowly.

The value of dried peat as fuel is known throughout the world, especially in the northern hemisphere where there are vast peat deposits. Ground up and pressed blocks of peat can yield more heat than hard coal. *Sphagnum* can be used in absorbent pads, and it is superior to absorbent cotton in its ability to absorb and retain moisture.

Hair-cap moss *(Polytrichum),* so called because the calyptra has a dense covering of hairs, and its relatives are the largest mosses (up to 2 ft in height). They are common and have been used in Europe for small brooms and for filling beds. The famous biologist, Linnaeus, is said to have slept on such beds. In times past, a decoction of the common hair-cap moss, *Polytrichum commune,* was used to aid the growing of hair. It was believed, and called the "doctrine of signatures," that the medicinal use of a plant is shown in its shape and structure; thus, the hairy cap (calyptra) of *Polytrichum* was believed, in accordance with the "doctrine of signatures," to aid in the growth of hair.

Occurrence   Mosses are worldwide in distribution. Most are perennial, but a few are annuals, frequently fall and winter annuals.

Very few mosses are aquatic (hydrophytic), but none grow in saltwater habitats; most live in mesic environments; and some are xerophytes. Following is a list of some of the many common habitats of mosses along with illustrative genera: (1) Attached to rocks below water in brooks or creeks (*Fontinalis,* water moss). (2) Bogs (*Sphagnum,* peat moss). (3) Banks of brooks or creeks (*Atrichum, Mnium, Climacium*). (4) Woods or forests (*Leucobryum,* cushion or white moss; *Dicranum,* broom moss). (5) Deep shady places growing over stones, earth, and logs (*Thuidium,* fern moss; *Mnium*). (6) Bases of stumps and trees in wooded swamps (*Climacium,* tree moss). (7) Meadows (*Polytrichum,* hair-cap moss). (8) Moist banks of clay or loam (*Pogonatum*). (9) Moist soil of an unplowed field or a roadcut (*Physcomitrium,* urn moss). (10) Tree trunks (*Orthotrichum*). (11) Exposed rock (*Grimmia*).

Mosses like *Pogonatum* and *Physcomitrium* serve as pioneer plants in secondary plant succession on old fields. Mosses like *Grimmia* are pioneer plants in primary plant succession on rocks.

Vegetative features   Mosses have a number of vegetative features that clearly are adaptations to life on land. (1) A waxy cuticle on the outer surface of the plant is an adaptation for decreasing the rate of water loss by evaporation or transpiration. The cuticle is characteristic of sporophytes of land plants, and it is not common on gametophytes, except those of mosses, which also have cutinized sporophytes. (2) The cuticle is a barrier against excessive water loss, but it is also a barrier against gas exchange between the atmosphere and photosynthetic tissue. An adaptive feature for enhancing or retarding gas exchange is the stoma. (3) Mosses have water- and food-conducting regions, but the cells are parenchymatous and not specialized into xylem and phloem elements as they are in vascular plants. Both lignin, which is a characteristic substance in the walls of water-conducting cells of vascular plants, and callose, found in the food-conducting cells of vascular plants,

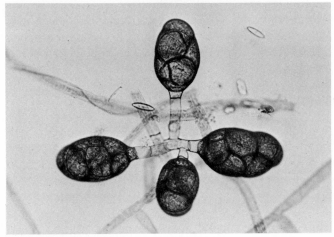

Fig. 37-4 (above, left) Closeup view of upright gametophytes of a monoecious species of *Mnium*. *(Courtesy Carolina Biological Supply Company.)*

Fig. 37-5 (above) Branching moss protonema. *(Photomicrograph courtesy Carolina Biological Supply Company.)*

Fig. 37-6 (at left) Multicellular gemmae of *Leptobryum*. *(Photomicrograph courtesy Carolina Biological Supply Company.)*

are present in some mosses; however, there are no tracheids, vessels, or sieve tubes in any mosses.

Moss plants range in height from 1.5–60 cm, but most are only a few centimeters tall (Fig. 37-4). The gametophytic thallus is biphasic: there is a protonemal phase and a gametophore phase. A germinating spore (shed from the capsule of a sporophyte) grows into a juvenile stage, which is usually a branching system of filaments, the protonema (Fig. 37-5); however, in *Sphagnum* the protonemata are irregularly lobed thalli somewhat resembling young liverwort thalli and fern prothalli. Buds develop on protonemata. Each bud starts as a small mass of parenchyma tissue, and through growth initiated by an apical cell, the bud develops into a leafy gametophyte (leafy gametophore) that produces filamentous, multicellular rhizoids on the basal portion. The leafy gametophyte of *Sphagnum* lacks rhizoids. Mosses lack vascular tissue, and for this reason moss stems are often called caulidia or caulids and the leaves are called phyllidia or phyllids. In most mosses the protonemal stage is transient, but a few, such as certain species of *Pogonatum*, have a long-lived, persistent protonema bearing relatively few and much reduced leafy gametophytes.

There is great diversity in morphology among different kinds of mosses. Most mosses are erect leafy plants, but many are much branched and creeping. The leafy gametophyte of *Sphagnum* is erect but otherwise unique in several ways. Individual *Sphagnum* plants are closely matted together. Each plant has a cluster of leafy branches at the apex and two kinds of leafy branches along the main stem: ascendant branches, which are more or less horizontal, and pendant branches (Fig. 37-1). The leaves are numerous, closely spaced, and essentially spiral in arrangement at maturity, as in most mosses, but they are unique in having large, colorless, nonliving, water-holding cells often marked with annular or spiral thickenings and perforated with large circular pores. Between these cells are smaller photosynthetic cells arranged end to end in such a way as to form a reticulum around and between the colorless, water-storage cells.

The leaves of many other mosses have a midrib-like region (costa, Fig. 37-4) from which extends the main portion of the blade, often a single cell in thickness. Some of the elongate cells of the midrib have thickened walls and function in support. There is considerable diversity in leaf form among mosses, but none are as complex as the complicate-bilobed leaves of certain leafy liverworts.

The stems of many mosses are differentiated into a central region, which may have both thick- and thin-walled cells, a thick cortex, and an epidermal layer. Stems as well as leaves can be photosynthetic. Also, during vegetative growth of the sporophyte of typical mosses (when the sporophyte consists only of a foot and elongating seta and before the capsule differentiates at the apex of the seta), the sporophyte is green and photosynthetic.

Asexual reproduction   Asexual reproduction by means of fragmentation of various parts of the gametophyte is common. Fragments of protonemata, stems, leaves, and even gametangia and paraphyses, in a favourable environment, can give rise to protonemata and then new leafy gametophytes. Also, rhizoids of leafy gametophytes may give rise to new protonemata, which in turn produce more leafy gametophytes.

Some mosses produce special parenchymatous masses of tissue, called gemmae, which can reproduce the gametophytic phase. *Leptobryum,* which is common in greenhouse pots, has gemmae on its rhizoids (Fig. 37-6). *Ulota* forms gemmae on its leaves. *Aulacomnium* develops a special stalk bearing a terminal cluster of gemmae, and *Tetraphis* forms gemmae in "cups" at the tips of leafy gametophytes.

Sexual reproduction   A leafy moss plant may be called a leafy gametophore because at sexual maturity it does bear the gametangia. The gametophores of some mosses are unisexual (Figs. 37-7, 37-8) and some are bisexual (Fig. 37-4). Most mosses are homothallic, but some are heterothallic.

In some mosses the archegonia and antheridia are borne on the apex of leafy gametophytes, which are usually erect. These are known as acrocarpous mosses. Pleurocarpous mosses bear their gametangia, and consequently their sporophytes, on special, short, lateral branches.

The methods of syngamy and early sporophyte development in mosses, as well as liverworts, hornworts, and vascular plants, are developmental features that clearly are adaptations to life on land. These are: (1) The male gametangia (antheridia) and female gametangia (archegonia) have a sterile jacket of cells (wall cells) that protect developing gametes from drying out. In mosses, developing gametangia are further protected by sterile filaments (paraphyses) or by vegetative leaves. Moss

Fig. 37-7 Gametophores of *Polytrichum* picked and placed together to illustrate an archegonial one (left) and an antheridial one (right). In the middle is a female gametophore bearing a mature sporohyyte. *(Courtesy Carolina Biological Supply Company.)*

Fig. 37-8 Stained longitudinal section of an antheridial head of *Polytrichum. (Photomicrograph courtesy Carolina Biological Supply Company.)*

Fig. 37-9 *Dicranum* with mature sporophytes. The light-colored distal portion of a calyptra on the apex of a capsule is indicated by an arrow. *(Courtesy Carolina Biological Supply Company.)*

Fig. 37-10 Closeup view of the apex of a *Sphagnum* gametophore with four sporophytes (S), each elevated on a gametophytic pseudopodium (P). *(Courtesy Carolina Biological Supply Company.)*

antheridia are generally elongate and borne on a multicellular stalk, but the antheridia of *Sphagnum* are globose like those of liverworts. The biflagellate sperm of mosses look and swim like those of liverworts and hornworts. Moss archegonia are stalked and extremely elongate. The long, often twisted neck is composed of six rows of wall cells enclosing a long row of neck canal cells, which break down at maturity, along with the ventral canal cell, and provide a chemical attractant for sperms and a medium through which sperms swim to the egg. (2) The method of syngamy is oogamy, and fertilization occurs within the archegonium, in the venter where the egg develops. (3) The zygote is retained, and the embryo develops within the protective confines of the venter. Further growth and early differentiation of the sporophyte into embryo and then young sporophyte composed of foot and seta continues in the enlarging old archegonium, which at this stage of development is called the calyptra.

In typical mosses the seta continues to elongate and soon ruptures the calyptra at its base, raising the distal portion of the calyptra on the apex of the sporophyte above the leafy gametophyte (Fig. 37-9). Although the moss sporophyte is green and photosynthetic during development, the attached foot absorbs dissolved food as well as water and mineral salts from the gametophyte.

In *Sphagnum* and *Andreaea* the seta does not elongate. Instead, the apex of the gametophore axis (the pseudopodium) elongates and elevates the entire sporophyte above the leafy gametophyte (Fig. 37-10).

In typical mosses, after the seta has grown to its full length, the distal portion, surmounted by the calyptra, differentiates into a capsule (sporangium or meiosporangium). In certain mosses the basal portion of the developing capsule enlarges, remains sterile, is actively photosynthetic, and has functional stomata with guard cells in its epidermis. This region is called the apophysis. The middle and largest part of the capsule differentiates an urn- or barrel-shaped sporogenous region surrounding a central, sterile columella. Like the sporocytes (spore mother cells) of liverworts and hornworts, the sporocytes of mosses undergo meiosis and form a tetrad of spores. Mosses do not form elaters. External to the sporogenous region is the capsule wall, composed of an outer epidermal layer and inner photosynthetic tissue.

The apex of the capsule of most mosses differentiates a cap (operculum) with a rim (annulus) at its base. In most mosses, cells at the base of the caps become differentially thickened, and, as they dry at maturity, they form a ring of toothlike segments called the peristome or peristome teeth. As the mature capsule dries, the calyptra and cap fall off and spores are free for release and air dispersal.

Spores may be passively emitted from the capsule or they may be discharged, aided by pressure from their contracting capsule wall or by hygroscopic movements of the peristome teeth. Spore discharge in *Sphagnum* is remarkable because it is explosive—spores under pressure inside the capsule explosively throw off the operculum as they are shot out of the capsule. *Andreaea* is unique because it releases its spores through four, longitudinal clefts in the capsule wall.

Mosses, like liverworts, hornworts, and all the other embryophytes or land plants, have an alternation of heteromorphic generations. The major phase in mosses and other bryophytes is gametophytic, and they may be said to have a haplo-diplontic type of sexual life cycle with heteromorphic alternating generations: the large and more conspicuous leafy gametophyte (the site of syngamy) alternates with the smaller stalk-like sporophyte (the site of meiosis).

Syngamy initiates the sporophyte generation and meiosis the gametophyte.

However, in bryophytes as well as in some other groups, vegetative portions of gametophytes can be induced in culture to develop directly (without syngamy) into haploid spore-producing plants that look essentially like ordinary diploid sporophytes—a process called apogamy. Similarly, setae and capsules can develop directly (without forming meiospores) into diploid gamete-producing plants that look essentially like ordinary haploid gametophytes—a process called apospory. Diploid gametophytes can continue the life cycle and establish polyploid mosses.

Project

I. **Typical moss** (representative genera: *Polytrichum, Atrichum, Pogonatum, Funaria,* and *Mnium*)

A. *Gametophyte*

1. Protonema. Carefully wash some protonema, mount it in water, add a cover slip, and with high power observe details of a few cells of a branching filament. Find chloroplasts and cross walls. Are the cross walls oblique or at right angles to the side walls? Using low power, look on the protonema for the "buds" that give rise to the upright "leafy moss plants."

2. Leafy gametophyte plant (upright shoot or gametophore). The "leaves" and "stems" of bryophytes are not true leaves and stems (they lack vascular tissue) and are more correctly called phyllidia and caulidia, respectively.

   a. Rhizoids. *Polytrichum* and *Atrichum* are excellent for the study of rhizoids. Separate a single gametophore from a clump of moss. Wash gently. Mount in several drops of water on a slide. Add a cover slip and press the mount as flat as possible. Using high power, find the points of origin of rhizoids from the stem. Is there any protoplasm in the rhizoids? Do the rhizoids branch? Are the rhizoids unicellular or multicellular?

   b. Leaves. *Mnium* is excellent for the study of leaves. Mount several leaves in water on a slide and add a cover slip. Using high dry, observe (1) the presence of a midrib, (2) the number of cells in thickness at the midrob, (3) the number of cells in thickness near the edge of the blade, (4) the shape of cells in the midrib, and (5) the shape of cells near the edge of the blade. Do all cells contain chloroplasts?

3. Antheridium

   a. Living or preserved material. At the tips of some erect branches observe that the leaves are closely packed, forming cuplike structures, antheridial heads. The jacket cells of mature antheridia may be reddish, giving the male head at maturity this color. With a pair of needles, tease out the antheridia in a drop of water on a glass slide and observe with your microscope. Look for the discharge of sperms. What is the shape of a sperm? How many flagella are there? Where are the flagella attached?

   b. Prepared slide. Study a longitudinal section of the fertile tip of a male gametophore. Find an antheridium (with its stalk, sterile jacket, and spermatogenous cells), paraphyses (multicellular sterile hairs), and gametophytic stem cells (to which the antheridia and paraphyses are attached).

4. Archegonium
   a. Living or preserved material. At the tips of other branches archegonia may be found. They can be dissected out by cutting off the tip of the branch, removing the leaves, placing the tip in a drop of water on a slide, and splitting it lengthwise.
   b. Prepared slide. Study a longitudinal section of the fertile tip of a female gametophore. Find an archegonium in median longitudinal section showing the venter (composed of egg, ventral canal cell, venter wall cells) and neck (composed of neck canal cells and neck wall cells). Also find paraphyses and stem cells.
5. Bisexual or monoecious mosses. Some mosses (e.g., *Mnium medium* and *Leptobryum* sp.) are monoecious and have antheridia and archegonia at the tip of a single gametophore. Study such material if it is available.
6. Culture. Directions for culturing mosses are given in Project 5, p. 38. If materials and time are available, start your own cultures.

B. *Sporophyte*
1. Embryo and stages of development. Young embryos are composed of an upper part and a lower part. The embryo develops into a sporophyte with three distinct parts: foot, stalk (seta), and capsule (sporangium or meio-sporangium). You may be able to find an embryo within an old archegonium as well as any number of stages in the maturation of the sporophyte.
2. Mature sporophyte. What reasons do you have for thinking that the sporophyte is parasitic upon the gametophyte? What evidence can you find to indicate that the sporophyte is autotrophic?
   a. Foot. Dissect the foot of a sporophyte out from the stem of the gameto-phyte. Does some gametophytic tissue adhere?
   b. Mature capsules. Using a dissecting microscope make the following observations:
      (1) Sporangium with calyptra on. The calyptra is gametophytic (the upper portion of the old archegonium) torn off and carried up on the growing sporophyte.
      (2) Sporangium with calyptra off, showing operculum (cap) and annulus (rim).
      (3) Sporangium with the cap pulled off, showing the peristome (teeth). Are the peristome teeth in one row or two? How many teeth are there in each layer (if there are two layers). In *Atrichum, Pogonatum,* and *Polytrichum* (Fam. Polytrichaceae) you will find a circular membrane, the epiphragm (this is an expansion at the top of the columella) that is attached to the tips of the teeth and helps control spore discharge. Wet the peristome with a drop of water. Notice the position of the moist teeth and the changes that occur during the subsequent drying out. How might this effect spore discharge?
   c. Dissected mature capsule. Dissect a mature sporangium in a drop of water on a slide. Find the sporangium wall, spore (meiospores), and columella. Remove the bulky tissue and add a cover slip. Using high power, observe several spores, finding the spore wall and chloroplasts.
   d. Longitudinal section of a mature capsule (prepared slide). Identify sporangium stalk (seta), operculum, sporangium wall, spore or meio-spore mother cells (sporocytes), and columella.

II. Bog or peat moss *(Sphagnum)*

A. *Gametophore (upright shoot)*

1. General appearance. Note the clustered branches at the apex. Note the pendant branches along the stem. These with their very fine leaves are important in the capillary rise of water along the outside.

2. Leaves. Mount several phyllidia in water, add a cover slip, and study one using low power. Is there a midrib? How many cells in thickness is a leaf? Using high power, find the smaller photosynthetic cells with chloroplasts and the larger, nonchlorophyllous water-holding cells, each with spiral thickenings of wall material, pores through the wall, and a lumen (internal space).

B. *Sporophyte*

1. Living or preserved material. Using a dissecting microscope, study a gametophore bearing a mature sporangium on the gametophytic pseudopodium. Carefully dissect the foot of the sporophyte out from the tip of the pseudopodium. With a needle remove the operculum of the sporangium. Break open the sporangium wall so as to reveal the spores and the dome-shaped columella.

2. Longitudinal section of a mature sporophyte (prepared slide). Find the mature sporophyte at the tip of an elongated, gametophytic pseudopodium. Identify foot, very short seta, and capsule (sporangium or meiosporangium) with its operculum, meiospores, wall, and dome-shaped columella.

Project **38** Lycopods or club mosses

Contents

Introduction

Taxonomy Lycopods or club mosses are plants of the group technically known
as Lepidophyta, Microphyllophyta, Lycophyta, or Lycopsida. There are 5 genera
and about 900 species. Although most lycopods do resemble mosses enough for
them to have the common name *club mosses*, the resemblance is deceptive: the
plant we commonly recognize as a moss plant is the mature gametophyte; whereas,
the plant we commonly recognize as a lycopod or club moss plant is the mature
sporophyte (Fig. 38-1).

Table 18-1 (page 132) summarizes the various ways of classifying lycopods:
lycopods, horsetails, and ferns are the pteridophytes. Lycopods and horsetails are
the microphyllous pteridophytes. Lycopods, horsetails, ferns, and seed plants are
the vascular plants. Lycopods, horsetails, and ferns are the vascular cryptogams.
And finally, lycopods, horsetails, ferns, seed plants, and bryophytes are the embryophytes or embryophytic eukaryotes.

As discussed under the taxonomy of liverworts (page 271), lycopods are like
other vascular plants, and also bryophytes, stoneworts, and green algae, in having
(1) similar photosynthetic pigments in their plastids, (2) storage of starch in
plastids, (3) motile cells (sperms in lycopods and other embryophytes) with only

Fig. 38-1 Habit view of *Lycopodium clavatum* with strobili. *(Courtesy CCM: General Biological Inc., Chicago.)*

Fig. 38-2 Closeup view of *Selaginella apoda* with terminal strobili. *(Courtesy Carolina Biological Supply Company.)*

Fig. 38-3 Habit view of *Isoetes bolanderii*. *(Courtesy Carolina Biological Supply Company.)*

the whiplash type of flagellum, and (4) cellulosic cell walls also containing pectic substances. In addition, lycopods and all other embryophytes have alternating haploid and diploid phases or generations, structurally are composed of tissues, and are oogamous. Only some green algae, and of these only some of the tetrasporine green algae, have all three of these features.

All the above fundamental features indicate that lycopods, the other vascular plants, bryophytes, stoneworts, and green algae are today's representatives of a single, complex evolutionary line or phyletic group, which can be called the green-plant evolutionary line or the green-plant phyletic group. Some biologists would call this the green-plant kingdom of organisms; others would call it the green-plant phylum or division of plants.

Basic features in the differentiation of primary vascular tissue in tracheophytes (lycopods, horsetails, ferns, and seed plants) are discussed at the end of the section dealing with the vegetative features of lycopods (p. 303).

Lycopods have the following features in common with other nonseed vascular plants (pteridophytes): (1) They have a diplo-haplontic type of sexual life cycle; the sporophyte is the conspicuous or dominant phase of the alternating heteromorphic generations. (2) They have multicellular gametangia (antheridia and archegonia). (3) They have multicellular sporangia (meiosporangia). (4) Their embryos are protected by female gametophytic tissue. (5) Their sporophytes are differentiated into three types of vegetative parts—roots, stems, and leaves. (6) They have conducting tissues (xylem and phloem) in a vascular system. (7) Water-conducting cells of the xylem are lignified. (8) There is a cuticle. (9) There are stomates, each with a pair of regulatory guard cells, in the epidermis. All the above features can be interpreted as adaptations permitting successful life on land for lycopods, horsetails, and ferns.

How far back in time lycopods and other pteridophytes evolved, differentiated, or diverged is a matter of conjecture, but there are known fossil lycopods, horsetails, and ferns (as well as bryophytes and gymnosperms) from the Devonian Period, and the fossil record of these plants continues through the more recent periods (Table 18-2, p. 134). Pteridophytes of the Carboniferous Period, especially in the Pennsylvanian Period when there were great coal-forming swamp forests, included members that were large trees, over 100 ft tall. As indicated in Table 18-2, arborescent lycopods and horsetails were an important component of these ancient forests, which were doomed to extinction during the Permian Period. Actually, the earliest fossil vascular plant comes from late Silurian rock. This was a simply constructed plant and has been placed with the Devonian *Rhynia* and other such fossils in a group called psilophytes, which became extinct during the Carboniferous Period. Some botanists have related these primitive land plants to the living genera *Psilotum* and *Tmesipteris*, calling them all psilopsids, but there is no compelling evidence that this is true. *Psilotum* and *Tmesipteris* are treated in this book as simple ferns (p. 321).

The progenitors of lycopods, horsetails, and ferns have not yet been identified in the fossil record. Each group seems to represent an independent evolutionary line, and there is no clear evidence that early members of any group gave rise to early members of any other group. Also, there is no evidence that primitive lycopods or other vascular plants evolved from early bryophytes; however, it is likely that pteridophytes and bryophytes had their origins in ancient, tetrasporine green algae, as discussed under the taxonomy of hornworts (p. 281).

Lycopods have the following important features: (1) The sporophyte, which is the dominant or conspicuous generation, is composed of vascularized (Fig. 38-4) roots, stems, and leaves. (2) The leaf is simple and scalelike (Figs. 38-2, 38-5) and is called a microphyll. a special name indicating that it probably evolved from an enation or protuberance from a previously smooth stem. Microphyllous plants lack leaf gaps. This means that there is no gap in the stem's vascular cylinder or that the vascular cylinder of the stem is not interrupted at the place where vascular tissue branches off (as a leaf trace) into the leaf. (3) The sporangium is in or near the axil of the leaf (Figs. 38-6, 38-7) on the upper or adaxial side of the leaf. This sporangium-bearing leaf is called a sporophyll. (4) There are both homosporous plants (with all spores morphologically alike) (Fig. 38-6) and heterosporous plants (with spores of two kinds and sizes) (Fig. 38-7). All the spores and sporangia of homosporous plants look alike. Heterosporous plants produce larger numbers of smaller spores (microspores or male spores, which grow into male gametophytes) in microsporangia on microsporophylls, and heterosporous plants produce smaller numbers of larger spores (megaspores or female spores, which grow into female gametophytes) in megasporangia on megasporophylls. (5) There are plants with biflagellate sperms and plants with multiflagellate sperms.

Although there are five living genera of lycopods, only three are common and well known: *Lycopodium* (with about 180 species), *Selaginella* (with about 600 species), and *Isoetes* (with about 65 species). These three genera are distinctive enough to be placed in separate orders (Lycopodiales, Selaginellales, and Isoetales). *Lycopodium* and *Selaginella* are somewhat mosslike in appearance (Fig. 38-2), and some species form clublike clusters of sporophylls; thus, *Lycopodium* and *Selaginella* are commonly called club mosses. *Isoetes*, quillwort, stands alone as a peculiar kind of pteridophyte; it looks somewhat like a tuft of grass (Fig. 38-3). The other extant genera are *Phylloglossum*, which is related to *Lycopodium*, and *Stylites*, which is related to *Isoetes*.

The above three orders also have members that became extinct in times past and are known only from the fossil record. In addition, there are a number of other known fossil genera that are such distinctive lycopods that they are placed in two additional orders, Lepidodendrales and Pleuromeiales. The former contains fossils of tree lycopods such as *Lepidodendron*, which had a trunk exceeding 35 meters in height and 1 meter in diameter. This and other members of the Lepidodendrales are known only from fossils of the late Devonian to early Permian Periods.

Importance   Lycopods contribute relatively little as primary producers in nature, but even so they are important as primary producers in their habitats. Although lycopods are of relatively little economic importance, the spores of *Lycopodium* are of some commercial value, including their use as a covering for pills and including because of their inflammability, their utilization in flares, fireworks, and tracer bullets. Some species of *Lycopodium* in the eastern United States are relatively rare and are in danger of extinction, primarily because they are collected in mass quantities and sold at Christmas time for decorative purposes, and also because their habitats are being destroyed by our expanding society. Like horsetails and ferns, lycopods of the past played an important role in the formation of our present-day coal deposits.

Occurrence   Lycopods are worldwide in distribution and are widespread in the tropics and temperate regions. *Lycopodium* and *Selaginella* have the same general geographic range. Most species are tropical and subtropical, where they are especially common in damp forests. Most live on soil substrates, but a number of tropical species grow as epiphytes. Habitats of *Lycopodium* range from rich woods and swamps (*L. lucidulum*) to dry woods, slopes, and pinelands (*L. flabelliforme*), to rock cliffs and barrens (*L. selago*). Habitats of *Selaginella* vary from wet, loamy meadows and muddy or grassy margins of ponds and streams (*S. apoda*) to dry, more or less exposed rocks (*S. rupestris*). *Isoetes* has a relatively wide distribution in temperate climates, where it commonly grows as a submerged aquatic in shallow water. It may be found in and on the edges of temporary pools, bogs, swamps, marshes, wet roadsides, and on stream edges. Rarely, *Isoetes* grows on exposed rock outcrops in the same habitats as xerophytic species of *Selaginella*. *Stylites* is found in the high mountains of Peru. *Phylloglossum* occurs only in Australasia.

Vegetative features   Discussed in this section are the vegetative features of what is commonly thought of as the lycopod plant: the mature sporophytic plant, which is the conspicuous, dominant, and perennial phase. This contrasts with the situation in bryophytes, where the conspicuous, dominant, and usually perennial

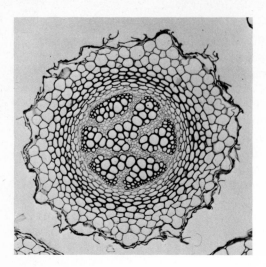

Fig. 38-4   Stained cross section of a root of *Lycopodium* showing the central vascular tissue. *(Photomicrograph courtesy Ripon Microslides Laboratory.)*

phase is the mature gametophyte. The vegetative features in lycopods of the rather cryptic gametophytic phase or gametophyte plant and also early sporophyte development (when the sporophyte is parasitic on the gametophyte) will be discussed in the section dealing with sexual reproduction. This is appropriate because the following developmental features are all intimately and immediately related to each other: (1) spore (meiospore) formation by the mature sporophyte, (2) spore germination and further development of the gametophyte plant, (3) formation of gametes, (4) syngamy, and (5) embryo development and sprouting of the embryo to initiate the independent sporophyte plant.

All living lycopods are herbaceous and are differentiated into three types of vegetative parts—roots, stems, and leaves—which have water-conducting tissue (xylem) and food-conducting tissue (phloem) in a simple vascular system (Fig. 38-4). The water-conducting cells (tracheids) of the xylem are lignified. Epidermis exposed to air is covered with a waxy layer (cuticle), and there are stomates, each with a pair of regulatory guard cells, in the epidermis.

The mature plants (sporophytes) of *Lycopodium* tend to be larger than those of *Selaginella*, but they are similar in having their sprawling stems covered with small, simple, sharp-pointed leaves; thus, laymen may call some of them mosses and others of them groundpine, trailing cedar, and similar names. Branching may be dichotomous or monopodial. The numerous leaves of most lycopods are spirally arranged, scalelike or awnlike, up to 13 mm long, appressed or spreading, and with a midrib only. The single vein does not form a leaf gap at the place where it emerges from the vascular cylinder (stele) of the stem; such leaves are called microphylls, and lycopod plants are said to be microphyllous. Roots are adventitous. The stele in all parts of a lycopod plant typically is a solid column of vascular tissue, and such a stele is called a protostele, but the stele of stems may be more complex. Surrounding the stele, in order, are cortex and epidermis.

In *Lycopodium* (Figs. 38-1, 38-5) such species as *L. lucidulum* have sprawling and loosely ascending stems that are not differentiated into horizontal and erect parts. Others, such as *L. flabelliforme* (*L. complanatum* var. *flabelliforme*), have extensively branched, superficial or subterranean rhizomes (usually elongate, horizontal, underground, or subsurface stems) from which arise upright branches, up to 8 in. in height, with many short branchlets. Typically, the leafy stems are rounded, but the upright branches of some species are flattened. Roots are adventitious along the creeping stem.

Selaginella is smaller and more mosslike than *Lycopodium*. Development of the shoot originates either from a single apical cell and its derivatives or from a group of apical meristem cells. The plant forms mats of slender, much-branched stems bearing scalelike, appressed, or spreading leaves (microphylls). The leaves are either spirally arranged, as in *Selaginella rupestris*, or they are arranged in four rows, as in *S. apoda* (Fig. 38-2). Each leaf has on its upper surface and at the base a small tonguelike structure called a ligule. Each leaf has an upper epidermis, mesophyll, and a lower epidermis with stomata that are localized near the single vein or the midrib. The delicate, fibrous roots of *Selaginella* are adventitious and arise from the tips of special leafless stems called rhizophores. A root's growth is initiated by a single apical cell. *Selaginella* is a unique lycopod in having vessels in the xylem of some species (e.g., *S. rupestris*) and in having some species with one or with two or more steles, the polystelic condition.

Plants of *Isoetes* are unique. In mass they resemble a clump or bed of grass and vary from about 3 in. to 2 ft in height (Fig. 38-3). Each plant is somewhat like an onion plant. Buried in the mud is a stubby corm (a short, verticle, fleshy, subterranean stem). A succession of sparsely branched roots are produced each year by the stem's basal meristem. An apical meristem produces fleshy leaves with an enlarged or dilated base. The bases of the leaves are buried in the mud or soil along with the stem and roots. Each leaf has four, large, internal air spaces through most of its length. As in *Selaginella,* each leaf has a ligule near its base on the adaxial side. A single plant may have 8–100 leaves that vary from 5–50 cm in length and are usually 1–2 mm broad at the middle. Although the leaves of *Isoetes* are long, they are actually microphylls. The cormlike stem develops a cambium-like layer that contributes to the increase in the girth of the stem.

Primary vascular tissue in lycopods and other vascular plants differentiates from elongate, narrow, highly vacuolated cells near the tips or apices of stems and roots. These cells are called procambial (or provascular) cells. Protoxylem is the term designating the earliest developed primary xylem. Protoxylem differentiates during the elongation phase of stems and roots, and it may be seen as a series of small strands referred to as the protoxylem poles of the procambium. After stem and root elongation is complete or nearly so, and after the protoxylem has matured, the remaining procambial cells differentiate into the last-formed primary xylem, called metaxylem.

Primary xylem develops in three ways: (1) Protoxylem may be at the outer margin of the xylem with metaxylem then differentiating inward (centripetally) toward the center of the stele (exarch development). The stems of lycopods and the fern *Psilotum* and the roots of all vascular plants have exarchly developed primary xylem (Fig. 38-4). Exarch development, which is characteristic of organs having protosteles, appears to be a primitive feature. (2) Protoxylem may be somewhere between the outer margin and the inside, and as the metaxylem develops it surrounds the protoxylem (mesarch development). The stems and leaves of many ferns have mesarch development. (3) Protoxylem may be at the inner margin of the primary xylem with metaxylem differentiating outward toward the periphery of the stele (endarch development). The stems of seed plants have endarch primary xylem, and this appears to be the most highly evolved or advanced condition.

A vascular strand extending through the cortex of a stem into a leaf or branch contains at least one protoxylem strand with associated metaxylem. Leaf gaps and branch gaps occur if the strands of protoxylem that enter leaves and branches originate from the inside (pith side) of a stem's stele (endarchly developed). Lycopods are exarch and lack leaf or branch gaps.

Protoxylem cells or elements are narrower than metaxylem cells and often develop their lignified secondary walls as series of rings (annular elements) or spiral bands (spiral elements). The wider metaxylem cells usually have more extensively deposited secondary walls, giving them the appearance of connected bars (scalariform elements) or a network (reticulate elements), and the metaxylem cells with the most extensive deposits of secondary wall material are pitted elements. Primary xylem may consist entirely of tracheids or (in those plants capable of developing vessels) of a mixture of tracheids and vessel elements, as in certain species of the lycopod *Selaginella,* in the horsetail *Equisetum,* in the ferns *Pteridium* and *Marsilea,* and in many monocotyledonous and dicotyledonous flowering plants.

Asexual reproduction   Asexual reproduction in *Lycopodium* and *Selaginella* commonly is accomplished through their sprawling or running and branching stems after death of old stems. Some species of *Lycopodium* have subterminal leaves bearing axillary gemmae or bulbils.

Sexual reproduction in *Lycopodium*   The sporangium-bearing leaves (sporophylls) of *Lycopodium* are more like the vegetative leaves in some species and less like them in other species. Sporophylls often occur in clusters called strobili. Strobili, each with several dozen sporophylls, occur at the tips of ordinary leaf-covered stems (e.g., *L. obscurum*) or they may be terminal on special upright stems clothed with scalelike leaves called peduncles (e.g., *L. clavatum*). In such species as *L. lucidulum,* bands of sporophylls about 1 cm in length alternate with longer zones of sterile leaves (Fig. 38-5).

Sporangia are produced on the upper (adaxial) sides of leaves (Fig. 38-6). They are solitary at the leaf base, massive, short stalked, and subglobose to reniform. The sporangium wall is three layered, and the inner layer of the wall functions as a nutritive layer called the tapetum. In *Lycopodium,* unlike most other pteridophytes, the tapetum does not disintegrate during spore formation. The diploid sporocytes (spore mother cells or sporogenous cells) in the central portion of the sporangium become separated and spherical, and after meiosis each produces a tetrad of spores. These separate and secrete a wall with ornamentations characteristic of the species. A sporangium releases its spores (meiospores) through a transverse slit in the sporangium wall. All the spores (and sporangia) of a species look alike, are of the same size, and grow into gametophytes each of which produces both male and female gametes; thus, *Lycopodium* is said to be homosporous. This is also true for the rare *Phylloglossum,* but it is not true for the other extant lycopods.

Spore germination and gametophyte (prothallus) development in most species of *Lycopodium* is slow, ranging from 8 months to 6–15 years. The slowest growing ones are those which have a colorless gametophyte nourished by a mycorrhizal fungus. Mature gametophytes (prothalli) are small and inconspicuous, commonly less than 1 cm in length and width.

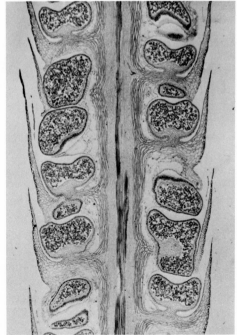

Fig. 38-5 Closeup view of four species of
Lycopodium with strobili, left to right:
L. obscurum, L. lucidulum, L. alopecuroides,
L. flabelliforme (complanatum var. flabelliforme).
(Courtesy Carolina Biological Supply Company.)

Fig. 38-6 Stained longitudinal section of part
of a strobilus of *Lycopodium.* At the lower right
is a clear view of the homosporous sporangium
on the adaxial side of a sporophyll.
*(Photomicrograph courtesy Ripon Microslides
Laboratory.)*

In nature, gametophytes of such species as *L. flagelliforme* and *L. obscurum* are subterranean, tuberous, or branching cylinders or top-shaped structures that lack chlorophyll and thus are heterotrophic. The taproot-like basal part of the gametophyte bears rhizoids and contains a zone of cells with an endophytic fungus, a phycomycete that may be *Pythium.* The upper part of a mature gametophyte is a cushion-like crown bearing antheridia and archegonia, both of which are partially embedded in crown tissue. When gametophytes of these species are grown axenically (without any other organisms) in agar cultures and in light, the gametophytes are green and, of course, autotrophic. Experiments with such cultures have shown that invasion of young gametophytes by the symbiotic fungus changes the morphology of the gametophyte. This is analogous to the situation in most lichens, where the fungus alone has a much different appearance than it has when growing with its algal symbiont as a lichen.

In nature, the gametophyte of such species as *Lycopodium cernuum* (a tropical species) differs from the previous kind in that it develops faster, is partially above ground where it is exposed to light, has cells with chloroplasts, and is autotrophic.

The gametangia of *Lycopodium* and other pteridophytes are smaller and simpler than those of bryophytes, but the archegonium of hornworts does somewhat resemble the archegonium of *Lycopodium.* The archegonium is sunken in the upper surface of the crown except for most of the neck. The protruding neck has three or four rows of neck wall cells surrounding one to thirteen neck canal cells. At maturity the ventral canal cell and the neck canal cells dissolve, the neck wall cells separate at the apex of the neck, and sperms are attracted to and have ready access to the egg. Antheridia are either intermingled among archegonia or segregated on different areas of the crown of the same gametophyte. Antheridia may be completely sunken or may protrude. The wall consists of a single layer of wall or jacket cells covering a mass of spermatogenous cells. Sperms are liberated after dissolution of one of the wall cells. Each sperm is fusiform with a broadly rounded base and has two apically attached and posteriorly directed whiplash flagella.

After fertilization, the zygote divides and produces an outer suspensor cell and an inner embryo-forming cell. The suspensor cell may divide once or twice, and the suspensor elongates and pushes the developing embryo deeper in the vegetative tissue of the gametophyte's crown. The mature embryo has a massive foot portion and an embryonic stem and leaf. The foot functions as that part of the embryo which absorbs food from the gametophyte during the sprouting of the rest of the embryo into a juvenile *Lycopodium* plant (sporophyte). The first embryonic leaf can be called the cotyledon. The first root develops adventitiously at the base of the cotyledon. The first shoot emerges from the gametophyte and up into the light. The gametophyte, attached to the developing sporophyte, ultimately disintegrates as the sporophyte becomes established as an independent, autotrophic plant.

It is clear that the sex life of *Lycopodium* involves two independant plants: a large, conspicuous, vascularized sporophyte (the site of meiosis) and a small, inconspicuous, nonvascularized gametophyte (the site of syngamy). The morphology as well as the size of these two phases is quite different; thus, *Lycopodium* has a diplo-haplontic type of sexual life cycle with anisomorphic alternating generations. This is true for all lycopods. Indeed, it is true for all other vascular plants.

Sexual reproduction in *Selaginella* The ligulate sporophylls of *Selaginella* look much like sterile leaves, and they occur in clusters, strobili, at the tips of the ordinary, much-branched, leaf-covered stems. Strobili are relatively inconspicuous (Fig. 38-2). Sporangia are produced singly in the adaxial leaf axils on short stalks. Both large and small spores are produced, a condition known as heterospory; the smaller spores are called microspores or male spores, and the larger spores are called megaspores or female spores. Their sporangia are, respectively, microsporangia and megasporangia, and their sporophylls are microsporophylls and megasporophylls (Fig. 38-7). In *Selaginella,* microsporangia may be located toward the apex of a strobilus with megasporangia below; however, there may be two vertical rows of microsporangia and two of megasporangia, and, also, the two kinds of sporangia may be irregularly arranged. Why some young sporangia differentiate as microsporangia and others as megasporangia is unknown. There are many microsporocytes in each microsporangium, but only one functional megasporocyte in each megasporangium (the other megasporocytes disintegrate); thus, following meiosis and spore formation, there are many small microspores but only four large megaspores per sporangium. The triradiate ridge (wall material deposited in three ridges when the spore is still in its tetrad of spores) is especially conspicuous on the large megaspore.

At least the early stages of microgametophyte (male gametophyte) and megagametophyte (female gametophyte) development in *Selaginella* occur entirely within the spore walls or cases; this is a developmental feature common to all other heterosporous plants (*Isoetes,* heterosporous ferns, and all seed plants). Also, early development of the gametophytes occurs before the spores are liberated from their sporangia. Not only that, gametophytes can complete their maturation while still in their strobili.

The male gametophyte is a greatly reduced one, consisting of but a single antheridium and only one vegetative cell, the prothallial cell. At maturity the prothallial cell and the antheridial wall cells disintegrate, water is absorbed, and the 128 or 256 biflagellate sperms, which are similar to those of *Lycopodium,* are released through the cracked open microspore wall. The male gametophyte is not green and develops entirely from food stored by the sporophyte in the microspore.

The megagametophyte is much larger. Early mitotic divisions of the nuclei within the megaspore wall are not accompanied by cytokinesis, and they are therefore referred to as free-nuclear divisions. The young female gametophyte, then, is coenocytic, and it has a large central vacuole. In this respect, the female gametophytic thallus resembles the thallus of coenocytic algae and fungi, but it differs from both in that it develops entirely from food provided by the sporophyte. As the female gametophyte matures, cross walls form in the end where the triradiate ridge is, and soon a mass of uninucleate cells are present. This parenchymatous mass of cells increases and causes the spore case to rupture. Rhizoids may develop from the protruding cushion of cells. Several small archegonia, similar to those of *Lycopodium,* develop in the protruding cushion of cells. When, as occasionally happens, gametophytes mature while still in the strobilus, and when microspores containing mature male gametophytes sift into the open megasporangia containing mature female gametophytes, a process suggestive of pollination has occurred.

After fertilization, the zygote develops into an embryo in much the same manner as in *Lycopodium.* Opposite the base of the suspensor is a foot. The rest

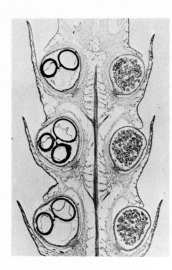

Fig. 38-7 Stained longitudinal section of part of a strobilus of *Selaginella* showing microsporangia to the right and megasporangia to the left. *(Photomicrograph courtesy Ripon Microslides Laboratory.)*

Fig. 38-8 Closeup view of a germling sporophyte of *Selaginella* showing the attached megaspore wall and the primary root (below) and cotyledons (above). *(Courtesy Carolina Biological Supply Company.)*

of the embryo is an axis with a primary root (radicle) at one end and a stem bearing two cotyledons at the.other end. The germling sporophyte, attached to the female gametophyte, still within its old megaspore wall, resembles a tiny seedling (Fig. 38-8).

The most interesting feature of the sex life of *Selaginella* is that megaspores may be retained in their strobili until after fertilization and embryo development, a condition that also is true in *Isoetes* and is always true in seed plants. This condition, then, represents part of the trend land plants had toward seed formation. Lycopods did not quite make it (seed formation), but they did come fairly close; however, there is no reason to believe that present-day lycopods will ever evolve into plants bearing seeds or that they stand in direct line of descent to existing seed plants.

Sexual reproduction in *Isoetes* Isoetes is heterosporous, all the sporophylls look alike, and they look like vegetative leaves. The sporangia, which of course are meiosporangia, are produced on the inner (adaxial) sides of the enlarged leaf bases (Fig. 38-9). The first leaves of the growing season may be sterile. The first sporophylls of the growing season may be megasporophylls, each producing many megaspores in a single megasporangium. The later ones may be microsporophylls, each producing even more microspores in a single microsporangium. The leaves produced at the end of the season (the inner leaves) are usually sterile or bear abortive sporangia. Thus, the outer leaves are often megasporophylls and these enclose the microsporophylls.

The sporangia are larger than those of *Lycopodium* and *Selaginella* and are up to 7 mm in length. A small ligule arises from just above the sporangium and an indusium-like covering (velum) grows down over the sporangium (Fig. 38-9). Male sporangia produce tremendous numbers of spores (meiospores), approxi-

Fig. 38-9 Stained longitudinal section of the base of a microsporophyll of *Isoetes* with a mature microsporangium. *(Photomicrograph courtesy Ripon Microslides Laboratory.)*

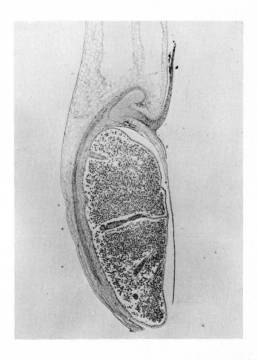

mately 150,000 to 1,000,000. Many of the megasporocytes disintegrate and only 50–300 megaspores develop in each female sporangium.

Unlike *Selaginella,* the spores of *Isoetes* do not begin development into male and female gametophytes until after liberation from their sporangia. The male gametophyte of *Isoetes* is like that of *Selaginella,* except only 16 sperms are produced and the sperms are multiflagellate, looking much like the sperms of horsetails and ferns. The female gametophyte develops essentially like that of *Selaginella.* Also, embryo development is similar, but there is no suspensor. As in *Selaginella,* the germling sporophyte, attached to the female gametophyte, still within its old megaspore wall, resembles a tiny seedling.

As in all lycopods, *Isoetes* has a diplo-haplontic type of sexual life cycle with heteromorphic alternating generations: the large, conspicuous, vascularized sporophyte (the site of meiosis) alternates with the small, inconspicuous, nonvascularized gametophyte (the site of syngamy).

Project

I. Homosporous club mosses (order Lycopodiales)

Lycopodium, giant club moss
A. *Sporophyte*
   1. Gross morphology. Identify adventitious roots, rhizome, upright branches (is branching dichotomous or monopodial?), and leaves (spirally arranged microphylls).
   2. Stem and root anatomy. Examine a cross section of a stem (rhizome) and a root showing protostele, with xylem and phloem, cortex, and epidermis. Identify protoxylem and metaxylem. Is the stele exarch, mesarch, or endarch?
   3. Strobilus
     a. Living or preserved material. Using a dissecting microscope, dissect a strobilus. Note that a bean-shaped sporangium (meiosporangium) is attached near the base to the upper surface (adaxial side) of a sporophyll. Note that all sporangia are similar in size and that they all produce similar spores, the condition known as homospory.
     b. Longitudinal section of a strobilus (prepared slide). Examine with both dissecting and compound microscopes. Find a place that shows the strobilus axis, attached sporophyll, sporangium stalk, and sporangium with its wall and either spores or spore mother cells.
B. *Gametophyte.* If they are available, study slides or whole material of developing gametophytes, mature gametophytes, and gametophytes bearing young sporophytes.

II. Heterosporous club mosses (orders Selaginellales and Isoetales)

A. *Selaginella, little club mosses*
   1. Sporophyte
     a. Gross morphology. Identify stem (is branching dichotomous or monopodial?); rhizophores, leafless branches producing adventitious roots at their tips; and leaves (microphylls).

b. Leaves. Some species of *Selaginella* have two kinds of vegetative leaves. Using both dissecting and compound microscopes, observe that leaves are arranged in four rows, two rows of larger leaves below and two rows of smaller leaves above. Examine a single mounted leaf using high power and find stomates and a leaf trace. Are tracheids of the ring, spiral, annular, or pitted type or types?

c. Strobilus

   (1) Living or preserved material. Using a dissecting microscope, dissect a strobilus. Note that there are two kinds of sporangia, microsporangia, with many small microspores, and megasporangia, with four large megaspores. Determine that the sporangia are attached near the base of the upper surface of the microsporophylls and megasporophylls. Using a compound microscope, examine the megaspores and microspores. Are the walls ornamented? In the same way?

   (2) Longitudinal section of a strobilus (prepared slide). Examine with both dissecting and compound microscopes. Identify megasporangia and microsporangia. Search for a place that shows strobilus axis, attached leaf, sporangium stalk, two-layered sporangium wall, and megaspores or microspores.

d. Embryo. Study a prepared slide with sections of megaspores that contain female gametophytes and developing embryos. Try to identify foot and embryonic stem, leaves, and root.

e. Juvenile sporophytes. Study megaspores with megagametophytes that have more mature sporophytes attached. Note the emergent young sporophytes with their two cotyledons, foliage leaves, and primary root. Where is the foot?

2. Gametophyte. Study prepared slides showing stages in the development of male and female gametophytes within the microspores and megaspores, respectively. What is the mode of nutrition of gametophytes? Does the material available show evidence of free-nuclear division? Can you see in Selaginella features that are forerunners of the pollination and seed habit?

B. *Isoetes, quillwort*. Observe the grasslike appearance of this aquatic and marsh herb. Study a longitudinal section of a plant. Identify root, stem (corm), sporophylls, and both megasporangia and microsporangia with their megaspores and microspores.

III. Fossil club mosses

Study the demonstration materials.

Project **39** Horsetails

Contents

Introduction

Taxonomy Horsetails are plants of the group technically known as Calamo-phyta, Arthrophyta, Sphenophyta, or Sphenopsida. There is a single genus with about 25–30 species.

Horsetails have a number of features in common with lycopods and ferns. These were discussed under the taxonomy of lycopods (p. 299). Horsetails them-selves are unique plants with a distinctive form or pattern of organization including (1) whorled appendages and ribbed stems, (2) small leaves (microphylls) arranged in whorls at nodes, and (3) sporangia borne on sporangiophores that are organized as a specialized strobilus (Fig. 39-1).

The progenitors of horsetails are not known, but it is likely that they had their origin in ancient, tetrasporine green algae. They represent an independent evolu-tionary line.

Although the horsetail group of plants is represented today only by a small number of species of *Equisetum,* the fossil record indicates that horsetails of past geologic times (in the Paleozoic Era) were an important part of the dominant land flora. All but *Equisetum* are extinct. The earliest known fossils (Table 18-2, p. 134) come from lower Devonian strata; they flourished in later Paleozoic times and reached their peak both in diversity and in size in the Carboniferous and Permian Periods. As examples, the tree *Calamites* and the herb *Sphenophyllum* were very common during Carboniferous times, as indicated by their fossils in

Fig. 39-1 Closeup view of *Equisetum arvense*. Fertile shoots (with strobili) at left and vegetative, sterile shoots at right. Note whorled appendages and ribbed stem (right) and microphylls in whorls at nodes (left). *(Courtesy Carolina Biological Supply Company.)*

many coal deposits. The fossil counterpart of *Equisetum* is *Equisetites,* which was common in the Mesozoic Era. It appears to have originated (evolved or differentiated) in the Pennsylvanian Period of the Paleozoic Era. The two genera are remarkably similar; this indicates that *Equisetum* had its origin in geologic times long past and that it has changed very little during its 300 million years of evolution.

Fossil horsetails are classified into four groups (orders): Hyeniales, Calamitales, Sphenophyllales, and Equisetales. The last order also contains the present *Equisetum.*

Importance Horsetails contribute very little to the primary productivity of our biosphere (Map 18-1, p. 135), but they are important as primary producers in their habitats. Like lycopods and ferns, horsetails of the past played an important role in the formation of our present-day coal beds. Coal is still of economic importance; however, the supply is dwindling and the burning of coal as a source of heat energy is discouraged because of its significant contribution to air pollution.

Some horsetails are commonly called scouring rushes, and as the name implies they were once used for scouring household utensils; their effectiveness is

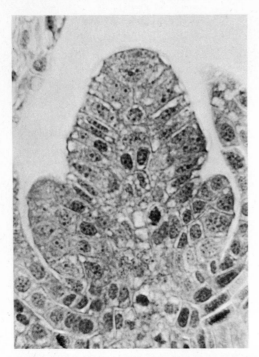

Fig. 39-2 Stained longitudinal section of a stem tip of *Equisetum arvense* showing the large apical cell. *(Photomicrograph courtesy Ripon Microslides Laboratory.)*

Fig. 39-3 Stained cross section of part of a strobilus of *Equisetum arvense* showing a median longitudinal section of one of the sporangiophores. *(Photomicrograph courtesy Ripon Microslides Laboratory.)*

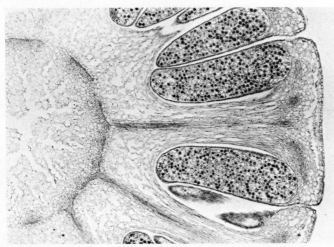

due to their stiff, ridged stems, with the walls of some of their epidermal cells having large amounts of silica. Six species of *Equisetum* have been found to cause poisoning to animals, and others may also be poisonous. The common *E. arvense* causes most cases of poisoning and it causes most trouble when in hay fed to horses. *Equisetum* is also injurious to mules, sheep, and cattle. *Equisetum* poisoning makes these animals sick and may even cause death.

Equisetum has been used for indicating the mineral content of the soil in which it grows. For example, up to $4\frac{1}{2}$ ounces of gold per ton of plant tissue may accumulate in *Equisetum* plants. The mineral content of the plants is determined either by chemical or x-ray analysis. Indicator plants like *Equisetum* can play an important role in prospecting for new mineral ores.

Occurrence   *Equisetum* has a worldwide distribution but occurs in greater variety in the northern hemisphere. It is commonly found along streams, in marshy areas, swamps, shallow ponds, moist meadows, and damp woods; however, some species live in dry meadows, roadsides, and other dry habitats. *E. arvense*, for example, commonly occurs along well-drained railroad embankments, but it also grows in moist habitats. Like the leaf of *Isoetes,* the internodes (stem) of *Equisetum* have large, long, internal air spaces. Large internal air spaces are characteristic of marsh plants. This may indicate that *Equisetum* evolved from plants that lived in wet habitats.

Vegetative features   Discussed in this section are the vegetative features of what is commonly thought of as the horsetail plant—the mature diploid sporo-phytic plant, which is the conspicuous, dominant, and perennial plant. Discussed in the section dealing with sexual reproduction will be the vegetative features of the ephemeral (though independent and autotrophic) gametophyte (Fig. 39-7) and also the embryo and germling sporophytic stages. The reasons for this are given in the section dealing with the vegetative features of lycopods (p. 302).

Equisetum is herbaceous. Species of the temperate zone rarely exceed 1–2 meters in height, but a tropical species grows to heights of over 6 meters. The form or appearance of the plant (sporophyte) is unique, including whorled appendages and ridged stems (Fig. 39-1). Horsetails resemble superficially the delicate aquatic algae called stoneworts and the gymnospermous, shrubby *Ephedra.*

Stems are erect, green, and cylindrical (terete), and they may be unbranched or have branches arising in whorls from the solid nodes. The internodes are hollow. The green stems are the site of almost all photosynthetic activity—mature leaves usually lose their green color and in some species the leaves are always achloro-phyllous. The inconspicuous leaves (microphylls) are scalelike, whorled, and fused laterally at their bases into a sheath (Fig. 39-1). This sheath protects the intercalary meristem at the base of each internode and also protects the whorls of tiny root primordia and lateral branch buds. The lateral buds occur alternately with the leaves instead of being in the axils of the leaves as in most vascular plants. Branches growing from these lateral buds break through the sheath of leaf bases.

Although each internode has a basal, intercalary meristem that contributes a large part of the tissues of both the node and internode, growth of a shoot or a root is initiated by a large apical cell (Fig. 39-2). The apical cell of a root is protected by a root cap.

Cross sections of the stem reveal many individual vascular bundles in the internodes and a complete, short siphonostele at the nodes. (A siphonostele has vascular tissue in the form of a hollow cylinder surrounding a pith.) The cell walls of the ridges of the stem are very thick and usually strongly silicified. Longitudinal sections through regions of the leaves reveal that there are no leaf gaps in the stele. Although the leaf of *Equisetum* has a single leaf trace, many fossil horsetails had leaves with a more complex leaf venation.

Rhizomes are subterranean, dark colored, extensive, branching, and with whorls of relatively delicate adventitious roots.

Asexual reproduction   As in lycopods, asexual reproduction in *Equisetum* commonly is accomplished through its extensive, running and branching rhizomes.

315

After death of old rhizomes, separate plants or colonies of plants are established. Asexual reproduction here is really just a result of vegetative growth; thus, it might properly be called vegetative reproduction. It appears to be more important in maintaining populations and in colonizing new habitats than sexual reproduction through spores and gametophytes. Because of the basal internodal meristems composed of delicate cells protected by sheathing whorls of leaves, stem segments become easily detached from parent plants. The existence of preformed root and branch primordia facilitates the development of detached stem segments into new plants.

Sexual reproduction *Equisetum* is homosporous, and all the sporangia look alike. They are borne in terminal, conelike strobili (Figs. 39-1, 39-4, 39-5) composed of several dozen whorls of close-fitting, stalked, peltate, and polygonal sporangiophore caps, each bearing several elongate sporangia on the inner side. The sporangiophore stalk is perpendicular to the axis of the strobilus; thus, the oblong sporangia are parallel to the sporangiophore stalk and are directed toward the strobilus axis (Fig. 39-3).

Some species of *Equisetum,* like *E. hyemale,* have their strobili at the tips of ordinary vegetative stems. Others, like *E. arvense* and *E. telmateia,* have dimorphic stems, and the special, nonchlorophyllous stems that bear strobili are pinkish white or bronze in color and arise separately from the rhizome (Fig. 39-4). *E. sylvaticum* is intermediate in that the strobilus at first is on an unbranched, nongreen stem, but soon the stem becomes photosynthetic and develops branches (Fig. 39-5).

The sporogenous tissue of a young sporangium is surrounded by a tapetum, which disintegrates during sporogenesis and contributes nutritive material to the developing tetrads of meiospores. Chromosome counts at meiosis in *E. arvense* and *E. hyemale* show the haploid number to be 108 ($n = 108$).

When sporangia are mature, the internodes of the strobilus axis and the stalks of the sporangiophores elongate enough and in such a way as to effectively expose sporangia to the air for spore dissemination (Fig. 39-1). Each sporangium develops a longitudinal slit through which spores are released.

Spores (meiospores) are green (chlorophyllous) and each bears four hygroscopic bands (elaters) derived from the outer wall of the spore (Fig. 39-6). When elaters are moist, they are wrapped spirally around the spore; as they dry out, the elaters open wide. These dry, opened elaters may aid in the wind dispersal of *Equisetum* spores. The elaters of *Equisetum* are not at all like the elaters of liverworts and hornworts; thus, the elaters of *Equisetum* are analogous to, rather than homologous with, liverwort elaters.

The spores of *Equisetum* are thin walled and dry out rapidly; they must germinate soon after liberation (within up to 2 weeks) on a suitable terrestrial site (Fig. 39-7). Young gametophytes (prothalli) range in size up to about 1 cm in diameter. They are green, thallose or cushion shaped, and bear a number of erect, multicellular lobes. The gametophyte is anchored to its substrate by numerous unicellular rhizoids.

Antheridia and archegonia are similar to those of *Lycopodium,* but the multiflagellate sperm resembles the sperm of *Isoetes.*

Unlike *Lycopodium* and *Selaginella,* and like *Isoetes,* embryo development in *Equisetum* does not involve the formation of a suspensor. The mature embryo consists of a foot, a primary root (radicle), and a shoot with embryonic leaves

Fig. 39-4 Closeup view of *Equisetum telmateia* in a field in Oregon. The fertile shoots seen here are the first to come up in the spring. *(Courtesy Carolina Biological Supply Company.)*

Fig. 39-5 Closeup view of a shoot of *Equisetum sylvaticum* bearing a terminal strobilus. *(Courtesy Carolina Biological Supply Company.)*

Fig. 39-6 Spores of *Equisetum* showing elaters. *(Photomicrograph courtesy Ripon Microslides Laboratory.)*

Fig. 39-7 Germinating spores (two young gametophytes) of *Equisetum*. *(Photomicrograph courtesy Ripon Microslides Laboratory.)*

and a stem. The primary root grows through the gametophyte into the soil and establishes the independence of the sprouting young *Equisetum* plant (sporophyte).

As in lycopods, *Equisetum* has a diplo-haplontic type of sexual life cycle with heteromorphic alternating generations: the large, conspicuous, vascularized sporophyte (the site of meiosis) alternates with the small, inconspicuous, nonvascularized gametophyte (the site of syngamy).

Project

I. Living horsetails: *Equisetum*

A. *Sporophyte*
  1. Gross morphology
     a. Observe the distinctive features of the vegetative plant. Identify rhizome, root, ridged aerial stem, whorl of tiny leaves (how many per whorl?), and branch.
     b. Make a longitudinal section of the stem to observe the origin of branches from the main stem. (Branches originate from buds just above the base of a whorl of leaves. In its development, a branch grows through the whorl of leaves.)
  2. Stem anatomy. Study a prepared slide containing a stained cross section of a stem. Identify pith (composed of parenchyma cells surrounding a large air space); vascular bundle, containing xylem, phloem, and air space; endodermis (inner layer of cortex cells); cortical chlorenchyma (the photosynthetic region); cortical sclerenchyma (supporting tissue); and epidermis, in which you may be able to find stomates.
  3. Strobilus (cone)
     a. Observe a living or preserved strobilus. Note the outer surfaces of the many sporangiophores.
     b. Sporangiophore. Dissect and pull out a single, complete sporangiophore. Examine it, noting its appearance as viewed from the under side (as it would be viewed from the strobilus axis). How many sporangia are there? Are they attached to the sporangiophore axis?
     c. Cross and longitudinal sections of strobili (prepared slides). Examine and find a place that shows a complete longitudinal section of a sporangiophore. Observe the sporangiophore axis, sporangium, and spores.
     d. Spores
        (1) On a microscope slide place dry spores from freshly collected or dried strobili. Examine and find spore body and elaters. One spore has how many elaters?
        (2) Moisten the dry spores by gently blowing your breath on them. What happens to the elaters when they absorb water vapor?
        (3) Add a drop of water to the spores, add a cover slip, and examine the spores using high power. (Instead, you may examine wet spores from preserved strobili.) Note the spirally wound elaters around each spore body. What is the ontogenetic origin of elaters?
B. *Gametophyte*. (Study living or preserved material or prepared slides.) Note that each gametophyte consists of a flattened cushion of tissue. From the

ventral side arise rhizoids and from the dorsal side arise multicellular erect lobes. (These relationships are difficult to see in most prepared slides.) Find antheridia. Using high power, identify sperms and antheridial wall cells. Find archegonia. How many rows of neck cells are there?

II. Fossil horsetails

Study the demonstration materials.

Project **40**   Ferns

Contents

Introduction

Taxonomy   Ferns are plants of the group technically known as Filicophyta, Pterophyta, or Filicineae. There are approximately 315 genera and 10,000 species.

Ferns are a highly diverse and distinctive group of plants, but they do have a number of features in common with lycopods and horsetails, as discussed under the taxonomy of lycopods (p. 299). The progenitors of ferns are not known, but it is likely that they had their origin in ancient tetrasporine green algae, as discussed under the taxonomy of lycopods (p. 300).

Ferns have the following important features: (1) The sporophyte, which is the dominant or conspicuous generation, is perennial and is composed of vascularized roots, stems, and leaves (*Psilotum* lacks roots and leaves). (2) Leaves, which are often called fronds, are megaphylls (large leaves, with several to many veins, which evolved from branch systems rather than from enations). Ferns and seed plants are the only plants with megaphylls (Table 18-1, p. 132). (3) Most fronds are large and feathery (Fig. 40-1) and are curled in the bud and uncurl during their rapid maturation, a condition called circinate vernation. (4) The stele may be a protostele or one of several types of siphonosteles. (5) There are leaf gaps—interruptions in the vascular cylinder above the departure of vascular bundles into leaves. (6) Typically, many sporangia develop in clusters (sori) on the margin or abaxial (lower) side of a sporophyll. (7) Most are homosporous but a few are heterosporous. (8) The gametophytes of some are heterotrophic, but most are autotrophic and independent, frequently heart shaped, and bear their gametangia on the lower side. (9) Sperms are coiled and multiflagellate.

Whether or not two genera, *Psilotum* and *Tmesipteris,* which comprise the family Psilotaceae, are modern representatives of primitive types of ferns is controversial. They have been related by some botanists to primitive vascular plants, which are known through the fossil record to have their beginning in the Silurian Period, their peak during the Devonian Period, and their extinction before or in early Carboniferous times some 400 million years ago. Indeed, it is conventional to place them in a separate group, Psilopsida, along with early Devonian fossil plants like *Rhynia* and other psilophytes. *Psilotum* and *Tmesipteris* have no fossil species, and it is difficult to believe that these vascular plants have survived for 400 million years without a fossil trace. Other botanists are of the opinion that *Psilotum* and *Tmesipteris* may be either lycopods or ferns, and that they may be simple plants not because they have retained primitive features but because of evolutionary reduction. Recent comparative studies of Psilotaceae with certain families of ferns indicate that all are ferns. Perhaps *Psilotum* and *Tmesipteris* are not modern representatives of very primitive ferns, but they are relatively simple ferns. They are so treated here.

Three groups (orders) of ferns exist only as fossils, and they are often called the preferns. They are known from middle Devonian to the Permian Periods, when they became extinct.

Existing ferns are usually classified in five orders: Ophioglossales, Marattiales, Filicales, Marsileales, and Salviniales. All but Ophioglossales also have fossil genera. Marsileales and Salviniales contain the five genera of heterosporous ferns,

Fig. 40-1 Closeup view of a typical woodland fern showing pinnately compound leaves arising in two clusters from the two growing fronts of a branched rhizome, which is out of view.
(Courtesy Carolina Biological Supply Company.)

which are aquatic and are called water ferns. How closely related these hetero-sporous ferns are to the homosporous ferns is still unclear. Marattiales, Ophio-glossales, and Filicales are homosporous and contain the typical ferns, most of which are in the large order Filicales, which has approximately 14 families, 200 genera, and 8,000 species. By far the largest family is Polypodiaceae (as defined by some fern taxonomists). Also, the simple or primitive Psilotaceae is placed in the Filicales.

Features important in the identification of ferns relate to features of the mature sporophyte—differences in the stem, vegetative leaf, sporophyll, sporan-gium (such as annulus type), position of sporangia, and the absence or presence of, as well as the shape of, the cover (indusium) protecting groups of sporangia.

Importance Although ferns are not the dominant plants of our land flora, they are important primary producers in their habitats, and ferns contribute more to the earth's primary productivity (Map 18-1, p. 135) than do other pteridophytes. Man has long cherished ferns for their aesthetically pleasing qualities, and a number of ferns are cultivated in gardens and grown as house plants for these pleasing visual sensations.

Ferns have moderate economic importance. Young fern leaves are eaten in the tropics, and in the Malayan and adjacent regions ferns are grown commercially as a food crop. "Fiddlehead greens" are eaten in the United States as a gourmet food. Ferns are used extensively by florists in floral arrangements and bouquets, and such ferns as maidenhair fern *(Adiantum)* and shield or fancy fern *(Dryopteris)* are grown in greenhouses especially for this purpose. Epiphytic orchids are frequently grown in greenhouses on the fibrous, water-holding, dead roots and stems of *Osmunda* and tree ferns.

The rhizomes and petioles of species of shield fern *(Dryopteris)* yield a drug known as aspidium that has been used for centuries for expelling tapeworms. Also, three ferns are known to cause sickness in varying degrees either when grazed by animals or when included in the hay fed to cattle, sheep, goats, or horses. These toxic ferns are the sensitive fern or meadow brake *(Onoclea sensibilis)*, cloak fern *(Notholaena sinuata)*, and brake fern or bracken *(Pteridium latiusculum)*.

Like lycopods and horsetails, ferns of the past played a role in the formation of coal beds. Present-day ferns are of interest to botanists because they reveal much about the nature of the early plants that were the forerunners of seed plants, the plants that play such an important role in man's economic and aesthetic existence.

Occurrence The geographic distribution of ferns is worldwide from the tropics to the subarctic; however, ferns are more common and diverse in tropical and subtropical regions, where many are epiphytic and where some may form stands of forest trees. Over 435 species of ferns have been found on a single mountain in Borneo. On the South Pacific island of Guam, approximately one fifth of all species of vascular plants are ferns; in contrast, only one fiftieth of the species in California are ferns. This has been interpreted as meaning that ferns had their evolutionary beginnings in the Australasian region of the world. Approximately 50 per cent of all living genera are restricted (endemic) to the Indo–Malayan–South Pacific area and 40 per cent to Central and South America and the Caribbean area. Most of the remaining genera of ferns are either cosmopolitan or pantropical.

Fig. 40-2 Clump of *Psilotum*, with sporangia, growing epiphytically on a cypress tree trunk in the Everglades. *(Courtesy Carolina Biological Supply Company.)*

Fig. 40-3 Closeup view of the water fern *Marsilea vestita* looking down on plants in a shallow pool. Note petioles below water and leaflets floating on the surface. Arrow points to a sporocarp. *(Courtesy CCM: General Biological, Inc., Chicago.)*

Fig. 40-4 Pressed leaves of five different ferns. *(Courtesy Carolina Biological Supply Company.)*

The whisk fern *(Psilotum)* is a tropical and subtropical plant that grows in the United States in Arizona, Texas, Louisiana, Florida, Georgia, and South Carolina. It grows either epiphytically (Fig. 40-2) or in humus-rich soil. One of the water ferns, *Marsilea* (Fig. 40-3), is worldwide in distribution and grows in the Pacific and southern regions of the United States. It is amphibious in the sense that it grows in shallow ponds and ditches but can survive if the water level falls, so long as the soil remains wet or moist.

Most of the common ferns of the temperate zone and most of the ferns in cultivation are members of the large family Polypodiaceae (order Filicales), and the majority of these genera range into the tropics. The most common habitat is moist, mesic woodlands (Fig. 40-1).

Following is a list of some common habitats along with common, illustrative ferns, many of which grow in other habitats as well: (1) Floating on ponds *(Azolla,* mosquito or water fern). (2) Rich, moist woods (*Botrychium virginianum,* grapefern or rattlesnake fern; *Osmunda cinnamonea,* cinnamon fern; *Onoclea sensibilis,* sensitive fern; *Adiantum pedatum,* maidenhair fern; and *Polystichum acrostichoides,* Christmas fern). (3) Dry woods (*Dennstaedtia punctilobula,* hay-scented fern). (4) Old fields and secondary woods (*Pteridium aquilinum,* bracken; *Asplenium platyneuron,* ebony spleenwort). (5) Mossy boulders and rock crevices

(*Asplenium rhizophyllum,* walking fern). (6) Epiphytically on trees (*Polypodium polypodioides,* resurrection fern).

Vegetative features   Discussed in this section are the vegetative or non-reproductive features of what is commonly thought of as the fern plant: the mature, diploid, conspicuous, dominant, perennial, sporophytic plant. The gametophytic plant and early sporophyte development, as well as spore formation, are discussed in the section dealing with sexual reproduction for the reasons stated previously (see lycopods, p. 301).

Ferns have a remarkable range in size and complexity—from the small floating aquatic *Salvinia* and *Azolla,* less than 2 cm in length, to the tall tree ferns *Cyathia* and *Dicksonia,* which can attain a height of over 60 ft; however, most ferns range up to but a few feet in height, and this height is accounted for primarily by their leaves. The climbing fern *Lygodium* has leaves up to 100 ft in length and in this respect it is a unique plant.

The macrophyllous leaf, often called a frond, is the dominant organ of most ferns. The leaves have many forms (Fig. 40-4) and those of most ferns are curled in the bud and uncurl during their rapid expansion to maturity, a condition known as circinate vernation. The leaves of some ferns are the largest and most complex in plants. The broad, feathery (pinnately compound) leaves of tree ferns may be over 15 ft long. The relatively narrow, perennial leaf of the climbing fern, which has continuous apical growth and may reach a length of nearly 100 ft, has pinnately dissected leaves that are subdivided four times. The ultimate lobe of a fern leaf is called a pinnule, and the leaves of many ferns have hundreds of pinnules. The leaves of some ferns are annual, as in *Ophioglossum* and *Botrychium,* which usually elevate from their short, fleshy, subterranean stems a single leaf each growing season. The clustered leaves of such ferns as *Osmunda* and *Athyrium* die back at the end of each growing season in temperate regions. A new cluster of leaves is produced at the apex of the rhizome at the beginning of each growing season. Such ferns as *Polystichum acrostichoides* (Christmas fern) have numerous, clustered, evergreen leaves ascending from the rhizome apex, and petiole bases remain alive for one to several years after the aboveground parts of the leaves die.

Leaves are absent in *Psilotum.* Although the leaves of most ferns are compound, some are simple, as in the adder's tongue fern *Ophioglossum,* the polypody fern *Polypodium lycopodioides,* the walking fern *Asplenium rhizophyllum,* and the water fern *Salvinia.* Although most other ferns have compound leaves with pinnately arranged pinnules, the water fern *Marsilea quadrifolia* has palmately arranged pinnules or leaflets and thus has a leaf resembling a four-leaved clover. Leaf venation is usually dichotomous but may be reticulate, the mesophyll often is divided into a more compact palisade layer and a spongy layer with large air spaces, and the guard cells surrounding leaf stomata are usually the only epidermal cells with chloroplasts.

Stems range in appearance from very delicate, much branched and superficial (represented by *Azolla*); long, thin, wiry, horizontal, and subterranean *(Marsilea)*; small, short, fleshy, erect, and subterranean (and with an endophytic fungus) *(Ophioglossum)*; subterranean rhizomes (with rhizoids and an endophytic fungus) that are stubby and much branched and from which arise thin, green, dichotomously branched, shrubby, aerial stem systems 1 ft or more in height *(Psilotum)*; rather massive, horizontal rhizomes *(Polystichum)*; rather massive erect or ascending stems *(Osmunda)*; to the erect trunks of tree ferns *(Cyathea).*

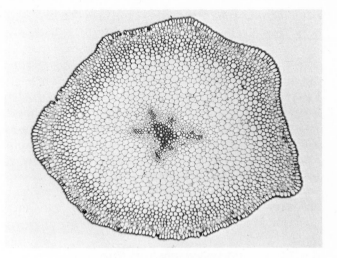

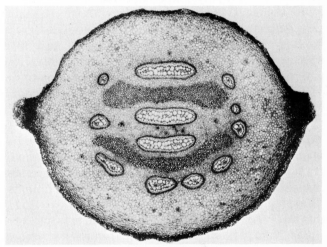

All roots except the ephemeral primary roots are adventitious, and most fern rhizomes are densely covered with these thin, dark, wiry roots that arise from internal stem tissue near the bases of leaves. The roots of some fern genera like *Ophioglossum* and *Botrychium* are fleshy and have a symbiotic, mycorrhizal fungus in their cortical cells (as do their stems). *Salvinia* has no adventitious roots and the mature plant is rootless. *Psilotum* and *Tmesipteris* never form any roots, but their rhizomes do have rhizoids.

Each of the three vegetative organs (root, stem, and leaf) of almost all ferns originates ontogenetically through the activity of a single apical cell. The root is protostelic throughout its life. The stems of some ferns are protostelic in juvenile stages but in mature or adult stages are siphonostelic. This ontogenetic change from protostelic to siphonostelic is used as evidence that "ontogeny recapitulates phylogeny"; for the fossil record indicates that the siphonostele evolved from the protostele. The stems of such ferns as the climbing fern *Lygodium* and *Psilotum* (Fig. 40-5) retain the protostelic condition throughout life, as do the roots of ferns. One to a few large leaf traces pass into the petioles of leaves as vascular bundles. Fern xylem ordinarily contains tracheids only, but vessel elements occur in the water fern *Marsilea* and the bracken fern *Pteridium aquilinum*, which has a complex stele (Fig. 40-6).

Most ferns have large numbers of chromosomes in their nuclei—often hundreds. Each diploid sporophytic cell of a tropical species of *Ophioglossum* has over 1,000 chromosomes, the largest number known for any plant.

Asexual reproduction   As in lycopods and horsetails, asexual reproduction in ferns commonly occurs through extensive and branching rhizomes. Multiplication is accomplished after death of old parts of rhizomes at points of branching— separate plants are then established. This can be called vegetative reproduction because it happens simply as a result of apical vegetative growth and posterior death of vegetative parts, and no specialized reproductive structures are involved. Occasionally, circles of fern plants (like the "fairy rings" of mushroom basidiocarps) are found in nature. They result from the type of growth and reproduction described above.

The walking fern *Asplenium rhizophyllum* has an unusual method of asexual reproduction. This fern has leaves with simple, entire, lanceolate, arching blades with long attenuate tips that root and produce new plantlets, a method of asexual reproduction similar to the production of new plantlets at the tips of arching, specialized branches called runners in the flowering plant strawberry; but in the walking fern, plantlets are produced at the tips of ordinary vegetative leaves. The roots of a few ferns, like *Ophioglossum*, produce adventitious buds that develop into new plants; as a result, extensive colonies can form.

Sexual reproduction in *Psilotum*   *Psilotum nudum*, which is easily grown in greenhouses, is used to represent a simple or primitive form of fern life. Sporangia are borne along the upright, green, aerial stems of *Psilotum* on very short stalks or branches (Figs. 40-2, 40-7), each of which contains a single vascular bundle that divides at the base of the globose, three-lobed and three-chambered sporangium into three vascular bundles. It is possible that this three-parted sporangium evolved from a plant, no longer in existence, which had three separate sporangia on a stalk. The sporangium is subtended by two scalelike emergences (enations). As in lycopods and horsetails, and also in some other ferns (Ophioglossales and

Fig. 40-7   Closeup view of aerial, dichotomously branched stems of *Psilotum* bearing sporangia. *(Courtesy Carolina Biological Supply Company.)*

Marattiales) and in all seed plants, sporangia develop in what is known as a eusporangiate (as opposed to leptosporangiate) manner. In eusporangiate development, the sporangial wall develops from superficial cells and the sporogenous tissue develops from internal cells.

Each of the three chambers of a mature sporangium contains a large number of colorless, kidney-shaped spores (meiospores) surrounded by wall tissue several cells in thickness. *Psilotum* is homosporous. The sporangium cracks open (dehisces) apically, exposing the spores to the air for dissemination.

Spores are slow to germinate and grow into gametophytes, which are small, subterranean, brownish, cylindrical (radially symmetrical), dichotomously branching, and with rhizoids. The gametophyte has an endophytic fungus and a saprobic (saprophytic) mode of nutrition. In all these ways the gametophyte of *Psilotum* resembles the young sporophytic rhizome of *Psilotum*. Some other ferns, such as *Tmesipteris, Ophioglossum, Botrychium, Stromatopteris,* and some species of *Schizaea,* have gametophytes similar to those of *Psilotum*.

Gametophytes are bisexual and bear antheridia and archegonia among the rhizoids around the cylindrical gametophyte. Antheridia are hemispherical, stick out from the surface of the gametophyte, and have a single layer of jacket or wall cells enclosing several dozen coiled, multiflagellate sperms similar to those of other ferns and to those of *Equisetum* and *Isoetes*. The venter of the archegonium is embedded in gametophytic tissue, and only the short necks protrude.

After fertilization, the zygote develops into a two-parted embryo (much as in bryophytes). The inner part is the foot. The outer part of the embryo—the primary stem—further develops, ruptures the calyptra (expanded archegonial wall), and becomes a young, dichotomously branching rhizome bearing rhizoids and with an endophytic fungus. This young sporophytic plant is still attached to the gametophyte, and the two look very much alike. In time, some of the tips of the young rhizome grow upward and develop into the green, aerial stems characteristic of the mature *Psilotum* plant (sporophyte). By this time the gametophyte has disintegrated.

As in lycopods and horsetails, *Psilotum* has a diplo-haplontic type of sexual life cycle with heteromorphic alternating generations; however, the striking resemblance between the gametophyte and the very young sporophyte should be noted again. Also, occasional gametophytes containing centrally located tracheids have been found. It may be said, then, that *Psilotum* comes closer than any other vascular plant to having isomorphic sporophytes and gametophytes, a condition found in a number of algal and a few fungal genera.

Sexual reproduction in typical ferns   Most ferns are polypodiaceous-like ferns of the large order Filicales. They are homosporous and produce their sporangia, which of course are meiosporangia, on large sporophylls. Sporophylls of most genera look like vegetative leaves; however; the sporophyll of *Onoclea* is very different from its vegetative leaf. Also, the sporangia of the Christmas fern *Polystichum acrostichoides* are restricted to the apical 25 or so pinnules (Fig. 40-4, second from left), and these are smaller than the apical pinnules of vegetative leaves.

Each sporophyll produces large numbers of sporangia on the edges or margin, as in *Pteridium,* or more commonly on the lower (abaxial) surface, as in *Polypodium*. Sporangia usually are clustered into sori, as in *Dryopteris* and *Polystichum,* but in such genera as *Adiantum* and *Pteris* sporangia occur in marginal rows. In the latter two genera, the margin of the pinnule is curled or rolled over the

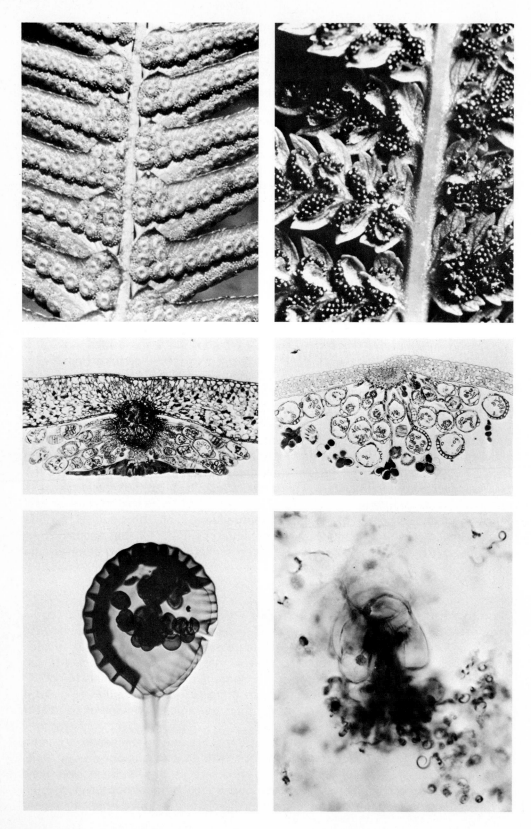

328

Fig. 40-8 (opposite, top row)   Closeup views of the under sides of sporophylls of two typical ferns. Left: Sori of sporangia with centrally attached indusia. Right: Sori with laterally attached indusia. *(Courtesy Carolina Biological Supply Company.)*

Fig 40-9 (middle row)   Stained cross sections of sporangial pinnules showing longitudinal sections of sori. Left: Centrally attached indusium. Right: Naked (without indusium). *(Photomicrographs courtesy Ripon Microslides Laboratory.)*

Fig. 40-10 (bottom left)   Stained sporangium of a typical fern containing some remaining spores. *(Photomicrograph courtesy Carolina Biological Supply Company.)*

Fig. 40-11 (bottom right)   Stained whole mount of a portion of a mature prothallus showing coiled sperms entering an opened archegonium. *(Photomicrograph courtesy Carolina Biological Supply Company.)*

sporangia, providing a false indusium, which protects developing sporangia. Abaxial sori may be naked, as in *Polypodium* (Fig. 40-9, right), or more commonly covered by a special membranous structure called an indusium (Figs. 40-8, 40-9, left). The sori of most ferns are round, linear, or kidney shaped, and they usually lie on or at the tips of veins.

Sporangia develop in a leptosporangiate manner, which means that the entire sporangium develops from an outer or superficial cell. (Filicales, Marsileales, and Salviniales are the only known leptosporangiate vascular plants.) Prior to meiosis, the sporangium consists of a thin, multicellular stalk at the apex of which is an enlarged portion with a wall one cell in thickness and with 12–16 centrally located sporocytes (spore mother cells or sporogenous cells) surrounded by a tapetum two cells in thickness. During meiosis and spore formation, the tapetum disintegrates and contributes nutriments to the developing meiospores. The mature spore sac is spheroidal or ellipsoidal and slightly flattened. The wall cells are thin walled except for an incomplete, vertical row called the annulus, which has its walls thickened on the inner tangential and radial surfaces only. The annulus extends from the top of the sporangium stalk (at the base of the spore sac) most of the way around the spore sac, where between the last cell of the annulus and the base of the spore sac are a few special thin-walled cells called lip cells (Fig. 40-10). The annulus and lip cells play important roles in the active liberation of spores. As spores mature, they (and their sporangia) change in color from light green to dark brown or black owing to the development of dark spore walls. When spores mature, indusia dry and shrivel up or revolute leaf margins unroll slightly and expose mature sporangia to a drier atmosphere.

Sporangial dehiscence and active propulsion of spores into the air depends on the evaporation of water through the thin outer walls of the cells of the annulus. Tension is established as water is lost from the annulus and, in time, this results in a breaking open of the sporangium between lip wall cells and on around between outer wall cells. Some spores are carried back with the upper part of the sporangium as the annulus bends back, and these spores are ejected when the annulus snaps back into its original position (Fig. 40-10).

A spore germinates readily on moist soil or other suitable substratum and produces a short, green filament several cells in length and with rhizoids. This rapidly develops into a parenchymatous, spatulate, dorsiventral gametophyte

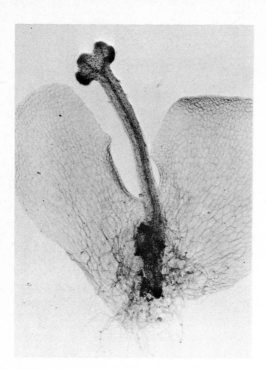

Fig. 40-12   Ventral view of a stained fern prothallus with a young sporophyte attached. *(Photomicrograph courtesy Ripon Microslides Laboratory.)*

(prothallus), one cell in thickness, with an apical cell and with rhizoids arising from the lower surface. Ordinarily, within a couple of months the gametophyte has matured into a somewhat heart-shaped structure with its apical cell in an apical notch (Fig. 40-12). The mature gametophyte is delicate and small (commonly up to about 1 cm in length), and it is autotrophic, thin, and one cell in thickness except along the center, where it is several cells in thickness. Archegonia develop in this cushion of cells on the ventral surface behind the apical cell. Antheridia, some of which usually develop before the initiation of any archegonia (a condition called protandry), are formed ventrally in great numbers, often more toward the base (posterior or spore end) of the gametophyte.

Antheridia are small and superficial. The relatively small number of spermatogenous cells are surrounded by only three wall cells. There is a stout, ring-shaped basal cell, a thin middle ring cell, and an apical cap cell, which is thin and circular in surface view. This cap wall cell pops off at the time of sperm liberation. The motile sperm of a fern is coiled and swims in a spiral path. It has a spiral nucleus and basal body from which arise many whiplash flagella, located toward the front end of the sperm.

Only the neck of an archegonium protrudes below the surface of its prothallus. The neck is composed of four tiers of wall cells surrounding a binucleate neck canal cell, above which is a ventral canal cell and then the egg. When the archegonium is mature, its canal cells disintegrate, and when this ripe archegonium is surrounded externally with water, the tiers of neck wall cells spread apart apically and provide ready access for sperms to the egg (Fig. 40-11). Sperms are chemically attracted to the open archegonium, and one of the attractants is known to be malic acid.

After fertilization, the zygote develops into a four-part embryo, and the embryo within the calyptra is said to have four quadrants: foot, stem, primary leaf (cotyledon), and root (radicle). As development continues, the radicle penetrates the calyptra and grows to the soil. The cotyledon grows out and up into the air, usually emerging through the apical notch of the prothallus (Fig. 40-12), and the embryonic stem grows and produces more juvenile leaves. By this time the gametophyte has withered and the sporophyte is an independent plant. The first-formed leaves are much smaller and simpler in form than those of mature fern plants (sporophytes). All secondary roots arise adventitiously from the stem.

The sexual life cycle of typical ferns is like that of *Equisetum* and some species of *Lycopodium* in that there is a regular alternation between an autotrophic, diploid sporophyte and an autotrophic, haploid gametophyte. Like all pteridophytes, this is a diplo-haplontic type of sexual life cycle with heteromorphic alternating generations, the sporophyte of which is large, conspicuous, and vascularized and the gametophyte of which is small, inconspicuous, and nonvascularized. In this cycle, syngamy and meiosis are normally the events that trigger the change from gametophyte to sporophyte and vice versa; however, occasionally sporophytes develop from gametophytes without syngamy (this is known as apogamy) and gametophytes develop from sporophytes without meiosis and not from spores (a process called apospory). It has been shown for a few ferns that when they display apogamy and apospory, the gametophyte and the sporophyte have the same number of chromosomes—both are either haploid or diploid.

Sexual reproduction in *Marsilea* *Marsilea* and the other four genera of water ferns are heterosporous, like the lycopods *Selaginella* and *Isoetes. Marsilea* is representative of water ferns. It produces both its microsporangia and megasporangia together in highly specialized structures called sporocarps, which arise on lateral branches of petioles (Fig. 40-3). A sporocarp, which is somewhat bean shaped and often about 1 cm in length, is a highly modified pinnule. The mature sporocarp is brown and very hard and nutlike. It can be air dried and remain viable for over a year.

A sporocarp is bilaterally symmetrical and each lateral half has a row of elongate sori containing both megasporangia and microsporangia surrounded by an indusium. After meiosis, the 32–64 young microspores all mature and become functional, but only one of the young megaspores enlarges and becomes functional, the others disintegrating. The megaspore is a great deal larger than the microspore.

When the hard outer coat of the sporocarp is weakened and water is imbibed, the swelling contents force apart the sporocarp wall, from which emerges a long gelatinous ring or horn bearing the two rows of sori (Fig. 40-13). After several hours, the sporangial walls and indusia gelatinize and passively release the spores into the surrounding water. Each tiny microspore is essentially spherical. The large, ovoid or ellipsoidal megaspore has a protuberance at one end.

The gametophytes now begin development and they develop very rapidly, in less than 1 day. The male gametophyte is somewhat like those of *Selaginella* and *Isoetes*. It consists of only two small antheridia and a single vegetative cell, the prothallial cell. At maturity, the antheridia protrude from the cracked open microspore wall, the prothallial cell and the antheridial wall cells disintegrate, and the large, coiled multiflagellate sperms are released (Fig. 40-14).

The protuberance at one end of the megaspore becomes cellular. As this small amount of vegetative or prothallial tissue enlarges, the megaspore wall is ruptursd and the single, apical, sunken archegonium is exposed. The mature female game-

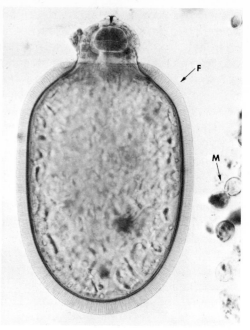

Fig. 40-13 Closeup view of a germinated sporocarp of *Marsilea* with its two rows of sori on a gelatinous ring. Arrow points to sporocarp wall. *(Courtesy Carolina Biological Supply Company.)*

Fig. 40-14 Stained female (F) and male (M) gametophytes of *Marsilea*. Males are liberating sperms. *(Photomicrograph courtesy Carolina Biological Supply Company.)*

tophyte, mostly within the megaspore wall, is surrounded by a gelatinous envelope having a watery, funnel-shaped portion extending up from the archegonium and out to the surrounding water. Sperms are attracted to and swim through this watery portion of the gelatinous envelope to the archegonium.

After an egg is fertilized by a sperm, the zygote immediately starts its development into a four-part embryo (foot, stem, primary leaf or cotyledon, and root or radicle). This embryonic sporophyte is surrounded by enlarged gametophytic tissue, the calyptra, which sends out rhizoids. After several days of growth, the radicle and cotyledon break out of the calyptra and initiate an independent life for the juvenile sporophyte. As in *Selaginella* and *Isoetes*, the germling sporophyte, attached to the female gametophyte, still with its old megaspore wall, resembles a tiny seedling.

The gametophytic phase of the alternating sexual generations of *Marsilea* is like that of *Selaginella* and *Isoetes* in that the gametophytic phase consists of two "plants," the male gametophyte and the female gametophyte. One of the most interesting features of the sexual life of water ferns is the retention of the female gametophyte within the megaspore wall, a condition found in all seed plants and also in *Selaginella* and *Isoetes*.

Project

I. **Macroscopic study of a variety of ferns** (mature sporophytes)

Study the ferns on demonstration, looking for differences in stems (e.g., rhizomatous vs. erect), vegetative leaves (e.g., simple vs. compound), sporophylls (e.g., autotrophic vs. not autotrophic), position of sporangia (e.g., marginal vs. superficial or not on the margin), and habitat (e.g., terrestrial vs. aquatic).

II. **A simple or primitive fern:** *Psilotum,* whisk fern

A. *Sporophyte*
  1. Macroscopic appearance. Examine a *Psilotum* plant growing in a pot. Note the photosynthetic, upright, dichotomously branched stem that bears scalelike appendages (enations). The underground part of the plant also is a dichotomously branched stem (rhizome). (Roots and leaves are lacking!)
  2. Anatomy
    a. Cross section of the aerial stem. Either make a freehand section or study a prepared slide. A freehand section stained by the phloroglucin technique (see Project 10: II.B.1) will give you a spectacular view of the xylem. What shape is the section? Identify xylem, the surrounding phloem, endodermis, and other thin-walled cortex cells, cortical sclerenchyma (supporting cells), cortical chlorenchyma (photosynthetic cells), and epidermis. How many protoxylem poles are there? Can you distinguish between protoxylem and metaxylem and determine whether the stele is exarch, mesarch, or endarch?
    b. Cross section of the rhizome. Look for the mycorrhizal fungi in the cortical cells.
  3. Sporangium
    a. Observe fresh or preserved material with sporangia at the tips of very short branches. Notice that they are associated with the tiny scalelike appendages (enations).
    b. Median longitudinal section of a sporangium (prepared slide). Identify the sporangial wall, sporogenous tissue or spores, sporangial stalk (stem), and the vascular trace to the stalk.
B. *Gametophyte*
  1. If available, study preserved gametophytes. Note the similarity in form of the gametophyte and the rhizome of the sporophyte.
  2. If available, study a cross section of a gametophyte. Find antheridia, archegonia, embryos, and mycorrhizal fungus.

III. **Typical homosporous ferns** (polypodiaceous ferns)

A. *Gametophyte*
  1. Macroscopic appearance. Observe gametophytes (prothalli) growing prostrate and close to soil (in nature in moist, shaded places) or growing on liquid or agar culture media. A prothallus seldom gets as much as $\frac{1}{2}$ in. across. Prothalli may be found in greenhouses growing on moist pots

or damp soil throughout most of the year if fern sporophytes are in the greenhouses.

2. Culture. Directions for culturing fern gametophytes are given in Project 6, p. 41. If materials and time are available, start your own cultures.

3. Study of development. Either study your own cultures at the intervals indicated or study the provided cultures that are about $\frac{1}{2}$, 1, 2, 3, 4, 5, 6, and 8 weeks old or older.

   a. Germling. Is the first cell to emerge from the germinating spore the initial rhizoid? Does the rhizoid have chloroplasts?

   b. Later stages of vegetative growth. As they appear, find spore wall, initial rhizoid, secondary rhizoids, chloroplasts, nuclei, apical cell, apical notch, and marginal gland cells.

   c. Sexual reproduction

      (1) Living material, whole mounts. As the prothallia mature, sex organs will form—usually the antheridia at first and then archegonia along with other antheridia. Archegonia can be recognized after fertilization of the egg by their brownish color. If you remove a mature gametophyte from an agar culture dish and place it ventral side up in a drop of water on a glass slide, you should be able to see the antheridia discharge their sperms and the archegonium neck open. When you see many sperms swimming in the mount, put on a cover slip and with high dry optics look for sperms swimming down the neck of an archegonium. (You may be provided with a prepared slide of a prothallium fixed at this stage.)

      (2) Sperms. Mount a drop containing swimming sperms and observe the mode of swimming. Stain them in order to see the numerous whiplash flagella and the spiral nucleus of each sperm. The simplest method is to kill, fix, and stain the cells in one operation by adding iodine solution. (Refer to Project 11, p. 62, if you want additional directions.)

      (3) Antheridium in longitudinal section (prepared slide). Find basal cell, ring cell, cap cell, and spermatogenous cells.

      (4) Archegonium in longitudinal section (prepared slide). Find neck (composed of neck wall cells and neck canal cells) and venter (composed of venter wall cells, ventral canal cell, and egg).

B. *Sporophyte*

   1. Embryo and early development

      a. Embryo. Look at living or preserved gametophytes for embryos inside old archegonia. Study a prepared slide (whole mount) of a gametophyte with its embryonic sporophyte. Identify the foot, root, stem, and leaf quadrants or segments of the embryo.

      b. Attached juvenile sporophyte. Study living or preserved material and a prepared slide of a young sporophyte still attached to the gametophyte. From which side of a gametophyte does the embryonic root, stem, and leaf emerge? Notice that the juvenile leaf is much smaller and of a different form than a mature leaf.

   2. Mature sporophyte

      a. Rhizome in longitudinal section. Make a longitudinal section of a rhizome. Be sure to include the stem apex and also include leaf bases.

(Christmas fern, *Polystichum acrostichoides* is excellent for this study.) Observe the origin of adventitious roots and of leaves and old leaf bases on the rhizome. Find "fiddleheads" (uncoiled leaves) at the apex of the stem. How many veins enter the pinnately compound leaf?

b. Stem in cross section. If suitable material is available, make thin cross sections of stems, mount them in water, stain by the phloroglucin technique (see Project 10: II.B.1), and study them. Also study a prepared slide and identify supporting tissue, cortical tissue, endodermis, vascular tissue (with its xylem and phloem), leaf gap, and leaf trace. Is the stele a protostele, siphonstele, or dictyostele? Can you distinguish between protoxylem and metaxylem and determine whether the stele is exarch, mesarch, or endarch?

c. Leaf
   (1) Study a leaf in cross section showing upper epidermis, palisade mesophyll, spongy mesophyll, ordinary lower epidermal cells, guard cells, stomata, and veins (with xylem and phloem).
   (2) Pull off a small patch of the lower epidermis and mount it in a drop of water. Do the same for the upper epidermis. Add cover slips and study from high dry. (Surface views of the mesophyll as well as the epidermal layers can be seen.)

d. Sorus
   (1) Living or preserved material. Study a spore-bearing leaflet, and observe details of structure and location of sori. Study the relation of the sori to the veins. (This can often be done best by holding the leaf up to a strong light. Pull or scrape off the sporangia from a sorus and note the position of attachment.)
   (2) Sorus in vertical section (prepared slide). Study a cross section of a leaf showing a vertical section of a sorus. Note the attachment of the sporangia and, if present, the indusium. (Some ferns have naked sori and others have either a true or false indusium.)

e. Sporangium
   (1) Living or preserved material. Scrape into a drop of water on a slide the sporangia of one or more sori. Examine both immature and opened sporangia, and, using high dry, find stalk cells, annulus, lip cells, and spores (meiospores).
   (2) Living material. Observe sporangia open and forcibly discharge spores by mounting nearly mature sporangia in glycerine, which acts as a drying agent. Also, spore discharge into air is easily observed in species lacking an indusium if a freshly collected sporophyll with mature but unopened sporangia is observed with reflected light using low power of a dissecting microscope. The heat of the lamp causes the sporangia to dry and discharge their spores. This is really fun to watch!

IV. **An advanced, heterosporous fern:** *Marsilea,* water fern

A. *Sporophyte*
   1. Macroscopic appearance. Examine a plant growing in wet soil or study preserved or herbarium material. Note its form and identify sporocarps

arising from short branches on the long petioles of compound leaves. Describe a leaf of *Marsilea*. Adventitious roots arise from the horizontal rhizome.

2. Emergence of sori from sporocarps. With a strong needle pierce one end of a number of sporocarps and place them in water, preferably fresh lake water or spring water in a petri dish. After about 1 hour examine a germinating sporocarp with very low power and observe the splitting of the sporocarp and the emergence of a gelatinous ring bearing several clusters (sori) of sporangia. Note differences in the sporangia and the meiospores that they contain. How long does it take for all of the sori to emerge?

3. Sporangia (heterosporangia). Find megaspores in megasporangia and microspores in microsporangia.

B. *Gametophytes*

1. Development. About 2–12 hours after the sporocarps are put in water, microspores and megaspores (each with a gelatinous sheath) are freed and the development of microgametophytes and megagametophytes is well under way. What changes occur that you can observe during and after discharge? Gametophytes are mature in 12–16 hours.

2. Megagametophyte and fertilization. Examine a mature magegametophyte, noting the structure and position of the archegonium. Look for sperms swimming to the neck of an archegonium prior to fertilization (syngamy).

V. Fossil ferns

Study the demonstration materials.

Project **41**   Cycads

Contents

Introduction

Taxonomy   Cycads are plants of the group technically known as Cycadophyta or Cycadales. There are 9 genera and approximately 100 species in this small but distinctive group of plants.

Table 18-1 (p. 132) summarizes the various ways of classifying cycads: cycads, *Ginkgo*, conifers, and the *Gnetum–Ephedra–Welwitschia* group are the gymnosperms. They (the gymnosperms) and the flowering plants (angiosperms) are the seed plants (spermatophytes or phanerogams). Cycads and other gymnosperms along with angiosperms and ferns are the megaphyllous vascular plants, and like all vascular plants they are embryophytes and eukaryotes.

Cycads are like all the plants in the green-plant evolutionary line (green algae and stoneworts, bryophytes, and vascular plants) in having (1) similar photosynthetic pigments in their plastids, (2) storage of starch in plastids, (3) motile cells (sperms only in cycads and *Ginkgo*, but no motile cells at all in any of the other gymnosperms or in any angiosperms) with only the whiplash type of flagellation, and (4) cellulosic cell walls also containing pectic substances. In addition, cycads and other embryophytes have alternating diploid and haploid phases or generations, structurally are composed of tissues (which in vascular plants are further organized into organs), and are oogamous (although most seed plants lack flagellated sperms and have a highly specialized and reduced type of oogamy).

Cycads and other gymnosperms have a number of features in common with pteridophytes: (1) They have a diplo-haplontic type of life cycle, and the sporophyte is the conspicuous or dominant phase of the alternating heteromorphic generations; however, in gymnosperms the gametophytes are completely dependent (parasitic) on the sporophyte. (2) They have multicellular archegonia, but these are highly reduced in gymnosperms, and no gymnosperms have clearly defined antheridia. (3) They have multicellular sporangia (meiosporangia); however, like only some pteridophytes, all gymnosperms are heterosporous. (4) Their embryos are protected by female gametophytic tissue; however, the gymnosperm embryo is additionally protected by female sporophytic tissue (seed coat). (5) They have conductive tissue (xylem and phloem) in a vascular system, but unlike nearly all pteridophytes, gymnosperms produce secondary vascular tissue. (6) They (their sporophytes) are differentiated into three types of vegetative parts or organs—roots, stems, and leaves. (7) Water-conducting cells of the xylem are lignified. (8) There is a cuticle on the epidermis of stems and leaves. (9) There are stomates, each with a pair of regulatory guard cells, in the epidermis. As with ferns and other pteridophytes, all the above features can be interpreted as adaptations permitting successful life on land. In addition, the protective epidermis of the roots and stems of gymnosperms usually is replaced by cork cells with suberized walls resulting from secondary (cambial) growth.

Two interdependent features strikingly distinguish cycads and other gymnosperms from ferns and other pteridophytes: pollination and seed formation. Pollination in gymnosperms, which is accomplished by wind, is the transfer of the young male gametophyte (pollen grain) to the receptive part of the female structure called the ovule.

An ovule is a megasporangium (also called nucellus) that has become overgrown with a protective layer, the integument. The integument does not quite close at one end, leaving a small hole called the micropyle. Commonly, only one megasporocyte develops in each megasporangium and, of the four spores formed by meiosis, the three closest to the micropyle degenerate soon after they are formed. The remaining megaspore develops into a megagametophyte without being discharged from the parent plant. Thus, the female gametophyte, which is contained within the enlarged megaspore wall, is parasitic, and it is completely enclosed within sporophytic tissue. The female gametophyte produces one to several archegonia after it has reached full size.

After pollination, the young male gametophyte (pollen grain) germinates in the micropyle of the ovule. The germ tube (pollen tube) grows through the nucellus (megasporangium) and eventually reaches the archegonium of the female gametophyte within the nucellus. By this time two sperm cells have formed near the tip of the pollen tube. In nonseed plants, flagellated sperms are released from antheridia into water, through which they must swim to reach and fertilize eggs. The evolution of the sperm-carrying pollen tube eliminated this aquatic phase in sexual reproduction and clearly was and still is of selective and survival advantage to the terrestrial, gymnospermous plants.

After fertilization, the seed with its three essential parts develops (1) the embryo from the zygote, (2) food-storage tissue from the female gametophyte, and (3) the hardened protective covering (seed coat) from the integument. Thus, the seed is a combination of two sporophytic generations and one gametophytic generation: the diploid seed coat derives from the integument of the old sporophyte, the food-storage or nutritive tissue develops directly from the haploid female gametophyte, and the embryo is the incipient new sporophyte. The seed is

Fig. 41-1 *Cycas revoluta* in cultivation. Arrows point to older portions of the stem. *(Courtesy William C. Dickison.)*

Fig. 41-2 Photograph of a model of an entire plant of *Zamia floridana* bearing a female strobilus. *(Courtesy CCM: General Biological, Inc., Chicago.)*

eventually detached from its parent plant and ultimately germinates and grows into a new plant (sporophyte).

There appear to be two major evolutionary lines or phyletic groups in these more primitive of the pollinating and seed-bearing plants, the gymnosperms. Both of these lines are traced back through the fossil record to the Paleozoic Era (Table 18-2, p. 134). (1) The cycadophyte line or phyletic group includes gymnospermous seed plants with somewhat fernlike (pinnately compound) leaves (Fig. 41-1), relatively short trunks (stems) that are usually unbranched, large pith and cortex regions in the stem, and relatively little secondary growth (through cambial activity). The vast majority of cycadophytes are extinct, including the two extinct orders Cycadofilicales (seed ferns) and Bennettitales. The modern cycads (Cycadales) are the sole survivors in this cycadophyte evolutionary line (Fig. 41-2). (2) The coniferophyte line or phyletic group includes gymnospermous seed plants with simple and often scalelike or needle-like leaves, tall and often much-branched trunks, small pith and cortex regions in the stem, and typically with a large amount of secondary xylem. In addition to the extinct order Cordaitales, coniferophytes include *Ginkgo biloba* and fossil Ginkgoales, living and fossil conifers, and the Gnetales (*Gnetum, Ephedra,* and *Welwitschia.*)

Cycads, and also the extinct Bennettitales, are thought by some botanists to have evolved from an extinct group of seed plants with fernlike foliage called seed ferns (pteridosperms or Cycadofilicales), but there is no compelling evidence that this is true. Fossils of seed ferns date back to carboniferous times in the Paleozoic

Era, and they were common in the Mesozoic Era along with the other cycadophytes, Bennettitales, and early members of the Cycadales. Living or extant genera are *Cycas, Zamia, Dioon, Ceratozamia, Microcycas, Bowenia, Macrozamia, Stangeria,* and *Encephalartos*.

Importance   Cycads have large, attractive, palmlike leaves and are commonly used in landscape gardening in Southern California, Louisiana, and Florida, where they are hardy outdoors. The commonest cultivated cycad is the sago palm (*Cycas revoluta*) and it is also grown as a house plant. The asiatic *Cycas circinalis* is the source of cycas gum, which is of slight commercial importance. *Zamia floridana* is a lesser commercial source of starch. The seeds of *Microcycas* in western Cuba are used as bottle corks and for this reason the plant is called "palma corcha".

Occurrence   All cycads are terrestrial and all are confined to limited areas of the tropics and subtropics. Rarely if ever do they form an extensive, conspicuous, or dominant feature of the landscape or vegetation. Four of the nine genera of cycads occur in the western hemisphere: *Microcycas* is endemic to Cuba; *Ceratozamia* and *Dioon* are endemic to Mexico; and *Zamia*, which is the only cycad native to the United States, occurs in southern Florida, the West Indies, Mexico, Central America, and northern and western South America. *Cycas* lives in Australia, India, China, southern Japan, Madagascar, and certain Pacific Islands. *Bowenia* and *Macrozamia* occur only in Australia, and *Stangeria* and *Encephalartos* only in Africa.

Present-day cycads are a remnant of a large, diversified cycad flora that extended widely over much of the earth during the Mesozoic Era. Ancient cycads reached their peak of development during the age of giant dinosaurs, and herbivorous dinosaurs probably used cycads as a source of food. Because so few cycads have survived and because of their now limited and isolated occurrence, today's cycads have been referred to as living fossils. Indeed, it is predicted that cycads will become extinct except for the intervention of man.

Vegetative features   The cycad plant (sporophyte) is evergreen and has a columnar, unbranched trunk with a crown of large, pinnately compound leaves (Figs. 41-1, 41-2). It resembles both a fern plant and the flowering plant called palm. Cycads range in size from the short, tuberous stemmed *Zamia floridana* but 1 ft or so in height to the tall tree *Macrozamia hopei*, which may reach 60 ft in height. Most cycads are extremely slow-growing plants. The oldest individuals are estimated to be over 1,000 years old.

The stems of cycads are covered with closely spaced leaf scars or are covered with persistent leaf bases. At the crown or apex of the stem is a cluster of pinnately compound leaves, each often about 3 ft long, arranged in a tight spiral. The dark green and leathery leaflets of *Cycas* exhibit circinate vernation, as in most ferns, but this is not characteristic of cycads. The outer walls of leaflets are very thick and cutinized. Stomata are sunken and are present on the lower surface only (Fig. 41-3). The leaflets of *Cycas* have but a single large midvein, but other cycads have dichotomously branched lateral veins, as in many ferns. The primary root of cycads develops into a prominent taproot (Fig. 41-2) that produces smaller secondary roots. In addition, several adventitious roots develop from the base of the stem. Branching roots of cycads may grow up above ground, and bacteria and the blue-

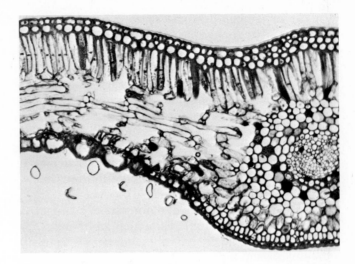

Fig. 41-3 Portion of a stained cross section of a leaflet of *Cycas* showing sunken stomata with overarching epidermal cells on the lower side and a multiple epidermis on the upper side. *(Photomicrograph courtesy Carolina Biological Supply Company.)*

green alga *Anabaena* are found in the cortex of nodules of these roots. *Anabaena* fixes gaseous nitrogen.

The fleshy nature of the mature root is due largely to the thick cortex, which increases in size as the root matures, and also to the many-layered pericycle, which is the region of parenchyma cells just inside the cortex. The innermost layer of cortex cells is differentiated and suberized and is called the endodermis. A vascular cambium has its origin in the procambial parenchyma cells between the areas of primary xylem and phloem, which like other primary tissues originate from a large multicellular apical meristem. A cork cambium develops in older roots, either in the pericycle or in the outer part of the cortex. Unlike those of other gymnosperms, the cambia of cycads produce sparse secondary tissue.

Between the large pith and cortex of cycad stems is a narrow cylinder of vascular tissue interrupted by numerous leaf gaps. The phloem is toward the outside and the cycad stem is said to have an ectophloic siphonostele. The phloem is composed of food-conducting sieve elements and also phloem parenchyma and fiber cells. The xylem contains very long water-conducting tracheids (largely scalariform-pitted tracheids), as well as wood parenchyma cells and parenchymatous wood rays. As in the root, the vascular cambium of the stem develops relatively little secondary xylem and phloem. The bulk of the stem is cortex and pith. These are food-storage areas and also abound with mucilage or gum canals. Also, the cortex is traversed by numerous leaf traces.

Asexual reproduction   In such species as *Cycas revoluta*, lateral buds developed in the axils of persistent leaf bases may become detached. These detached buds, after sprouting adventitious roots, grow into new plants.

Sexual reproduction   The features of sexual reproduction fundamental for all gymnosperms are given in the section dealing with taxonomy (p. 338), and it is well to remember that the most distinctive features are pollination and seed formation. The following account describes the aspects of male and female meiospore formation, male and female gametophyte development, syngamy, embryo and seed formation, and seed germination that characterize the cycads. Some of these features are shared with other gymnosperms.

All cycads are dioecious, which means that there are both male individuals and female individuals; thus, a single strobilus consists of only male or female sporophylls, and the male and female strobili occur on different plants. The large strobili of cycads are the largest of any plants. The female strobilus or cone of *Macrozamia denisoni* may reach 2 ft in length, 1 ft in diameter at the base, and weigh 70 lb.

Strobili are borne apically on the upright stem among the terminal cluster of vegetative leaves (Figs. 41-2, 41-4, 41-5). The female strobilus of *Cycas* is considered to be primitive and consists of several spirally and loosely arranged and spreading female sporophylls, which are thick, leathery, and somewhat leaflike in appearance. The apical part of the female sporophyll of *Cycas* is flattened and with pinnate lobes or a serrate margin. Below this bladelike region are 4–8 large ovules in two rows along the margin. The female strobilus of most other cycads, such as *Zamia*, is a compact cone (Fig. 41-4). The female sporophyll of *Zamia* is a woody, scalelike, peltate structure bearing only two ovules on its inner surface.

The ovule of cycads varies from $\frac{1}{2}$-2 in. in length. Ovules project straight out, with the micropylar end opposite the point of attachment of the ovule to the sporophyll. The massive integument is three-layered: the outer and inner layers are fleshy and the middle layer becomes hard or stony. The integument surrounds the remaining tissue of the ovule, the nucellus (female sporangium). One of the internal cells of the nucellus differentiates as a megasporocyte (female spore mother cell) that undergoes meiosis and forms four female meiospores in a row parallel to the long axis of the ovule. As in all gymnosperms, the three closest to the micropylar end disintegrate and the fourth, functional megaspore enlarges and has a period of free-nuclear divisions within the enlarging female spore wall. This young female gametophyte soon becomes cellular and then continues to grow, surrounded

---

Fig. 41-4 (top left)   Terminal portion of a female *Zamia* plant with its female strobilus. *(Courtesy Carolina Biological Supply Company.)*

Fig. 41-5 (top right)   Terminal portion of a male *Cycas* plant with its male strobilus. *(Courtesy Carolina Biological Supply Company.)*

Fig. 41-6 (middle row, left)   Stained cross section of a microsporophyll of *Cycas* showing numerous microsporangia or pollen sacs on the lower surface. *(Photomicrograph courtesy Carolina Biological Supply Company.)*

Fig. 41-7 (middle row, right)   Portion of a stained section of an ovule of *Zamia* showing a longitudinal section of an archegonium with its neck and huge egg. Also seen are portions of the megagametophyte, archegonial chamber, and megasporangium. *(Photomicrograph courtesy Ripon Microslides Laboratory.)*

Fig. 41-8 (bottom row)   Stained longitudinal sections showing early embryo development in *Zamia*. Left: Many free diploid nuclei at the base of an old archegonium surrounded by the female gametophyte. Right: Cellular proembryo with suspensor cells and an apical meristematic zone. *(Photomicrographs courtesy Ripon Microslides Laboratory.)*

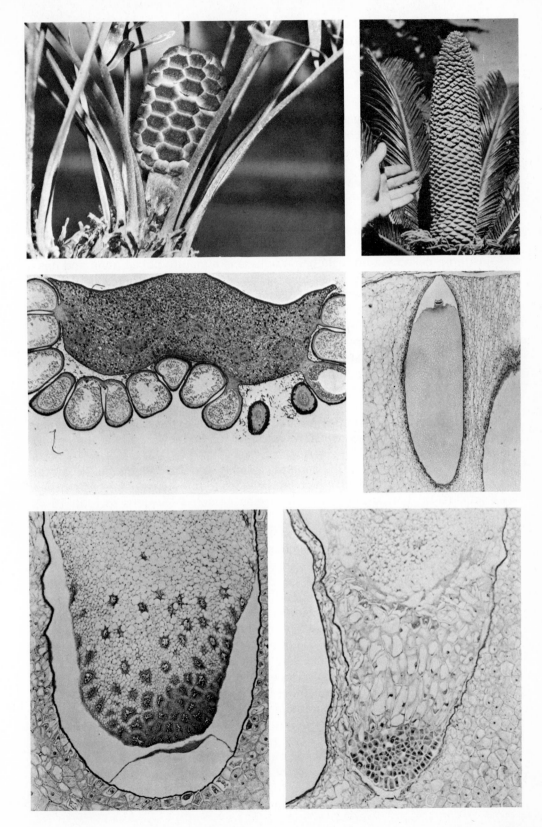

by cells of the nucellus. The nucellar jacket functions as nutritive tissue for the enlarging female gametophyte. The mature gametophyte develops three to ten highly reduced archegonia submerged at the surface of its micropylar end. Each archegonium consists of two neck cells and a huge egg, which is up to 1.5 mm in diameter (Fig. 41-7). The archegonium has a ventral canal nucleus that disintegrates prior to maturation of the archegonium.

The male strobilus in cycads is usually smaller than the female strobilus of the same species. The male strobilus (Fig. 41-5) is a compact cone consisting of many spirally arranged, thick, brownish male sporophylls, each bearing a few dozen to over 1,000 male sporangia (depending on the species) on its lower surface (Fig. 41-6), a feature reminiscent of ferns. A nearly mature sporangium (pollen sac) contains numerous tetrads of male meiospores (young pollen grains) surrounded by a nutritive tapetal layer and a sporangium wall several cells in thickness. The uninucleate spore immediately divides and forms first a small prothallial cell and then a small genetative cell. At this stage the large main cell is called the tube cell, and this three-celled young male gametophyte is a mature pollen grain and has a thick, two-layered wall, the inner layer called intine and the outer exine. At this stage the sporophylls separate, each pollen sac opens by a longitudinal slit, and the pollen grains are set free for wind dissemination.

A pollen grain blown to a female plant and into spaces between female sporophylls may lodge at an ovule's micropyle, which at this time is filled with a viscous liquid that formed at the micropylar end of the nucellus, where a space or cavity called the pollen chamber also has formed. Either the pollen grain germinates in the liquid and grows in it through the micropyle or, as the liquid dries, it contracts, thus pulling the pollen into the pollen chamber and eventually up against the megasporangium. A pollen grain germinates by rupturing the exine, and the pollen tube grows through the nucellus toward the archegonial end of the female gametophyte.

As the pollen tube grows, the generative cell within the pollen tube cell divides into a stalk cell and a body cell, which later divides to form two sperms. *Microcycas* is exceptional in that its body cell undergoes repeated divisions to form 16–22 sperms.

While the pollen tube (male gametophyte) is growing through the nucellus, a small chamber called the archegonial chamber forms between the archegonial end of the female gametophyte and the adjacent inner part of the nucellus (Fig. 41-7). After the pollen tube has traversed the nucellus, its tip ruptures and it discharges its sperms into the archegonial chamber. Each large sperm (up to 300 microns in length) is top shaped with a rounded base and has a long, spiral band in the front part to which are attached numerous, short, whiplash flagella. A sperm swims to the neck of an archegonium, and the sperm nucleus enters the egg. The time interval between pollination and fertilization may be 4–6 months or longer.

After fertilization, seed formation begins. The zygote nucleus divides mitotically but no cross wall forms. Many more free-nuclear divisions result in a cell (the former egg and zygote) with hundreds of nuclei (Fig. 41-8, left). Then walls form around uninucleate portions of the young, free-nuclear sporophyte, and the lowermost of these cells (those in the basal part of the old archegonium) become a meristematic zone, which later develops into the mature embryo. But first the cells behind this meristem become a suspensor, and as the suspensor cells elongate they push the meristem deeper into the vegetative tissue of the large female gametophyte (Fig. 41-8, right). This structure with its multicellular suspensor and basal meristem is called a proembryo. The meristem is the embryo-forming region. It differentiates an axis consisting of embryo root (radicle), which is directed toward the micropyle, embryo stem (hypocotyl), and a tiny terminal bud (epicotyl or plumule). The epicotyl is between the two seed leaves (cotyledons), which are attached laterally to the hypocotyl just behind the epicotyl. The radicle is covered by a special sheath, the coleorhiza. As the embryo is developing within the vegetative tissue of the female gametophyte, from which it derives food, the developing seed (or transforming ovule) increases in size, and striking changes occur in the integument as it becomes the seed coat. The outer fleshy layer becomes very thick and, in *Zamia*, bright orange. The middle layer becomes very hard and stony, and the inner layer of the integument remains soft. The mature seed, then, consists of an embryonic sporophyte surrounded by a lot of food-storage tissue (female gametophyte), which is surrounded by the thin remains of the nucellus, which in turn is surrounded by the three-layered seed coat. The tightly spaced female sporophylls of *Zamia* and most other cycads separate during seed maturation and permit abscission of mature seeds.

In a suitable habitat, seed germination is initiated by protrusion of the coleorhiza and its enclosed primary root through the micropyle of the seed coat. The primary root soon ruptures the coleorhiza and continues its downward growth in the soil. In time, the two cotyledons partially emerge from the seed, and then the first foliage leaves appear on the shoot that developed from the epicotyl. The young, slow-growing sporophyte is then established as an independent plant.

Cycads and all other seed plants have a diplo-haplontic type of sexual life cycle with heteromorphic alternating generations: the large, conspicuous, vascularized, and heterosporous sporophytic phase (the site of meiosis) alternates with the small, inconspicuous, nonvascularized gametophytic phase (the site of syngamy). Like the lycopods *Selaginella* and *Isoetes* and the water ferns (e.g., *Marsilea*), the gametophytic phase of cycads and all other seed plants consists of two reduced and highly specialized "plants," the male gametophyte and the female gametophyte. Cycads and other seed plants differ from the heterosporous pteridophytes in having their megaspores retained entirely within and never shed from their sporangia, in having their gametophytes develop completely within their spore walls, and in having gametophytes with a parasitic mode of nutrition. Both male gametophytes (pollen grains and pollen tubes) and female gametophytes take food and water from their host sporophytes while they are growing and developing within them.

Project

I. Living or extant cycads (order Cycadales)

A. *Vegetative plant (sporophyte)*

1. Macroscopic appearance. Study *Zamia, Cycas, Dioon,* or any other cycads that may have been brought from the greenhouse into the laboratory. (*Zamia floridana* is native to southern Florida. *Cycas revoluta,* commonly called sago palm, is a small palmlike tree cultivated for landscaping in southern latitudes.) Notice the short, stout stem of each plant. If young leaves are present, observe their unfolding and note their fernlike appearance.

2. Stem anatomy. Study a cross section of a stem (prepared slide). Identify pith, xylem, phloem, cortex, mucilage canals, and narrow, curved leaf traces. Find the protoxylem. Is the primary xylem exarch, mesarch, or endarch? Can you find a cambium, secondary xylem and secondary phloem?

B. *Reproduction*

1. Strobili on plants. Look for cones or strobili on the living plants provided.
2. Strobili and sporophylls of *Zamia*. Examine living or preserved strobili of *Zamia*. Study carefully specimens that have been cut longitudinally. Note that two kinds of strobili are produced, microstrobili and megastrobili. They develop on different plants. Remove a single sporophyll from each kind of cone and look for the sporangia on each of them. Megasporangia are in the ovules of the megasporophylls. How do these microsporophylls and megasporophylls compare with those of *Selaginella* as to number of sporangia, their position on a sporophyll, and their color, size, and texture?
3. Sporophylls of *Cycas*. Examine the sporophylls of *Cycas revoluta* and compare them with those of *Zamia*. How do the megasporophylls and microsporophylls of *Cycas* resemble and differ from the vegetative leaves of *Cycas*?
4. Pollen. Mount the contents of a maturing microsporangium, add I_2KI solution, and study the pollen grains with high power. Can you see both the intine and exine? Look for the prothallial cell, generative cell, and tube cell of a pollen grain.
5. Ovule of *Zamia* in longitudinal section (prepared slide). Identify the micropyle, layered integument, nucellus, and megagametophyte with archegonia.
6. Seed of *Zamia*
   a. Split seed. With a razor blade bisect a mature seed of *Zamia*. Identify the seed coat (formerly the several layers of the integument) and the embryo, surrounded by the female gametophyte and the remains of the nucellus.
   b. Sectioned embryo (prepared slide). Identify cotyledons, epicotyl, hypocotyl, and radicle.
7. Germination of *Zamia* seed
   a. Before planting viable seeds of *Zamia*, remove the leathery covering and carefully remove the stony layer from some of them to permit immediate germination. Treat the seeds with a fungicidal agent to prevent molding.
   b. Plant seeds, smaller end down, in a mixture of peat moss and sand (1:1), and examine from time to time for germination and the development of juvenile sporophytes or seedlings. Is germination epigean or hypogean?

II. Fossil cycads

Study the demonstration of fossil cycads including cycadeoids and pteridosperms or seed ferns, if available.

Project **42**   Ginkgo or maidenhair tree

Contents

Introduction

Taxonomy   *Ginkgos* or maidenhair trees are plants of the group technically known as Ginkgophyta or Ginkgoales. There is a single extant genus and species, *Ginkgo biloba*.

Ginkgo biloba is the sole surviving member of an ancient and formerly widely distributed and diversified group of gymnospermous seed plants. It is even doubtful if *Ginkgo* now exists in the wild state, and it is appropriate to think of *Ginkgo* as a living fossil. Indeed, unless man continues to cultivate this beautiful tree (Fig. 42-1), it appears doomed to extinction.

The following points about *Ginkgo* were made in the section dealing with the taxonomy of cycads (p. 337): where *Ginkgo* fits in the classification of vascular plants; how *Ginkgo* is like all green plants and more specifically like all embryophytes; how *Ginkgo* and other gymnosperms are like ferns and other pteridophytes; how *Ginkgo* and other gymnosperms are strikingly different from pteridophytes; and finally, the likelihood that *Ginkgo* is a member of a different evolutionary line of gymnosperms than cycads. The two major lines or phyletic groups of gymnosperms are the cycadophyte line (the cycadophytes, with only cycads still in existence), and the coniferophyte line [the coniferophytes, which include the extinct order Cordaitales, *Ginkgo biloba*, and many fossil Ginkgoales, living and fossil conifers, and the Gnetales (*Gnetum, Ephedra,* and *Welwitschia*)]. These coniferophytes contrast with cycadophytes through their simple and often scalelike or needle-like leaves, tall and often much-branched trunks, small pith and cortex regions in the stem, and their large amount of secondary xylem.

347

Fig. 42-1 (this page) *Ginkgo* tree (arrow) on the campus of the University of North Carolina showing its unusual form and interesting appearance. *(Courtesy Marion Seiler.)*

Fig. 42-2 (opposite, top left)   Leafy branch of *Ginkgo* (foreground). *(Courtesy Marion Seiler.)*

Fig. 42-5 (bottom left)   Looking up into a *Ginkgo* tree. Arrow points to a spur shoot with an apical cluster of several leaves. *(Courtesy Marion Seiler.)*

Fig. 42-3 (opposite, top right)   Fanlike blade of a *Ginkgo* leaf, yellow in color, after it has fallen from its spur branch in autumn. Note the dichotomously branched veins. *(Courtesy Marion Seiler.)*

Fig. 42-4 (right column, second from top) Portion of a *Ginkgo* tree in winter showing long shoots and spur shoots. *(Courtesy Marion Seiler.)*

Fig. 42-6 (bottom right)   Closeup view of *Ginkgo* branches after their leaves have fallen from their spur shoots. Note the large terminal bud and the numerous, tightly spaced leaf scars of a spur shoot. *(Courtesy Marion Seiler.)*

349

Over a dozen genera of extinct *Ginkgo*-like plants have been described, primarily based on the fossils of leaves. The ancestral origin of ginkgophytes is not known, but it was probably a group of seed-bearing ferns presently unknown in the fossil record.

Ginkgo biloba is one of the older species of living plants and *Ginkgo* may be the oldest genus of living seed plants. It appears to have had its beginning in the Permian Period, and it was common during the Triassic and Jurassic Periods (Table 18-2, p. 134). *Ginkgo* has persisted to the present time apparently with remarkably little change during its nearly 300 million years of evolution, much like the pteridophyte *Equisetum*.

Importance   *Ginkgo* is valued as a cultivated plant in temperate regions. It makes a fine shade tree during warm weather (Fig. 42-1); its green, fanlike leaves are interesting to look at (Figs. 42-2, 42-3, 42-8); its golden-yellow autumn leaves (Fig. 42-3), most of which fall from a tree at one time, make a spectacular sight; and its winter twigs are unusual and pleasing (Fig. 42-4).

Ginkgo seeds have a thick, outer coat that emits an extremely unpleasant odor, rendering female trees unsuitable as ornamental plants, but the kernel of the *Ginkgo* seed, which technically is the embryo and female gametophyte, is highly nutritious. It is used as food in Japan and China and seeds can be purchased in this country in "Chinatowns."

Occurrence   *Ginkgo* appears to have been worldwide in distribution during the Triassic and Jurassic Periods. Since the Mesozoic Era it has declined in its distribution and China either is or was the last natural site of this ancient seed plant. Apparently there still are native stands of *Ginkgo* trees in a mountainous area of southeastern China south of the Yangtze River, but it has been suggested that these plants may have escaped from cultivation. *Ginkgo* has been cultivated in oriental temple grounds for centuries.

Vegetative features   The *Ginkgo* plant (sporophyte) is a profusely branched tree bearing many fan-shaped and often bilobed leaves (Fig. 42-5). *Ginkgo* trees are deciduous; their leaves live only one growing season, and an entirely new set of leaves develops each year.

Young trees have strong apical dominance and a pronounced excurrent pattern of branching from a prominent main trunk; thus, young trees are essentially conical in shape, like many conifers. Older trees are more rounded and irregular in outline because, as they grow, older lateral branches become more prominent (Fig. 42-1). Large trees may be 100 ft tall.

Ginkgo has two types of shoots or branches: long ones (called long shoots) with long internodes and a single leaf at each node, and short lateral ones (spur shoots) with very short internodes and an apical cluster of several leaves arranged in a tight spiral (Figs. 42-5, 42-8). The rest of a spur shoot is covered with closely spaced leaf scars (Fig. 42-6). The apical buds of both types of branches are protected during the winter by several overlapping bud scales. Similar but smaller axillary buds occur on long shoots. Although the spur shoots of the ancient *Ginkgo* are unique, they are somewhat like a diminutive version of the stout stems of the also ancient cycads (Figs. 41-1, 41-2).

The foliage leaf of *Ginkgo* is also distinctive and unique. Arising from a petiole is a broad, thin, fan-shaped blade, which may be nearly entire, notched,

Fig. 42-7   Stained cross section
of a young *Ginkgo* stem.
*(Photomicrograph courtesy
Ripon Microslides Laboratory.)*

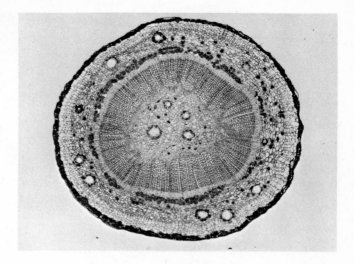

or conspicuously two lobed. The two vascular bundles in the petiole branch dichotomously many times in the blade. Both the form and venation of the *Ginkgo* leaf (Figs. 42-3, 42-8) resemble a pinnule of the maidenhair fern *Adiantum,* and this is why *Ginkgo biloba* is commonly called maidenhair tree.

A root's apical meristem is protected by a cover of parenchyma cells called the root cap. The vascular system of the root is a protostele; that of the stem is a siphonostele dissected or interrupted by the departure of two leaf traces to each leaf.

The extensively branched root and stem systems are characterized anatomically by a lot of secondary growth, which as in all woody, perennial plants is initiated by cambial activity in primary tissues derived from apical meristems. The vascular cambium is initiated in undifferentiated parenchyma cells between the primary xylem and phloem and produces xylem toward the inside (centripetally) and phloem toward the outside (centrifugally) (Fig. 42-7). Because cambial activity is seasonal, the large amount of secondary xylem (wood) appears in zones called annual rings. The cork cambium (phellogen) develops in outer cells of the cortex. Cells that mature toward the inside of the cork cambium become cortex cells, and those which mature toward the outside are suberized cork cells that replace the epidermis as a protective layer. Gas exchange between living cells and the atmosphere occurs through breaks in the cork called lenticels.

Reproduction   *Ginkgo* does not reproduce itself asexually. Although *Ginkgo* and cycads are not closely related (their vegetative plants and their strobili are very different), both have retained a primitive or ancient pattern of seed-plant sexual reproduction that was probably shared by many of the now extinct Late Paleozoic and Mesozoic gymnosperms.

Ginkgo is dioecious and has many additional reproductive similarities with the cycads: method of microspore formation, pollination, and pollen tube formation; method of megaspore formation and female gametophyte development; archegonial structure; sperm structure and egg fertilization; embryo development; the general structure of the ovule and mature seed; and seed germination. Indeed, sexual reproduction in *Ginkgo* is so much like that in cycads (p. 341) that only the distinctive and important differences will be mentioned here.

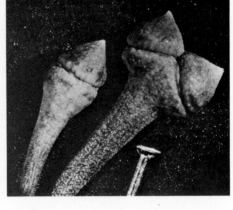

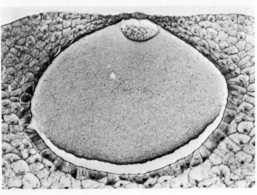

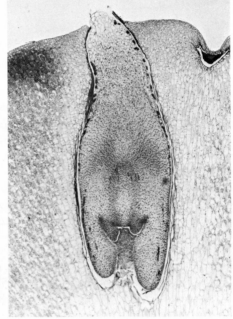

Fig. 42-8 Detail of a female spur shoot of *Ginkgo* with pairs of stalked ovules. Note the dichotomously branched veins of the leaves. *(Courtesy CCM: General Biological, Inc., Chicago.)*

Fig. 42-10 Stained longitudinal section of an archegonium in a female gametophyte of *Ginkgo* showing the large egg with its nucleus close to two neck cells. *(Photomicrograph courtesy Carolina Biological Supply Company.)*

Fig. 42-9 Closeup view of two ovuliferous stalks of *Ginkgo* showing the rimlike outgrowth at the base of each ovule. *(Courtesy Carolina Biological Supply Company.)*

Fig. 42-11 Stained longitudinal section of an embryo surrounded by enlarged female gametophyte in a seed of *Ginkgo*. *(Photomicrograph courtesy Ripon Microslides Laboratory.)*

The strobili of *Ginkgo* are unique. They are tiny when compared with those of cycads and they do not look at all like cycad strobili. Several strobili arise at the end of a spur shoot, along with several vegetative leaves, when the terminal bud of the spur shoot opens in spring (Fig. 42-8). The male (microsporangiate) strobilus (microstrobilus or androstrobilus) of male trees is a loose, limp, catkin-like structure having an axis and numerous spirally arranged microsporophylls, each of which is but a stalk bearing two terminal, pendant microsporangia (pollen sacs). Each of the microsporophylls of *Ginkgo* looks much like a stamen in flowering plants. The female (ovuliferous) strobilus (megastrobilus or gyno-strobilus) of female trees consists of a stalk or peduncle bearing at its tip usually two, erect, small ovules, each subtended by a rimlike outgrowth or collar, which has been interpreted as a reduced, vestigial sporophyll (Fig. 42-9).

The young male gametophyte (a mature pollen grain) has two prothallial cells instead of one as in cycads. Also, the flagellated sperm of *Ginkgo* is smaller, but it is the second largest sperm of known plants. The archegonium of *Ginkgo* (Fig. 42-10) is somewhat like that of cycads (Fig. 41-7). Fertilization and embryo development in *Ginkgo* (Fig. 42-11) may occur while the ovule is on the tree, as one would expect, or after the ovule has fallen to the ground. A final difference of note between *Ginkgo* and cycads is that the proembryo of *Ginkgo* has an inactive or only a slight or poorly defined suspensor.

The basic type of life cycle for *Ginkgo* and other seed plants is discussed in the last paragraph dealing with sexual reproduction in cycads (p. 345).

Project

I. **Maidenhair tree,** *Ginkgo biloba*

A. *Vegetative Plant (sporophyte)*

1. Tree. Observe cultivated trees or pictures of them showing, in younger trees, the prominent main trunk (excurrent or monopodial branching) and conical form. Older trees have a more rounded form.

2. Leafy branch. Provided are living or herbarium specimens of leafy branches of this deciduous tree. Examine them and find long shoots and spur shoots (short, lateral branches). Are spur shoots found on the most recent year of growth? Why are there no leaves at the bases of spur shoots? Identify leaf scars. Describe the difference you see in leaf arrangement on long and spur shoots. Notice that *Ginkgo* has leaves that are very different from those of cycads, but the spur shoots of Ginkgo do resemble the relatively short, stout stems of cycads.

3. Leaf. Examine several leaves. Note their characteristic shape (with many variations) and look for the apical notch of some leaves. Observe the fern-like dichotomous venation of *Ginkgo* leaves.

4. Stem anatomy. Compare cross sections (prepared slides) of the stems of long shoots and spur shoots. Observe that the long shoots have a small pith and cortex, a large amount of secondary xylem, and few mucilage canals. Observe that, in contrast, spur shoots have a relatively large pith and cortex, a small amount of secondary xylem, and many mucilage canals. Is the stem of cycads anatomically (and morphologically) more like the long shoot or the spur of *Ginkgo*?

B. *Reproductive structures of a male tree*
   1. Whole microstrobilus (androstrobilus). Observe the catkin-like cluster of microstrobili emerging, along with several vegetative leaves, from the tip of a spur shoot. Each strobilus contains many spirally arranged, highly modified microsporophylls.
   2. Whole microsporophyll (androsporophyll). Using a dissecting microscope, examine the individual microsporophylls of a strobilus. How many microsporangia (pollen sacs) are there on each sporophyll?
   3. Whole pollen (young microgametophyte) and its development. On a microscope slide crush out the contents of several microsporangia in a drop of I_2KI solution or acetocarmine stain. Using high dry and oil immersion, study stages in either microspore development or pollen grain (young microgametophyte) development (depending on the age of the material you are studying). How many cells and nuclei are there in mature pollen grains?
   4. Microstrobilus in sectional view. Study prepared slides with stained sections of microstrobili. Identify the several-layered wall and (depending on the age of the sporangia) either microspore mother cells undergoing meiosis, microspores, or pollen grains. If mature pollen is present, try to identify the two prothallial cells, generative cell, and tube cell. How does the pollen of *Ginkgo* compare with that of cycads?
C. *Reproductive structures of a female tree*
   1. Whole megastrobilus (gynostrobilus). Observe the cluster of highly reduced megastrobili emerging, along with several vegetative leaves, from the tip of a spur shoot. Using a dissecting microscope, observe that each is reduced to a single stalk (peduncle), near the apex of which there are two ovules, each subtended by a collar (which may be the rudiment of the sporophyll).
   2. Young ovule in sectional view. Study prepared slides with stained, median longitudinal sections through young ovules showing either the megaspore mother cell, linear tetrad of megaspores, or early free-nuclear megagametophyte. Identify these and also the micropyle, the pollen chamber, megasporangium, and integument.
   3. Mature ovule in sectional view. Study a prepared slide showing one or two archegonia at the apex of a mature megagametophyte.
   4. Embryo in sectional view. Study a median section through a mature seed showing the enlarged megagametophyte and the embryo.
   5. Whole seed. How many mature seeds usually occur on each peduncle? A seed of *Ginkgo* resembles what common type of flowering plant fruit? Study a split *Ginkgo* seed. Note the central megagametophyte. What is its function at the time of seed germination? Can you see the embryo, micropyle, and nucellus? The integument is differentiated into three seed-coat layers: an outer fleshy, inner stony, and thin innermost soft or dry one. Identify these.

II. Fossil ginkgos

Study the demonstration materials.

Project **43**   Conifers

Contents

Introduction

Taxonomy   Conifers are plants of the group technically known as Coniferophyta, Coniferinae, or Coniferales. There are about 50 genera and 550 species.

The following points about conifers were made in the section dealing with the taxonomy of cycads (p. 337): where conifers fit in the classification of vascular plants; how conifers are like all green plants and more specifically like all embryophytes; how conifers and other gymnosperms are like ferns and other pteridophytes; how conifers and other gymnosperms are strikingly different from pteridophytes; and, finally, the likelihood that conifers are members of a different evolutionary line of gymnosperms than cycads, and it was pointed out that members of the coniferophyte evolutionary line or phyletic group differ from members of the cycadophyte line through their simple and often scalelike or needle-like leaves, tall and often much-branched trunks, small pith and cortex regions in the stem, and their large amount of secondary xylem.

The ancient and extinct order Cordaitales has been regarded as the ancestral stock from which modern Coniferales and Gnetales may have originated. Cordaites appear to have had their origin in the late Devonian Period along with the ancient seed ferns, ferns, horsetails, and lycopods (Table 18-2, p. 134). Cordaites were conspicuous during the Carboniferous Period and became extinct by the end of the Paleozoic Era. Conifers appear to have arisen from the cordaites during the relatively dry Permian Period.

Pinus (Fig. 43-1), *Podocarpus,* and *Juniperus* are the largest coniferous genera—they have the largest number of species—and they also have a very wide distribution. Furthermore, all are widely cultivated and grown even in regions where they do not occur naturally.

Conifers commonly are grouped into six families on the basis of such features as (1) whether their leaves are spirally or cyclically arranged, (2) whether leaves occur singly or sometimes in bundles, (3) whether their their members are mostly monoecious or mostly dioecious, (4) whether or not ovules are borne in cones, (5) whether or not seeds are berry-like or drupelike, (6) whether or not pollen grains are winged, and (7) differences in the complexity of their gametophytes.

Following are the families and some of their more familiar genera. (1) Pinaceae (Abietaceae): pine *(Pinus),* fir *(Abies),* hemlock *(Tsuga),* Douglas fir *(Pseudo-tsuga),* spruce *(Picea),* cedar *(Cedrus),* and larch or tamarack *(Larix).* (2) Taxo-diaceae: redwood *(Sequoia),* dawn redwood *(Metasequoia),* Chinese fir *(Cunning-hamia),* and cypress or yew-cypress *(Taxodium).* (3) Cupressaceae: juniper *(Juniperus),* arbor vitae *(Thuja),* incense cedar *(Libocedrus),* and cypress *(Cupressus).* (4) Araucariaceae: *Araucaria* and *Agathis,* the only genera. (5) Podo-carpaceae: *Podocarpus.* (6) Taxaceae: yew *(Taxus)* and plum-yew *(Cephalotaxus).*

Importance   Conifers contribute a great deal to the earth's terrestrial produc-tivity (Map 18-1, p. 135), vastly more than all the other gymnosperms. Huge and awesome coniferous trees surely have been an inspiration to man from earliest human times.

Economically, conifers are by far the most important gymnosperms. They are especially important in providing building materials and also fuel. They supply most of our timber, pulp, paper, resin, and turpentine, and several species are widely cultivated to provide sources for these materials. Pine *(Pinus)* is the major lumber tree in eastern North America. The Douglas fir *(Pseudotsuga taxifolia)* is the principal lumber tree of western North America, and its seeds are exported in large numbers for reforestation in Australia, Japan, and South Africa, where it does not grow natively.

Araucaria of the southern hemisphere is cultivated as an exotic ornamental tree in California and is becoming a favorite house plant in the United States. *(Araucaria bidwilli* is used for reforestation in South Africa.) Conifers are of great importance in landscape gardening. Evergreen conifers are generally used, often in great abundance, when newly constructed houses and buildings are landscaped.

Although conifers are not troublesome as poisonous plants, cattle, horses, sheep, goats, and wild animals have been poisoned by browsing the leaves and twigs of yew *(Taxus)* because of an alkaloid that is a heart depressant. When large amounts of the bark, leaves, or seeds are eaten, death may result.

Occurrence   Most conifers live in mesic environments, but many, such as *Pinus,* have adaptations for living under xeric conditions. Swamp- and pond-cypress *(Taxodium)* may grow either in well-drained soil or in swamps and ponds (Fig. 43-2).

Conifers are worldwide in distribution, from the arctic to the tropics, and they commonly form extensive forests in the north and south temperate zones. The few tropical representatives occur at high altitudes.

Fig. 43-1 Habit view of *Pinus monticola.*
(Courtesy Carolina Biological Supply Company.)

Fig. 43-2 Cypress trees *(Taxodium)* growing in
shallow water showing "knees" sticking up
above water away from the tree trunks. The
epiphytic angiosperm *Tillandsia* (spanish moss)
hangs down from the branches of the cypress
trees. *(Courtesy Carolina Biological Supply
Company.)*

Fig. 43-3 Habit view of *Pinus edulis.*
(Courtesy Carolina Biological Supply Company.)

Pinus, with about 90 species, is the dominant species of the northern hemisphere; whereas *Podocarpus*, with about 70 species, is its counterpart in the southern hemisphere. There are an unusually large number of coniferous genera and species in western North America. Members of the Pinaceae (Abietaceae), Taxodiaceae, and Taxaceae are almost entirely confined to the northern hemisphere. The Cupressaceae is represented in both hemispheres. The Podocarpaceae is almost exclusively of the southern hemisphere, and the two genera of the Araucariaceae are widely distributed in the southern hemisphere only. With respect to distribution, conifers strikingly contrast with cycads: in cycads, more than half the genera are in the southern hemisphere; whereas in conifers, more than half the genera are in the northern hemisphere. Also, not even one of the nine cycad genera is common to both the eastern and western hemispheres.

Conifers were widespread and numerous during the Mesozoic Era, during which time they became diversified into the six families presently on earth. Redwood *(Sequoia)* and the dawn redwood *(Metasequoia)* were widely distributed in the northern hemisphere during Triassic times, but now they are restricted to small areas of the earth. *Sequoia* now grows natively only in California and Oregon. *Metasequoia,* formerly known only as a widely distributed fossil, rather recently has been discovered in a remote forest of western China. *Metasequoia* was correctly hailed as a living fossil when it was discovered in China.

Vegetative features   Most conifers are trees, but a few are bushes or trailing shrubs. In the northern hemisphere all conifers are evergreen except *Taxodium* and *Larix.* Typically, trees have strong apical dominance (Fig 43-3) with a pronounced excurrent pattern of branching from a prominent main trunk (Fig. 43-1). The tall, stout, and stately conifers have a majestic quality possessed by no other trees.

All conifers are autotrophic and apparently independent from other vascular plants with one known exception: *Podocarpus ustus,* a woody shrub in remote forests of New Caledonia, grows parasitically on the roots of forest trees. On the other hand, it is common for the roots of forest conifers to live in close association with certain mycorrhizal fungi, mostly basidiomycetes.

The largest and oldest individual plants on earth appear to be conifers. The bristlecone pine *(Pinus aristata),* growing at high altitudes in the White Mountains of California, may reach an age of 4,000 years even though it does not become a huge tree. The giant sequoia *(Sequoia gigantea)* of California, growing mostly south of San Francisco at higher elevations on the western slopes of the Sierra Mountains, is known to live for over 3,500 years, and it can be huge; an individual called "General Sherman" was 272 ft high and with a trunk over 32 ft in diameter with a perimeter of 101 ft, as measured several feet above ground above the swollen base. The coastal redwood, *Sequoia sempervirens,* extending from San Francisco north into southern Oregon, attains heights of up to 385 ft and diameters exceeding 35 ft. A fantastic specimen of *Taxodium mucronatum,* called "Big Tree of Tule," growing near Oaxaca in southern Mexico, has a trunk over 52 ft in diameter. At the other extreme, the Englemann spruce *(Picea engelmanii)* growing on rocky and windswept places may be stunted and with a trunk less than 6 in. in diameter, even though the tree is 200 years old. And on Vancouver Island of western Canada a tree of *Picea sitchensis* less than 1 ft in height and with a trunk only 19 mm in diameter was 86 years old, looking like a Japanese artificially dwarfed bonsai tree.

Conifer leaves are small and simple. They are spirally arranged, except in the Cupressaceae, where they are cyclic; for example, leaves of *Juniperus* are in whorls of three or in alternating pairs. The leaves of most conifers arise only on stems of unlimited growth; however, in *Pinus, Cedrus,* and *Larix* both long shoots and dwarf or spur shoots occur, somewhat as in *Ginkgo.* The conspicuous leaves of *Pinus* are needle-like, and the juvenile leaves of seedlings are borne singly and spirally on the stems for the first year or two. *Pinus* produces its leaves in bundles of one to eight, depending on the species, on very short spur shoots wrapped at the base with scalelike sheath leaves (Fig. 43-4). The apical meristem of the spur shoot is inactive. Each spur shoot or bundle of vegetative leaves arises from the axil of a subtending leaf or bract. When pine drops its leaves—after 2 or 3 years— the entire bundle or spur shoot abscisses and falls; however, only the leaves in *Cedrus* and *Larix* fall, and new leaves develop from the apical meristem of the spur shoot, as in *Ginkgo.*

Although the leaves of conifers are small and simple, technically they are macrophylls. The needle-like leaf of *Pinus* and *Abies* is characteristic of conifers, but the leaf may be broad and flat, as in *Agathis* and species of *Podocarpus* and *Araucaria.* Scalelike vegetative leaves are characteristic of the Cupressaceae, and the adult scalelike leaves of most species of *Juniperus,* for example, are preceded by needle-like juvenile leaves of seedlings. Flat coniferous leaves have several to many parallel veins; needle-like and scalelike leaves usually have but a single vein.

The leaf of *Pinus* and many other conifers is adapted for growth under arid conditions (Fig. 43-5). Beneath the thickly cutinized epidermis are one or more layers of thick-walled hypodermal cells. Stomata are sunken in pits. The mesophyll is compact and contains resin ducts. The central tissue of the leaf is enclosed by a conspicuous endodermis. There are one or two centrally located collateral vas-

Fig. 43-4 Closeup view of a cluster of over 12 mature male pine cones just prior to shedding pollen. T, terminal bud of the branch; B, one of the many bundles of vegetative leaves (pine needles), each bundle on a very short spur shoot wrapped at the base with scalelike sheath leaves. *(Courtesy Carolina Biological Supply Company.)*

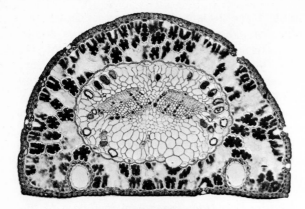

Fig. 43-5 Stained cross section of a leaf of *Pinus resinosa* (which has two leaves in each bundle). *(Photomicrograph courtesy Ripon Microslides Laboratory.)*

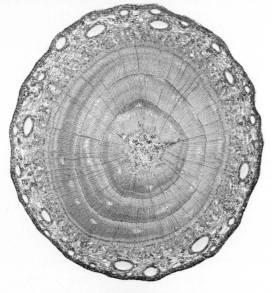

Fig. 43-6 Stained cross section of a young stem of pine showing several annual rings. *(Photomicrograph courtesy Carolina Biological Supply Company.)*

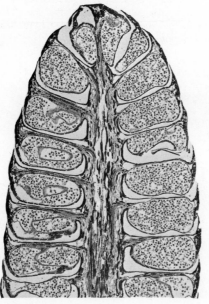

Fig. 43-7 Stained longitudinal section of the apical part of a male pine cone showing the cone axis, micro-sporophylls, and microsporangia containing mature pollen grains (young microgametophytes). Only one of the two microsporangia of each sporophyll can be seen in longitudinal section. *(Photomicrograph courtesy Carolina Biological Supply Company.)*

cular bundles with xylem and phloem, largely secondary in origin, in nearly equal amounts.

A root's apical meristem is protected by a root cap. The vascular system of the root is protostelic; that of the stem is an ectophloic siphonostele of an advanced type. The extensively branched root and stem systems of conifers are characterized anatomically by a large amount of secondary growth (as in all gymnosperms of the coniferophyte evolutionary line), and, as in all woody plants, this secondary growth is initiated by cambial activity. The woody stem (Fig. 43-6) has a minute pith, a thick vascular cylinder, and a thin cortex. Wood consists almost entirely of long, thick-walled tracheids with bordered pits, and each year's growth of wood appears as an annual ring. The numerous parenchymatous wood rays extend into the phloem. Resin canals lined with secretory parenchyma cells occur in the wood and in the cortex. The phloem of conifers consists primarily of sieve cells, and there are no companion cells. The cork cambium, early established in the outer cells of the cortex, produces centrifugally massive amounts of cork (outer bark), much as the vascular cambium centripetally produces massive amounts of xylem. As in woody angiosperms, the outer bark often has an appearance characteristic for the genus or species and often is not only an aid in identification but also a feature of great beauty.

Asexual reproduction   Conifers rarely reproduce themselves asexually or vegetatively. In nature conifer branches very seldom develop adventitious roots, and rarely do adventitious shoots develop from roots. Rarely in *Pinus,* the normally inactive apical meristem of the spur shoot of a bundle of pine needles that has fallen to the ground may become active, rooted, and develop into a new plant. Although with some difficulty, most conifers can be propagated by man through the rooting of branch tips cut off from plants, and this is known as propagation by means of cuttings. This is not, of course, a conifer's means of reproduction.

Sexual reproduction   Sexual reproduction in conifers and other gymnosperms is strikingly different from sexual reproduction in pteridophytes because of the two interdependent processes, pollination and seed formation. Their basic developmental features for all gymnosperms are described in the taxonomy section of cycads (p. 338).

The microsporangia and megasporangia of conifers are borne in separate strobili or cones; thus, there are male strobili or pollen-bearing cones and female strobili or seed-producing cones. Most conifers are monoecious, with both male and female cones occurring on the same plant; but some are dioecious, as in *Juniperus, Podocarpus, Araucaria,* and *Taxus* and the other members of the Taxaceae.

The male cone (Fig. 43-4) bears few to many microsporophylls along the cone axis, and each sporophyll bears two to sixteen microsporangia (pollen sacs), depending on the genus. In the pine family the microsporophyll consists of a slender stalk and an expanded tip, and two pollen sacs are produced on the lower (abaxial) surface (Fig. 43-7). A nearly mature male sporangium contains numerous microsporocytes surrounded by a sporangium wall a few cells in thickness, the innermost layer forming a nutritive tapetum. In *Pinus,* microsporocytes undergo meiosis in the spring as the male cones enlarge, and counts of chromosomes during meiosis show that the haploid number of chromosomes is twelve ($n = 12$). Following cytokinesis, each microspore develops a two-layered wall, an inner intine and an outer exine, and these two layers separate at two points and enlarge, forming the characteristic winged pollen grain (Fig. 43-8). As in *Ginkgo,* the young male gametophyte (mature pollen grain) of *Pinus* is four celled: it has in series two small, ephemeral prothallial cells, a generative cell, and a large tube cell. At this stage the sporophylls separate, each pollen sac opens by a longitudinal slit, and the pollen grains are set free for wind dissemination.

The formation of two ephemeral prothallial cells by the male gametophyte is found in all genera of the pine family; however, in Araucariaceae and Podocarpaceae, the two prothallial cells divide and form a tissue of many cells, and this is thought to be a more primitive condition. In addition, no prothallial cells at all are formed in the Taxodiaceae, Cupressaceae, and Taxaceae, and this condition is the most advanced found in conifers.

The female strobilus (cone) of most conifers is a compound structure consisting of an axis bearing spirally arranged bracts (Fig. 43-9), each of which subtends and often is fused with an ovule-bearing scale (ovuliferous scale) with one to many ovules, depending on the genus. In *Pinus* and other genera of the pine family, each large cone scale in the axil of its small bract bears two basal ovules on the upper (adaxial) side (Fig. 43-10). The ovuliferous scale is usually interpreted as the evolutionary modification of a primitive, ovule-bearing lateral branch.

Not all female strobili in conifers are like the typical kind found in *Pinus.* The female strobilus of some of the Podocarpaceae is reduced and bears only one or two ovules, and in most members of the Taxaceae there is only one ovule.

The ovule has a single integument (Fig. 43-11), and in *Pinus* and other genera in its family the ovule is inverted, with the micropylar end directed toward the cone axis (Fig. 43-10). As in cycads and *Ginkgo,* the three-layered integument has outer and inner fleshy layers and a middle stony layer. The integument is free from the remaining tissue (megasporangium or nucellus) of the ovule at the micropylar end, and the space between the nucellus and integument is called the pollen chamber (Fig. 43-11). One of the internal cells of the nucellus differentiates as a megasporocyte (female spore mother cell) that undergoes meiosis and forms four female meiospores (megaspores) in a row parallel to the long axis of the ovule. As in all gymnosperms, the three closest to the micropylar end disintegrate and the fourth (functional) megaspore enlarges and has a period of free-nuclear divisions within the enlarging female spore wall. This young female gametophyte soon becomes cellular and then continues to grow, surrounded by cells of the nucellus. The nucellar jacket functions as nutritive tissue for the enlarging female gametophyte. The mature gametophyte of *Pinus* usually has two to five archegonia submerged at the surface of its micropylar end (Fig. 43-12, top left). There may be up to and over 100 archegonia in a gametophyte of conifers in other familes. Each archegonium of *Pinus* and other genera of the pine family usually has two to eight neck cells arranged in two tiers, but in other conifers there may be up to twelve or more neck cells in several tiers. The archegonium of pine has a ventral canal cell that disintegrates prior to maturation of the archegonium. The female gametophyte of pine reaches this mature condition about 1 year after the ovule has been pollinated.

Pollination of the young female cone occurs soon after it emerges from the bud. Its scales separate slightly and a viscus pollination droplet is exuded through the micropyle of each ovule. This droplet captures the windblown pollen grains

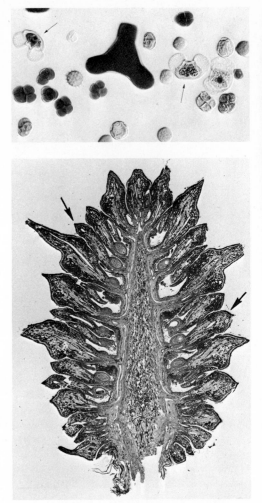

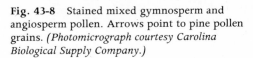

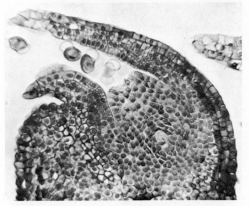

Fig. 43-8 Stained mixed gymnosperm and angiosperm pollen. Arrows point to pine pollen grains. *(Photomicrograph courtesy Carolina Biological Supply Company.)*

Fig. 43-9 Closeup view of a female pine cone (arrow) at the time of pollination. *(Courtesy Carolina Biological Supply Company.)*

Fig. 43-10 Stained longitudinal section of a young female pine cone at the time of pollination. Arrows point to two ovuliferous scales, each showing clearly its subtending bract and a young ovule. Only one of the two ovules on each ovuliferous scale can be seen in longitudinal section. *(Photomicrograph courtesy Carolina Biological Supply Company.)*

Fig. 43-11 Stained longitudinal section of an ovule of pine showing pollen grains in the pollen chamber, the single integument, and the megasporocyte in the megasporangium (nucellus). *(Photomicrograph courtesy Ripon Microslides Laboratory.)*

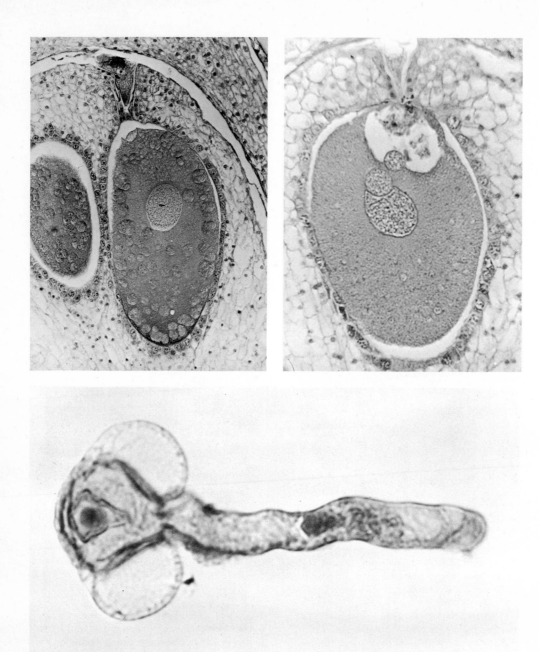

Fig. 43-12   Stained, median longitudinal sections of pine archegonia within megagametophytic tissue, which is surrounded by megasporangial tissue. Top left: The archegonium at the right shows its large egg and egg nucleus and its small ventral canal cell and neck cells. Top right: Archegonium at the time of fertilization. *(Photomicrographs courtesy Ripon Microslides Laboratory.)*

Fig. 43-13 (below)   A stained microgametophyte of pine grown in liquid culture medium. Note, from left to right, the two thin prothallial cells, the generative cell, and the nucleus in the tube cell. *(Photomicrograph courtesy Carolina Biological Supply Company.)*

Fig. 43-14   Three female cones of a species of *Pinus* as they appear in successive stages of maturation. Left, in the winter following spring pollination. Middle, in the next summer. Right, in the second autumn and with mature seeds ready to be shed. *(Courtesy Carolina Biological Supply Company.)*

(young male gametophytes), and, as the droplet dries, the pollen is drawn into the pollen chamber to the nucellus, where it germinates (Fig. 43-13). After pollination, the cone scales close and the cone begins its long period of growth (Fig. 43-14).

The pollen tube grows through the nucellus toward the female gametophyte. The tube nucleus moves into the pollen tube (Fig. 43-13), and the generative cell, remaining at the basal end, divides into the stalk cell and the body cell. These move into the pollen tube, and much later the body cell divides into two relatively undifferentiated sperm cells that lack flagella. No conifer sperms ever form flagella. While this male gametophyte is maturing, so also is the female gametophyte. Finally, the pollen tube comes in contact with the archegonial neck, and the tip of the pollen tube ruptures and discharges at least one of its sperms into the egg. A sperm nucleus fuses with the egg nucleus (Fig. 43-12, top right) and immediately the diploid fusion nucleus divides mitotically, initiating embryo development (Fig. 43-15, top left).

After fertilization in *Pinus,* four free diploid nuclei are formed, and they move to the base of the cell (formerly the egg) where they become arranged in a plane horizontal to the long axis of the ovule (which is now beginning its transformation into a seed). Each of the four nuclei again divides and all eight nuclei then are incorporated into walled cells, resulting in two tiers of four cells each at the base of the old egg cell (Fig. 43-15, top center). After several cell divisions, the pro-embryo is established. Each of the four cells of the lowermost tier is pushed deep into the female gametophyte through elongation of cells above, called the suspensor. Each of the four terminal cells gives rise to a separate embryo; however, all but

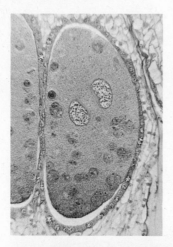
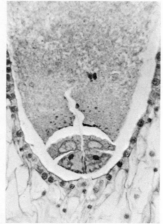
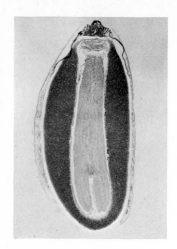

Fig. 43-15 Stained longitudinal sections of early proembryo development in old archegonia of *Pinus*. Top left: The zygote nucleus has divided to form two free nuclei. Top center: The two tiers of young proembryo cells at the base of an old egg cell. *(Photomicrographs courtesy Ripon Microslides Laboratory.)*

Fig. 43-16 (top right) Stained longitudinal section of a mature pine seed showing embryo, enlarged female gametophyte, and seed coat. *(Courtesy Ripon Microslides Laboratory.)*

Fig. 43-17 (at left) Pine seedlings in three stages of development; the earliest seen here is to the right. H, hypocotyl; C, cotyledons. *(Courtesy Carolina Biological Supply Company.)*

one of the developing embryos usually aborts, and the mature seed has only one embryo. In many conifers the cells of the lowermost tier do not separate and form four embryos, as in *Pinus,* but instead remain together and form a single embryo.

The mature conifer embryo consists of a radicle (embryo root) at the suspensor end, followed by the hypocotyl and terminated at the opposite end by a minute epicotyl or plumule (embryo bud), which is surrounded by two to eighteen cotyledons (embryo or seed leaves). As the embryo is developing within the vegetative tissue of the female gametophyte, from which it derives food, the developing seed (or transforming ovule) increases in size, and the integument becomes the seed coat. The inner and outer layers of the integument become very thin, and the seed coat consists essentially of cells derived from the middle stony layer. The mature seed, then, consists of an embryonic sporophyte surrounded by a great deal of food-storage tissue (enlarged female gametophyte), which is surrounded by the seed coat (Fig. 43-16). In *Pinus* the remains of the nucellus usually can be found at the micropylar end of the female gametophyte. The mature seed of conifers usually is brown, and the tightly spaced seed-bearing scales of most conifers separate after seed maturation and permit abscission of the mature seeds (Fig. 43-14). In many species of *Pinus*, seeds are shed in the autumn of the second year after pollination.

The female cone of most conifers becomes dry and woody at maturity, but in some genera, as in *Juniperus,* the mature cone is berry-like. An even more striking variation in seed development occurs in the Podocarpaceae and Taxaceae, where an outer fleshy covering grows up around the integument of the ovule. In yew *(Taxus)* an ovule occurs singly on a short lateral branch and has a fleshy, cuplike structure (aril) at the base. This fleshy aril grows up around the developing seed and surrounds the mature, drupelike seed.

In a suitable habitat, seed germination in conifers is initiated by protrusion of the radicle through the micropyle of the seed coat. Seed germination in *Pinus* is epigean (Fig. 43-17). The hypocotyl elongates and the entire embryo emerges from the ruptured seed coat, which often adheres for a short period of time to the tips of the photosynthetic cotyledons. The primary shoot soon develops from the small upright epicotyl.

The basic type of life cycle for conifers and other seed plants is discussed in the last paragraph dealing with sexual reproduction in cycads (p. 345).

Project

I. Macroscopic study of a variety of conifers (order Coniferales)

Coniferous trees and shrubs are of common occurrence in nature and are widely cultivated for landscaping. Study the demonstration branches of such conifers. Look for differences in their (1) general appearances and in their (2) cones. You may be able to tell that (3) some are deciduous and others (most) are evergreen. Find differences in (4) leaf form or shape, (5) leaf size, (6) leaf color, (7) whether or not leaves are in fascicles, and, if in fascicles, (8) differences in the number of leaves in each fascicle. Can you see other distinguishing features?

II. Pine, *Pinus*

A. *Vegetative plant (sporophyte)*
1. Tree. Observe native or cultivated pine trees, noting their prominent main trunks (excurrent or monopodial branching) and characteristic appearance. Why do lower branches die and fall off as trees grow older?
2. Leafy branch. Study a branch and identify stem, buds, and leaves. How many years of growth are represented on this branch? Identify the following leaves: foliage leaves in fascicles, sheath leaves (bud scales) at the base of a fascicle of foliage leaves, and subtending or scalelike leaves, in the axils of which arise and arose the fascicles of foliage leaves.
3. Leaf. Make your own cross sections of foliage leaves, mount them in water, and add a cover slip. Study your leaf sections and also stained sections on a prepared slide. Identify the thick cuticle and sunken stomata, each surrounded by a pair of guard cells. Are stomata a part of all epidermal

surfaces? Also find ordinary epidermal cells, mesophyll, and the central vascular region with xylem and phloem.

4. Stem. Make cross sections of a young stem, mount them in water, and add a cover slip. Study your stem sections and also stained sections on a prepared slide. Identify pith, primary and secondary xylem, rays, resin canals, vascular cambium, secondary and primary phloem, cortex, cork cambium, and cork. Identify protoxylem and metaxylem. Is the stele exarch, mesarch, or endarch?

5. Root. Study a prepared slide with a stained cross section of a root. Can you identify all the regions, except pith, found in the stem?

B. *Microstrobilus (male cone)*

1. Whole Microstrobilus

a. Observe a mature microstrobilus and find the numerous spirally arranged scales bearing pollen sacs and the bud scales at the base of the cone.

b. Using a dissecting microscope, study several scales. How many pollen sacs are there on each scale? Are they on the proximal side (the side next to the cone axis) or on the distal side (the side away from the cone axis)?

2. Whole pollen. On a microscope slide crush out the contents of several pollen sacs in a drop of water. Using high dry, examine pollen grains. Find the wings, which are really air sacs. Do all pollen grains have two? Examine the wall closely and suggest the origin of wings. Stain with I_2KI solution. What does this demonstrate with respect to the food stored in pollen? Are nuclei visible? When does a microspore become a young microgametophyte (mature pollen grain)? Does this happen before or after pollen is shed?

3. Microstrobilus in sectional view. Study prepared slides with stained sections of microstrobili. Identify the strobilus axis, pollen sac wall, and either microspore mother cells (microsporocytes) undergoing meiosis, microspores, or pollen grains (young microgametophytes). If mature pollen is present, try to identify the two prothallial cells, generative cell, and tube cell. Also identify intine and exine. Determine the origin of wings.

C. *Megastrobilus (female cone)*

1. Observe a branch that shows young (up to 6 months old) and mature (about $1\frac{1}{2}$ years old) female cones. How many years of growth are represented on this branch? Approximately how old is each cone?

2. Very young megastrobilus. Observe a very young megastrobilus and find the numerous, spirally arranged ovule-bearing scales. Using a dissecting microscope, dissect out and examine several scales. How many ovules are there on each scale? Are they on the proximal or distal side? Is the micropyle (small hole through the integument) directed toward or away from the axis of the strobilus?

D. *Study of prepared slides showing megaspore, megagametophyte, and seed development*

1. Ovule with a megaspore mother cell. Identify megastrobilus axis, ovule-bearing scale, and ovule, consisting of an integument (incipient seed coat), micropyle, megasporangium, and a large megaspore mother cell (megasporocyte).

2. Ovule with a young megagametophyte in the free-nuclear stage of development. Identify the integument and megasporangium, as well as the young gametophyte, in the free-nuclear stage of development, with a large space in the central portion.

3. Ovule with a mature megagametophyte. Using low power, identify the integument, micropyle, megasporangium. and mature megagametophyte with portions of one or two archegonia at the micropylar end. Put the most complete archegonium you can find under high power and identify the two neck cells (which do not protrude from the gametophyte) and the egg with its huge nucleus. (No ventral canal nucleus can be seen.)

4. Immature seed. Identify the matured, enlarged megagametophyte containing a young embryo (proembryo). The young embryo is made up of suspensor cells and embryo-forming cells, which will develop into the embryo proper.

5. Mature seed. (The seed coat and what was left of the nucellus were removed before sectioning.) Find the mature embryo surrounded by the enlarged megagametophyte. Identify the parts of the embryo: radicle or first root (at the micropylar end), hypocotyl portion of the embryonic stem, cotyledons or seed leaves, and the epicotyl and plumule (the first bud).

E. *Mature female cone and seeds*

1. Examine a mature female cone. Approximately how old is it? Find mature seeds on the upper (proximal or adaxial) surface. How many seeds are there on each scale? Study a mature seed with its attached wing. Can you see evidence relating to the origin of the wing? What do you suppose is the function of the wing? Can you produce evidence for this? Find the micropyle, which is now seen as a small scar.

2. Carefully dissect a seed. Just beneath the seed coat (matured integument) is a thin, paper-like layer, the remains of the megasporangium. Cut away the megagametophyte and find the mature embryo. How many cotyledons are there? What is the function of the enlarged megagametophyte at the time of seed germination?

F. *Calendar of events.* From your own observations and with help from your text and other resources, can you determine the approximate times of (1) pollination, (2) syngamy, and (3) seed maturation and dispersal?

G. *Seed germination.* Plant viable seeds in a mixture of peat moss and sand (1:1) and examine from time to time for germination and the development of juvenile sporophytes or seedlings. Is germination epigean of hypogean?

III. Fossil conifers

Study the demonstration materials.

Project **44**

The gnetum or *Gnetum–Ephedra–Welwitschia* group

Contents

Introduction

Taxonomy   The gnetum group or the *Gnetum–Ephedra–Welwitschia* group of plants is technically known as Gnetophyta or Gnetales. There are 3 genera and about 70 species. *Ephedra, Gnetum,* and *Welwitschia* are unusual, peculiar gymnosperms, and the differences between the three genera are great enough that each is now regarded as a member of a distinct family and order. *Welwitschia* has but a single species, *W. mirabilis* (Fig. 44-1). *Ephedra* and *Gnetum* each contain a number of species.

Ephedra, Gnetum, and Welwitschia are thought to have their ancestors in the ancient and extinct Cordaitales (which also has been regarded as the ancestral stock from which modern conifers arose), but their evolutionary history is obscure. They have no fossil record except for remains of *Ephedra* pollen from the Tertiary and perhaps Upper Cretaceous Periods and pollen like that of *Ephedra* and *Welwitschia* from the Permian Period.

Ephedra, Gnetum, and Welwitschia are highly specialized plants and are best regarded as end points in evolution that are not closely related to any present-day seed plants. They are more like flowering plants (angiosperms) than are any other gymnosperms. Distinctive features common to the three genera are (1) the occurrence of vessels (as well as tracheids) in their secondary xylem, (2) strobili that are compound and resemble flowers and inflorescences, (3) perianth-like bracts and bracteoles in male strobili and envelopes (fused bractioles) around

370

Fig. 44-1 *Welwitschia mirabilis* photographed near Brandburg in southwest Africa by R. J. Rodin. *(Courtesy William C. Dickison.)*

ovules, and (4) a very long micropyle that projects as a long tube. Additional features shared by the three genera are opposite or whorled leaves and embryos with two cotyledons.

Importance Several Asiatic species of the shrubby *Ephedra* have been used for over 5,000 years in China as a source of the medicinal drug ephedrin, an alkaloid extracted from the entire plant. In the United States, ephedrin has been used in the treatment of colds, hay fever, asthma, and for other medicinal purposes. In some arid parts of the southwestern United States, *Ephedra* grows in abundance and is grazed by livestock. *Gnetum gnemon* is a tree cultivated in Malaysia for its edible young reproductive shoots and seeds. Its bark yields fibers used for making rope.

Occurrence The xerophytic *Ephedra* (Fig. 44-2) occurs in tropical and temperate North and South America and Asia, from the Mediterranean to China. Six or more of the approximately 40 species of *Ephedra* occur in the southwestern part of the United States, where it is commonly called joint fir. *Gnetum* is mesophytic and occurs in the moist tropical forests of South America (in the Amazon basin), Africa, and Asia (India, South China, and Malaysia). The xerophytic *Welwitschia* is restricted to deserts in a narrow coastal region about 600 miles long in southwest Africa. *Welwitschia* can grow in areas receiving less than 1 in. of rain per year.

Vegetative features The plants (mature sporophytes) of *Ephedra, Gnetum,* and *Welwitschia* are perennial woody plants that differ in general appearance as greatly from one another as from other gymnosperms.

Most species of *Ephedra* are shrubby plants (Fig. 44-2) very superficially resembling *Psilotum* and *Equisetum,* and their form also is somewhat like that of the Charales. *Ephedra* has green stems with reduced scalelike and ephemeral

Fig. 44-2 *Ephedra nevadensis,* the desert switch plant or joint fir. *(Courtesy Carolina Biological Supply Company.)*

leaves, and lateral branches often arise in fasciculate whorls. Several species of *Ephedra* are woody vines called lianas, and one species can grow into a small tree. The scalelike leaves, each with two veins, are fused basally to form a sheath around the stem. The leaves of *Ephedra* are green only in early development, and the stem is the main photosynthetic organ.

Most of the 30 or so species of *Gnetum* are woody vines, lianas, but some are shrubs, and *Gnetum gnemon* is a tree that may attain a height of 30 ft. The leaf if *Gnetum* is unique among gymnosperms. It has a petiole and a broad blade with pinnately netted venation. It resembles the broad leaves of dicotyledonous angiosperms.

Welwitschia is a most unusual plant, perhaps the strangest of terrestrial plants. It has a short, broad stem, up to 4 ft in diameter, and a large taproot. Its stem and root system resemble a gigantic turnip. The mature *Welwitschia* plant has only two leaves, and these persist throughout the life of the plant by growth from their perennial, basal leaf meristems. As a *Welwitschia* plant ages, these two strap-like, leathery leaves become split into longitudinal strips and the tips become worn away, so that plants even over 100 years old have leaves only about 6 ft long. Their main veins are parallel, but smaller lateral veins anastomose and form an irregular network of veins.

Gymnosperms other than *Ephedra, Gnetum,* and *Welwitschia* lack vessels. Angiosperms also are characterized anatomically by having vessels. This is not evidence that the gnetum group is closely related to angiosperms, because the perforations of the vessels originated differently in the two groups. In the gnetum group, perforations of the vessel elements originated by the disappearance of the membranes of circular bordered pits of tracheids. In angiosperms, perforations of the vessel elements originated by the loss of membranes of transversely elongate pits of scalariformly pitted tracheids. The evolution of vessels in the gnetum group and in angiosperms is interpreted as evidence of parallel evolution rather than of phylogenetic relationship.

Asexual reproduction   *Ephedra* plants can spread and reproduce vegetatively by means of rhizomes or new plants that develop from underground buds from roots.

Sexual reproduction   The strobili of *Ephedra, Gnetum,* and *Welwitschia* are compound and they resemble inflorescences of flowers. As in most gymnosperms, most strobili are either microstrobili or megastrobili, but most plants of the gnetum group are dioecious.

In *Ephedra* the compound strobilus is one in which the cone axis has pairs of bracts that subtend either microsporangiate or ovulate branches. Each microsporangiate branch consists of a pair of fused bracteoles (sometimes called "perianth") and a short axis with one to eight microsporangia (pollen sacs) at the tip. Each megasporangiate branch consists of an ovule surrounded by a pair of fused bracteoles (sometimes called "outer integument").

In *Ephedra,* after microsporogenesis in the microsporangium, endosporal development of male gametophytes proceeds in a manner typical of many conifers. The mature pollen grain contains two prothallial cells (the second one is a free nucleus without cleaved cytoplasm around it), a stalk cell nucleus, a body cell nucleus, and a tube nucleus. This five-nucleate male gametophyte (mature pollen grain) is shed from the microsporangium or pollen sac. The male gametophytes of *Gnetum* and *Welwitschia* are more reduced. Both have a prothallial cell, but there is no stalk cell and the generative nucleus divides directly into two sperm nuclei.

A unique feature of the gnetum group of plants is that the integument at the micropylar end of an ovule elongates and forms a micropylar tube that protrudes through the fused bracteoles surrounding the ovule. Megasporogenesis and megagametophyte development within the nucellus of the ovule of *Ephedra* proceed in a manner typical of conifers; however, the one to several archegonia have longer necks, each containing 30–40 cells. *Gnetum* and *Welwitschia* differ strikingly from *Ephedra* and all other gymnosperms in lacking archegonia. The female gametophytes of *Gnetum* and *Welwitschia* also differ from those of *Ephedra* in several developmental features.

Ephedra has a unique feature. While archegonial development is in progress, the nucellar cells directly above the female gametophyte disintegrate, producing a large pollen chamber and exposing the female gametophyte directly to the bottom of the pollen chamber. Windblown pollen grains (young male gametophytes) of *Ephedra* drop through the long, exserted micropylar tube into the pollen chamber and are in direct contact with the archegonial portion of the female gametophyte. The prothallial cells disintegrate and the body cell of the pollen grain divides, forming two sperm nuclei. The pollen tube then grows or pushes between the neck cells of the archegonium to the egg. The tip of the pollen tube ruptures and the nuclear contents are discharged into the egg cytoplasm. The egg is fertilized by one of the sperm nuclei, and it then develops into an embryo with two cotyledons and the general features of typical conifer embryos. The embryo is embedded within the female gametophytic tissue and a membranaceous nucellar layer surrounded by the true seed coat, derived from the integument, and an outer coat derived from the fused bracteoles. Fertilization and embryogeny in *Ephedra, Gnetum,* and *Welwitschia* differ in a number of ways with respect to details of development.

The basic type of life cycle for the gnetum group of plants and other seed plants is discussed in the last paragraph dealing with sexual reproduction in cycads (p. 345).

Project

I. *Ephedra*

A. *Vegetative plant (sporophyte)*
1. Shrub. Observe living, preserved, or herbarium specimens of this straggling shrub. Note its superficial appearance to *Equisetum*, its fluted green stems, opposite and whorled arrangement of branches and minute scalelike leaves. Are roots present on your material?
2. Leaf. Count the number of scaly leaves at each of several nodes.
3. Stem. Examine a stem as viewed in cross section. A stained section on a prepared slide should reveal the cuticle, epidermal cells, stomata, cortex, primary and secondary phloem, vascular cambium, secondary and primary xylem, and pith.

B. *Microstrobilus*
1. Whole microstrobilus
   a. Observe the characteristic shape of a microstrobilus. Identify the opposite pairs of bracts. Are microsporangia (pollen sacs) protruding?
   b. Using a dissecting microscope, dissect off the bracts and find in the axil of each bract a pair of bracteoles enclosing a microsporophyll ("stamen"), which is a stalk terminated by microsporangia (pollen sacs).
2. Whole pollen. On a microscope slide crush out the contents of several microsporangia in a drop of water. Using high dry, examine pollen grains. Notice their surface markings.
3. Microstrobilus in sectional view. Study prepared slides with stained sections of microstrobili. Identify microsporangium wall and pollen.

C. *Megastrobilus*
1. Whole megastrobilus
   a. Observe the characteristic shape of a megastrobilus. Identify the opposite pairs of bracts. Are micropylar tubes protruding from one or two apical fertile bracts?
   b. Using a dissecting microscope carefully dissect off a fertile bract. Remove the ovule from its surrounding bracteoles, which are fused and sometimes referred to as an "outer integument." If the ovule is old enough, note that the micropylar tube (elongated, tubular portion of the integument) protruded through the fused bracteoles.
2. Megagametogenesis and embryogeny. Study available demonstration preparations. When it is possible, identify megasporangium, megagametophyte, pollen chamber, archegonium, embryo, and seed coat.

II. *Gnetum* and *Welwitschia*

Study available demonstration materials of these rare plants.

Project 45   Flowering plants or angiosperms

Contents

Introduction

Taxonomy   Flowering plants or angiosperms are technically known as Antho-phyta or Angiospermae. There are over a quarter of a million species of flowering plants (approximately 285,000) that are grouped into over 10,000 genera, 300 families, and 32 orders. Angiosperms are divided into two large groups: Mono-cotyledoneae (monocots) (Fig. 45-1) and Dicotyledoneae (dicots) (Fig. 45-2). Monocots have approximately one fifth as many species as dicots.

Table 18-1 (p. 132) summarizes the various ways of classifying flowering plants. Angiosperms and gymnosperms are the seed plants. Angiosperms, gymno-sperms, and ferns are the megaphyllous vascular plants, and like all vascular plants they are embryophytes and eukaryotes.

Angiosperms are extremely diverse and complex land plants. Nevertheless, there are important general features characterizing angiosperms, and these are

Fig. 45-1 (at left)   A group of *Yucca* plants with their tall, showy inflorescences, growing among grasses. *(Courtesy Carolina Biological Supply Company.)*

Fig. 45-2 (above)   A dogwood *(Cornus)* tree in flower. *(Courtesy Carolina Biological Supply Company.)*

(1) broad leaves that, as in gymnosperms and ferns, are megaphylls with leaf gaps where leaf traces leave the stele; (2) vessels in the xylem of all but about 100 primitive dicots and companion cells in the phloem; (3) the development of male and female meiosporangia and reduced male and female gametophytes in modified, highly specialized strobili called flowers; (4) ovules enclosed or surrounded by tissue, forming a structure called a carpel (specialized megasporophyll), which may be a single carpel or may be compound and consist of two or more fused carpels; (5) pollination by means of insects and other agents as well as wind; (6) having tissue of the carpel wall (the stigmatic surface of a carpel or pistil) as the site of pollination; (7) double fertilization, with endosperm development accompanying embryo development; (8) the lack of free-nuclear divisions during early development of the embryo; and (9) the development of seeds within fruits, with the fruit coat (pericarp) developing from the carpel or pistil wall.

The fossil record gives few clues to the origin of angiosperms. There is no reason to think that they evolved from any existing group of plants; however, like cycads and the extinct Bennettitales, it is possible that angiosperms could have had their ancestral stock in an extinct group of seed plants with fernlike foliage called the seed ferns (pteridosperms or Cycadofilicales), the fossils of which date back to the Carboniferous Period of the Paleozoic Era, but there is no compelling evidence that this is true. The first fossils of angiosperms (pollen grains, leaves, and other parts) appear in the Cretaceous Period (some pre-Cretaceous angiosperms have recently been reported), and during the Cretaceous Period angiosperms evolved or diversified rapidly and spread to worldwide dominance on land, which they have maintained to the present (Table 18-2, p. 134). Many modern families and genera of angiosperms were differentiated by mid-Cretaceous. It is possible that the sudden appearance and high degree of specialization and diversification of angiosperms in the Cretaceous period indicates that angiosperms evolved at a faster rate than other groups of vascular plants. It is also possible that angiosperms originated long before the Cretaceous Period and that the fossil record may be lacking, because early flowering plants might have evolved on upland sites where fossilization was unlikely.

The two large groups of flowering plants, monocotyledons and dicotyledons, have several features that generally separate the two groups. (1) Usually the protostelic root of monocots has many protoxylem poles in contrast to the few protoxylem poles of the primary xylem of dicot roots. (2) Whereas monocot roots and stems rarely develop cambial activity, many dicot roots and stems have secondary growth from cambia. (3) Most monocot stems have numerous, scattered vascular bundles, whereas most dicot stems have a single cylinder of vascular bundles or vascular bundles appearing in a circle in cross-sectional view. (4) Monocots usually have parallel-veined leaves in contrast to the typically net-veined leaves of dicots. (5) Whereas the floral parts of monocots are usually in threes (Fig. 45-3) or multiples of three, the floral parts of dicots are generally in fours, fives, or multiples of these. (6) The monocot embryo usually has a single cotyledon, an epicotyl covered by a coleoptile and a hypocotyl and radicle covered by a coleorhiza; in contrast, the dicot embryo usually has two lateral cotyledons and an epicotyl, hypocotyl, and radicle not covered by sheaths (Fig. 45-4).

Because of evidence indicating that vessels evolved from tracheids independently and unidrectionally in monocotyledons and dicotyledons, it has been suggested that these two great groups of angiosperms evolved separately from a common, vesselless ancestral type; however, other evidence can be used to indicate that either group arose first and that either group evolved from early members of the other group. Botanists agree that the origin of the two major phyletic groups of angiosperms remains a perplexing problem that will require for its resolution much more information from both living and fossil plants. Within the families of angiosperms, it is widely believed that the woody genera represent the primitive condition and that herbaceous genera are derived, having arisen by the curtailment or cessation of cambial activity.

Importance Angiosperms are of great biological and economic importance. They are of major importance as primary producers in the food chains and webs of nature. Up to one half of the earth's photosynthesis occurs on land (Map 18-1, p. 135), and the major terrestrial primary producers are the dominant, ubiquitous angiosperms.

By far the most important plants for man are angiosperms. They serve as our main source of food, either directly through crops or indirectly through livestock and certain other animals. Not only do angiosperms play an important part in providing man with the three basic necessities of life—food, clothing, and

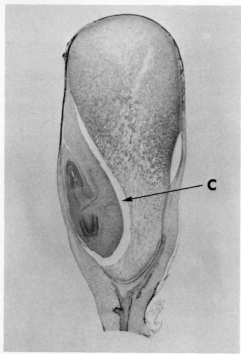

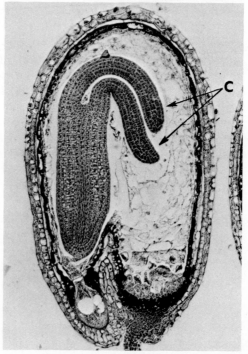

Fig. 45-3 (opposite, top)   Closeup view looking down on an
open tulip flower showing its floral parts arranged in groups of
three. *(Courtesy Carolina Biological Supply Company.)*

Fig. 45-4   Stained longitudinal sections of two seeds (C,
cotyledons). Bottom left: Corn *(Zea)*, a monocotyledon. (A corn
grain is really a fruit with one seed.) Bottom right: Shepherd's
purse *(Capsella)*, a dicotyledon. *(Photomicrographs courtesy
Ripon Microslides Laboratory.)*

---

shelter—they provide a great variety of other useful products such as drugs, rubber, cork, dyes, essential oils, perfumes, and waxes. For many who live in forested regions of the world, wood is still the principal fuel because of its cheapness, and angiosperms are the major source of fuel wood in some of these regions. Angiosperms are important in water and wildlife management and other aspects of conservation.

Most of man's valuable economic plants (including cereals, vegetables, fruits, coffee, tea, cocoa, and fiber plants) were discovered and cultivated by man thousands of years ago. Some examples of plants cultivated for over 4,000 years are wheat and rice (cereals); cabbage and onion (vegetables); apple, date, and grape (fruits); flax and hemp (fiber plants); and tea.

Now as always, the most important sources of plant food for man are the cereals wheat, maize (corn), rice, barley, oats, and rye. They are members of the large grass group of monocotyledonous angiosperms. The fruit is called a grain and so is the plant that produces it. Grains or cereals have played an important role in the development of civilization, because one or more of them grows well in each kind of climate, they have a wide range of moisture and soil requirements, are easy to cultivate, have a large yield, are easy to handle and store, and are high in food value.

Leguminous dicots (such as field and garden peas, string and lima beans, soybeans, peanuts, and lentils) are next in importance to cereals as sources of food for man. They are easy to grow and mature rapidly, and they are relatively high in protein. Many legumes have nitrogen-fixing bacteria growing within their roots in nodules.

The dicotyledonous white or Irish potato *(Solanum tuberosum)* is one of our most important sources of food. Potatoes are adapted to many climates and soils and are grown the world over, except in the low tropics, but most of the potato crop of the world is grown in Europe. The family to which Irish potato belongs (Solanaceae, the nightshade family) contains another food plant, tomato *(Lycopersicon esculentum),* and also three drug plants containing dangerous alkaloids: *Nicotiana tabacum* (tobacco), *Datura stramonium,* and *Atropa belladona,* which produces the narcotic drug belladona. Weed species of this family of dicots often cause poisoning to livestock, to children who eat the attractive berries of some species, and to adults who occasionally use some of them for their hallucinogenic qualities. Also in this family is the attractive ornamental plant or flower *Petunia.*

Cut flowers play a significant role in the lives of most people, and the commercial production and sale of flowers (floriculture and floristry) are important businesses. Both the natural landscape and the landscape that is designed by man have an enormous impact on the quality of human existence. Landscaping assumes greater importance as man becomes more urbanized. The designing, arranging, and placing of lawns, trees, shrubs, and flowering herbs on plots of ground to make them more attractive and functional for man provide incomes for increasing numbers of people, and most of the plants they work with are angiosperms.

The importance of trees is not sufficiently appreciated in the United States, where an estimated 1,000,000 trees are eliminated each year through paving, urban sprawl, and other developments. Trees play an important part in combating man's environmental problems by controlling water runoff, wind, dust, odors, and noise. Tree and shrub barriers (Fig. 45-2) can reduce noise levels by 50 per cent or more and should play a significant role in the design of parks, playgrounds, hospitals, parkways, and other places where noise is a problem. All trees have natural odors that help improve the odor of polluted air, and trees are important producers of oxygen. Certain trees are sensitive indicators of air pollution, as are the lichens that grow upon them. Trees filter out dust particles; for example, a 100-year-old beech tree may have over 1,600 square yards of leaf surface that catch dust. Trees stabilize and condition soil for retaining rainwater. This is an important consideration in flood control and the maintenance of watersheds that drain into water-supply lakes and rivers.

Occurrence Angiosperms are ubiquitous land plants found in practically all habitats from the tropics to near the poles and from the intertidal margins of the oceans to the highest altitudes at which land plants can exist. Angiosperms include species that are xeric (Fig. 45-1), mesic (Fig. 45-2), and hydric (Fig. 45-5). The aquatic habit is a secondarily derived condition in angiosperms.

The major kinds of vegetation covering large or wide geographical areas of the earth are called plant formations. These plant formations are called biomes when the animals are considered along with the plants in the systems. Seven major categories of biomes can be recognized: tropical rain forest, savanna,

Fig. 45-5 Closeup view looking down on many plants of the tiny aquatic duckweek *Lemna* floating on a pond. *(Courtesy Carolina Biological Supply Company.)*

desert, grasslands, temperate deciduous forest, northern coniferous forest (taiga), and tundra. These biomes are controlled by climate, and change from biome to biome occurs both with latitude and with evelation. The characteristic appearance of each of the earth's biomes is for the most part due to its dominance by angiosperms (except for the coniferous forest).

Vegetative features   Morphological and anatomical features of the leaf, stem, and root of angiosperms are highly diverse and varied. Some of the important basic features were brought out in the section dealing with taxonomy (pp. 376-77).

Angiosperms have a wide range in size, varying from the tiny, floating, rootless watermeal *(Wolffia),* which is about 1 mm long or broad, to such huge broad-leaved trees as the tulip tree *(Liriodendron tulipifera)* in deciduous forests of eastern United States, where it may reach a height of 250 ft and a diameter of 14 ft. Another large flowering tree is *Eucalyptus regnans,* which may be over 300 ft tall and 9 ft in diameter.

Angiosperms may be deciduous or evergreen and may be trees, shrubs, vines, or herbs. They may be annual, biennial, or perennial. Woody trees, shrubs, and vines are perennial. Perennial angiosperms having herbaceous aerial shoot systems survive inclement seasons by such underground structures as rhizomes, bulbs, and corms.

The vast majority of angiosperms are independent autotrophs, but some autotrophic species can also be parasitic, as for example, mistletoe *(Phoradendron),* which is a small, evergreen shrub that grows parasitically on the branches and trunks of flowering trees. Also, some autotrophic angiosperms, like venus's flytrap *(Dionaea),* sundew *(Drosera),* and pitcher plant *(Sarracenia),* enhance their nutrition through insect-catching and digesting mechanisms (Fig. 45-6). Some angiosperms lack chlorophyll and are parasitic, like dodder *(Cuscuta),* which is a rootless and leafless yellow to orange vine that attaches itself to its host by means of haustoria (Fig. 45-7). Some other angiosperms, like indian pipe *(Monotropa uniflora),* lack chlorophyll and are saprophytes with mycorrhizal fungi, which may be attached to the roots of autotrophic angiosperms (Fig. 45-8).

Angiosperm leaves vary greatly in size, shape, form, and anatomy. Much of this variation clearly has adaptive value and is correlated with the different environmental stresses of the highly varied habitats of angiosperms. Although the leaf is the major photosynthetic organ, many leaves perform other functions in addition to or in place of photosynthesis. It is the vegetative leaves of the insecti-vorous plants mentioned earlier that trap insects (Fig. 45-6). Such xeric angiosperms as *Portulaca* have thick, succulent, water-storage leaves. The fleshy bulb scales (leaf bases) of such flowering plants as onion and daffodil store food and water. The scales of the dormant buds of angiosperms are protective leaves, and the spines of barberry are actually modified leaves. Some vines support themselves through tendrils, which in garden peas and vetch are modified terminal leaflets of the compound leaf. The vegetative leaves of such angiosperms as *Kalanchoe* and duckweeds (Fig. 45-5) function in asexual reproduction. The bright, eye-catching floral or involucral bracts of poinsettia and flowering dogwood (Figs. 45-2, 45-9) are specialized leaves and are not flower parts.

Angiosperms also have members with stems and roots modified for special functions. The stem is the photosynthetic organ of cactus and mature asparagus plants. Also, the large, succulent stem of the xeric cactus stores large amounts of water. The spines or thorns of the hawthorn plant are stems (branches). Grape

Fig. 45-6 Three autotrophic angiosperms with insect-catching leaves. Top left: *Dionaea*, venus' flytrap. Top right: *Drosera*, sundew. At left: *Sarracenia*, pitcher plant, here with four open flowers. *(Courtesy Carolina Biological Supply Company.)*

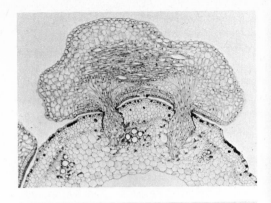

Fig. 45-7   Stained cross section of a dodder *(Cuscuta)* stem (above) showing two of its haustoria inside its host's stem. *(Photomicrograph courtesy Ripon Microslides Laboratory.)*

Fig. 45-8   Closeup view of several flowering plants of the nongreen indian pipe *Monotropa uniflora* growing in a forest floor. *(Courtesy Carolina Biological Supply Company.)*

Fig. 45-9   Closeup view looking down on an inflorescence of dogwood *(Cornus)*. The four large involucral bracts surround the cluster of tiny flowers, a few of which are open. *(Courtesy Carolina Biological Supply Company.)*

vines climb or support themselves by means of stems specialized as tendrils. In twining vines like morning glory, the twining main stem itself is functionally modified for supporting and elevating the plant. The numerous adventitious roots arising on the stems of vines like English ivy and poison ivy cling to supporting objects and facilitate the elevation of these vines. Special, aerially produced, adventitious roots called prop roots, in such plants as *Pandanus* and corn, give added support and anchorage to these plants. Stems and roots that function in asexual reproduction are discussed in the next section.

Asexual reproduction   Asexual or vegetative reproduction in angiosperms is common. Stem or shoot fragments of such plants as the aquatic *Elodea* and the desert cacti can become detached and grow into new plants. The extensive, branching rhizomes of such angiosperms as many grasses, cattail, iris, and banana enable them to colonize new areas and to establish new plants or colonies after the death of old rhizomes. The plant of such angiosperms as Irish potato and Jerusalem artichoke produces many rhizomes, the end portions of which enlarge and become thick and somewhat fleshy structures called tubers. When the main part of the parent plant dies, the tubers may survive and serve as reproductive structures. The long slender aerial stems of such plants as raspberry, dewberry, and wild rose droop and touch the ground, where they develop adventitious roots and new shoot systems. Such branches in the strawberry plant are specialized and are called stolons. Tiger lilies produce large specialized buds in the axils of their leaves. These fall to the ground and develop into new plants. The bulbs of such angiosperms as daffodils, tulips, lilies, and onions produce small bulbs that reproduce the plants, as do the corms of crocus and gladiolus.

The horizontal roots of many angiosperm trees, shrubs, and woody vines (for example, poplar, sweet gum, beech, sumach, and poison ivy) produce new plants from adventitious buds, and the somewhat fleshy, clustered roots of such angiosperms as sweet potato develop adventitious buds that grow into new plants.

Some angiosperms reproduce asexually or vegetatively by means of their leaves. Some species of the life plant *Kalanchoe (Bryophyllum)* develop tiny plantlets in the notches of their fleshy leaves. The plantlets fall to the ground and grow into mature plants. Duckweeds, which are very small floating aquatic angiosperms, commonly develop new plants from their leaves (Fig. 45-5).

Even flowers (which are sexual structures) can be involved in asexual reproduction. Some grasses replace flowers with vegetative propagules, and the onion plant develops aerial bulbs in place of some of the flowers of their inflorescences. Some botanists consider the parthenogenetic development of seeds (from ovules without fertilized eggs), as in dandelion, to be a form of asexual reproduction, but this is actually a modification of the sexual method.

Sexual reproduction   The flower is interpreted as a highly specialized determinate sexual branch or sporogenous shoot. Its sepals, petals, stamens, and carpels are considered by some to be specialized leaves, or at least the morphological equivalent of leaves (Fig. 45-10). Stamens are microsporophylls and carpels are megasporophylls. The most important general features characterizing sexual reproduction in angiosperms are listed in the section dealing with taxonomy (pp. 376-77). Basic structural features of flowers and certain other aspects of sexual reproduction are described in the Project (p. 391) and need not be repeated here.

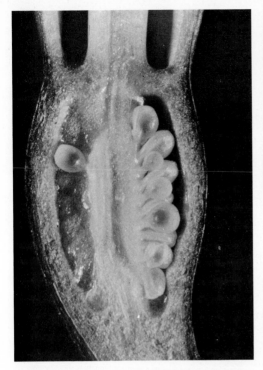

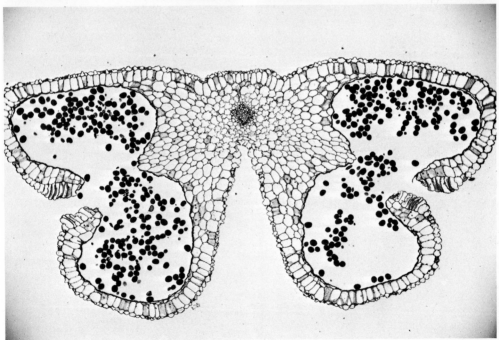

Fig. 45-10 (top) Bisected jonquil flower (right) showing the various floral parts, and a closeup view (left) of its bisected, inferior ovary containing many ovules. *(Courtesy Carolina Biological Supply Company.)*

Fig. 45-11 (below) Stained cross section of a *Lilium* anther with microsporangia containing mature pollen grains. *(Photomicrograph courtesy Carolina Biological Supply Company.)*

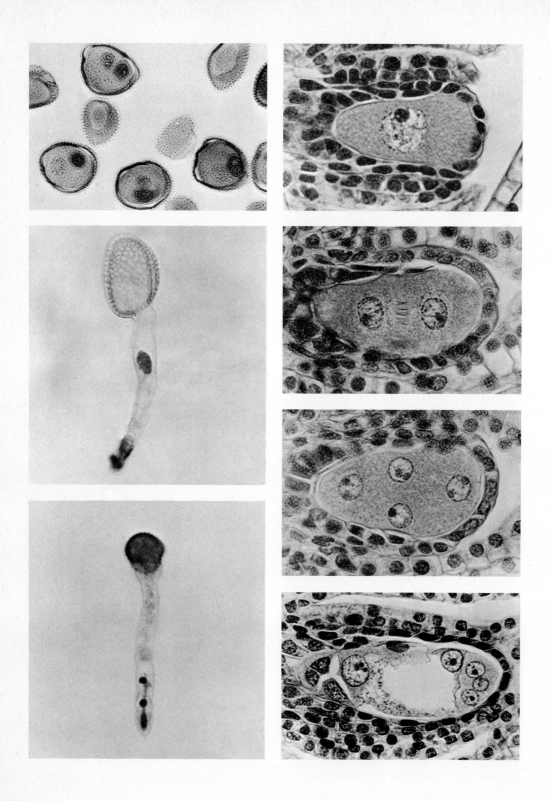

Fig. 45-12 (opposite, top left)   Stained two-nucleate, mature pollen grains (young male gametophytes) of *Lilium*. *(Photomicrograph courtesy Ripon Microslides Laboratory.)*

Fig. 45-14 (Left column, center and bottom photos)   Stained angiosperm male gametophytes grown in liquid culture medium. Center: *Lilium*. Two nucleate with both nuclei in the pollen tube. Bottom: A three-celled mature male gametophyte. *(Photomicrographs courtesy Carolina Biological Supply Company.)*

Fig. 45-13 (right column, opposite)   Stained cross sections of *Lilium* ovules showing four stages in female gametophyte development. Top: The huge megasporocyte (in the nucellus) with its large nucleus about to undergo meiosis. Second photo: Two-nucleate stage. Third photo: First four-nucleate stage. Bottom: Eight-nucleate, mature female gametophyte surrounded by the megasporangium (nucellus). *(Photomicrographs courtesy Ripon Microslides Laboratory.)*

Great diversity exists among flowering plants. The following account deals with the main sexual events in the life cycle.

Microsporogenesis occurs in the anther of a stamen, which usually has four microsporangia (pollen sacs) (Fig. 45-11). A nearly mature microsporangium contains numerous diploid microsporocytes (microspore mother cells) surrounded by a sporangium wall several cells in thickness, the innermost layer forming a nutritive tapetum. Meiosis and cytokinesis in each microsporocyte result in the formation of four uninucleate microspores. As in other seed plants, male or microgametophyte development begins inside the microspore within the microsporangium. The male gametophyte is extremely reduced. No prothallial cells are formed and usually the mature pollen grain (young male gametophyte) contains only two haploid cells: a larger tube cell and a smaller generative cell (Fig. 45-12). However, the generative nucleus may divide and form two sperm nuclei before pollen is shed. Each pollen grain has a two-layered wall (intine and exine) with thin areas, germ pores or germ furrows. At this stage the anther dehisces and pollen grains are disseminated. Pollination (in angiosperms, the transfer of pollen from microsporangia to the stigmata of carpels) is effected by gravity, wind, insects, birds, bats, rain, or water currents, depending on the species. Much of the diversity in color, odor, shape, and structural features of flowers is correlated with the diversity of animals, especially insects, that serve as pollinating agents.

The development of female gametophytes occurs while pollen is developing. The ovary (ovulary) wall of a carpel may contain and protect one to many ovules (Fig. 45-10), depending on the genus. The ovule is a megasporangium, also called nucellus, that has become overgrown with one or often two integuments, in contrast to only one integument in gymnosperms. The integuments do not quite close at one end, leaving a small hole, the micropyle. A subepidermal cell in the micropylar region of the megasporangium enlarges greatly and becomes the functional megasporocyte (megaspore mother cell) (Fig. 45-13, top). In the majority of angiosperms, the megasporocyte undergoes meiosis and cytokinesis to form four megaspores arranged in a row, but deviations of this are known (for example, in *Lilium*). Usually, as in gymnosperms, the three megaspores closest to the micropyle degenerate soon after they are formed. The remaining megaspore stays in the megasporangium, where it develops into a female gametophyte.

The female gametophyte of angiosperms is highly reduced and is commonly called an embryo sac. In most angiosperms its development proceeds as follows. The haploid nucleus of the functional megaspore undergoes three consecutive free-nuclear divisions within the enlarging megaspore cell. Four of the nuclei migrate to the micropylar end or pole of the developing female gametophyte; the other four nuclei migrate to the opposite (chalazal) pole. After cytokinesis, six of the eight nuclei are incorporated into uninucleate cells, three at each pole. The three at the micropylar pole differentiate as an egg cell flanked by two synergid cells, and the three at the opposite pole are known as antipodal cells. The two remaining nuclei migrate from each pole toward each other, and they are called polar nuclei. The polar nuclei may fuse before fertilization. This mature female gametophyte has only seven cells. The three at each pole are haploid and the larger cell in between may have either two haploid nuclei or a single diploid nucleus (fused polar nuclei). Archegonia are lacking in angiosperms, a condition found elsewhere in embryophytes only in the gymnosperms *Gnetum* and *Welwitschia.*

Ontogeny of the female gametophyte in lily *(Lilium)* represents one of the variant types of development found in angiosperms (Fig. 45-13). The difference begins in the megasporocyte. Meiosis is not followed by cytokinesis and all four of the free nuclei, which are actually meiospore nuclei, are involved in the development of a female gametophyte (Fig. 45-13, third photo). This is the first four-nucleate stage of the female gametophyte in *Lilium.* One of these haploid nuclei stays at the micropylar pole of the enlarging female gametophyte. The other three haploid nuclei migrate to the opposite (chalazal) pole where they simultaneously fuse and divide, giving rise to two large triploid nuclei. At the same time, the nucleus at the micropylar pole divides to form two smaller haploid nuclei. This is the second four-nucleate stage of female gametophyte development in *Lilium.* After another mitotic division, there are four haploid nuclei at the micropylar pole and four triploid nuclei at the opposite pole. Further development proceeds in the usual way, as described above, but one of the two polar nuclei is triploid and so are the three antipodal cells (the other polar nucleus is haploid and so are the egg and two synergids) (Fig. 45-13, bottom photo).

In many angiosperms the female gametophyte reaches maturity at or just prior to the opening of the flower. After pollen grains (young male gametophytes) are transferred from dehisced anthers to the receptive stigmata of carpels (the process known as pollination), they germinate by a tube (pollen tube) that grows through the style to the ovary (Fig. 45-14). If the generative cell did not divide within the pollen grain, it does so in the pollen tube. The mature male gametophyte (Fig. 45-14, second photo) is a three-celled structure: within the elongate tube cell are two male gametes (sperm cells), which never have flagella. The tip of a pollen tube usually enters the ovule through the micropyle and then penetrates the thin nucellar tissue (megasporangium) and the wall of the embryo sac (female gametophyte). Both the sperm cells, and sometimes the nucleus of the tube cell, are discharged into the female gametophyte.

One of the most distinctive features of angiosperms—a feature found only in angiosperms—is the process called double fertilization in which both of the male gametes fuse with cells in the female gametophyte (Fig. 45-15). One sperm fuses with the egg, resulting in a diploid zygote that will develop into an embryo. The other sperm fuses with the polar nuclei, resulting in a primary endosperm nucleus that will develop into nutritive endosperm tissue (found only in angiosperms). After fertilization in angiosperms that have female gametophytes developed in the "normal" way, the primary endosperm nucleus is triploid, but angiosperms having female gametophytes with the *Lilium* type of development have a pentaploid primary endosperm nucleus.

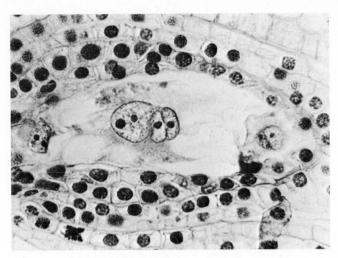

Fig. 45-15 Stained cross section of a *Lilium* ovule showing double fertilization in the female gametophyte. One sperm nucleus is fusing with the egg, which is at the micropylar end (right). The other sperm nucleus is fusing with the two polar nuclei. *(Photomicrograph courtesy Ripon Microslides Laboratory.)*

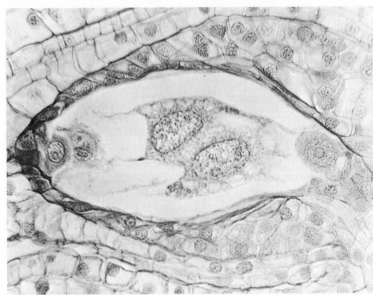

Fig. 45-16 Stained cross section of a *Lilium* ovule showing an embryo sac or old female gametophyte with a zygote (right) and the first two free endosperm nuclei (center). *(Photomicrograph courtesy Ripon Microslides Laboratory.)*

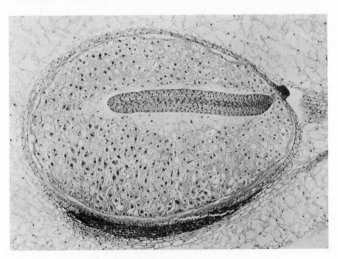

Fig. 45-17 Stained section of a developing *Lilium* seed showing a young elongate embryo surrounded by cellular endosperm. *(Photomicrograph courtesy Ripon Microslides Laboratory.)*

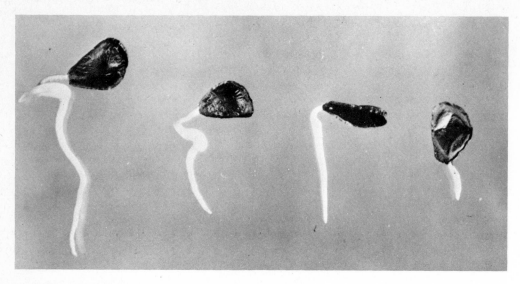

Fig. 45-18 Germinating seeds of *Yucca* showing the young primary root, the first part of a seedling to grow from an embryo. *(Courtesy Carolina Biological Supply Company.)*

Endosperm development usually starts before embryo development (Fig. 45-16). Young endosperm may be cellular tissue from the beginning or the early divisions may be free nuclear, in which case the endosperm later becomes cellular. The zygote divides, and the cell at the micropylar end of the two-celled young embryo is called the basal cell and the other cell is known as the terminal cell. The basal cell usually produces the suspensor cells, and the terminal cell usually develops into the bulk of the embryo (Fig. 45-17). The ovule enlarges and keeps pace with the growing embryo and endosperm. Most or all of the surrounding nucellus (megasporangium) disappears as the seed matures, but if there is a distinguishable remnant in a mature seed, it is called perisperm. The integuments thicken and develop into seed coats. The mature embryo consists of a radicle (embryo root) at the suspensor or micropylar end, hypocotyl, epicotyl, and one or two cotyledons (embryo leaves) (Fig. 45-4). In such angiosperms as common bean and pea, the endosperm is used up as it nourishes the developing embryo, and the cotyledons contain the bulk of the food stored in the seeds of these plants. Other angiosperms, such as corn (Fig. 45-4, left) and castor bean, have massive endosperms in their mature seeds. While the seed or seeds are developing within the ovary, the ovary wall enlarges and develops into the fruit coat or wall, the pericarp. In many angiosperms, such as apple and corn (Fig. 45-4, left), the receptacle and other floral organs develop and become part of the structure known as the fruit.

The seeds of some angiosperms (e.g., some of the oaks and maples) germinate immediately if they are dispersed into a suitable environment, but others have a period of dormancy. Some angiosperm seeds can remain viable for years. As an extreme example, seeds of lotus *(Nelumbo)* germinated after lying dormant in a peat bog for several centuries.

During seed germination, the radicle first ruptures the seed coat at the micropylar part of the seed and develops as the primary root (Fig. 45-18). In seeds with epigean germination, the hypocotyl elongates and causes the cotyledons and epicotyl to emerge from the seed coat and become elevated. In seeds with hypogean germination, the hypocotyl elongates little or none and the cotyledons remain within the seed coat. The epicotyl or embryonic bud grows out and elevates the young shoot system. Seed germination in most dicots is epigeous; in most monocots it is hypogeous.

The basic type of life cycle for angiosperms and other seed plants is discussed in the last paragraph dealing with sexual reproduction in cycads (p. 345). It should be mentioned that deviations from the ordinary sexual events described above exist in the highly diversified angiosperms. Some examples follow. A female gametophyte may be diploid as a result of its development (by apospory) from a diploid cell, and the diploid egg may then develop parthenogenetically (by apogamy) into a diploid embryo. Haploid embryos may develop from unfertilized eggs or even from other cells of the female gametophyte. A diploid embryo may develop from cells of the megasporangium or integuments rather than from a zygote. Even so, it is correct to say that angiosperms have a diplo-haplontic type of sexual life cycle with heteromorphic alternating generations: the large, conspicuous, vascularized, and heterosporous sporophytic phase (the site of meiosis) alternates with the small, inconspicuous, nonvascularized gametophytic phase (the site of syngamy).

Project

I. Inflorescence

An inflorescence is the flowering portion of an angiosperm—an axis bearing flowers. Examine the various inflorescences on demonstration. Identify the pedicel of the individual flower of each inflorescence. Classify the inflorescences, using another book as a guide. Available for study may be spikes and racemes (indeterminate inflorescences) and cymes, umbels, and heads (determinate inflorescences). The head (capitulum) type of inflorescence may have two kinds of flowers, central disc flowers and marginal ray flowers.

II. Variation in flower structure

Study and compare the various provided flowers as follows:

A. *How to look at each*
   1. External view. Look at each for the flower stalk or pedicel and those parts and features that are visible from different external views.
   2. Sectional view. Make a longitudinal section (median) of each flower by cutting with a single-edge razor blade upward, starting through the pedicel. Study the various parts and features.
B. *What to look for*
   1. Common flower. A common type of flower is one that consists of four whorls of organs attached to the receptacle: an outer calyx composed of sepals, a corolla composed of petals (sepals and petals collectively are called the perianth), an androecium composed of stamens, and a gynoecium composed of carpels. The flower is said to be complete if all these whorls are present; it is incomplete if one or more of the whorls are absent. A flower is perfect if both androecium and gynoecium are

391

present, and it is imperfect (either staminate or carpellate) if one or the other of these whorls is missing.

2. Microsporophyll (stamen). A stamen usually consists of an enlarged terminal portion, the anther (pollen sac or sacs), and a slender stalk or filament.

3. Megasporophyll (carpel). A carpel consists of a swollen basal portion, the ovary (ovulary), and usually a more or less elongated style and a terminal stigma (the site of pollination).

4. Position of the ovary. In primitive flowers the stamens and perianth are attached below the base of the ovary and the flower is said to be hypogynous and the ovary is superior. In more advanced types the sepals, petals, and stamens are attached to a floral tube or hypanthium surrounding but free from the ovary—the flower is perigynous and the ovary is still superior. The most advanced type is the epigynous flower in which the floral parts arise above the ovary (the floral tube is adnate to the ovary). In this case the ovary is said to be inferior.

5. Primitive flower. The primitive flower consists of a strobilus-like aggregation of spirally arranged parts or organs attached to a receptacle. Numerous carpels (megasporophylls) are arranged spirally near the apex. Immediately below are numerous spirally arranged stamens (microsporophylls), and below these are numerous spirally arranged sterile leaflike flower parts, the perianth, at the base.

6. Advanced flower. More advanced or highly evolved flowers have the perianth differentiated into an outer calyx and inner corolla, and the arrangement of these parts is whorled. Further evolutionary advancement involves cohesion (the fusion of similar parts), adnation (the fusion of unlike parts), abortion (the incomplete development or loss of parts), and change of symmetry from actionomorphic (radial or regular) to zygomorphic (bilateral or irregular).

III. Microspore and microgametophyte development

A. *Whole pollen.* Examine the pollen of several of the flowers. Look for differences in form and in ornamentation of the wall. How many cells and nuclei are usually present in angiosperm pollen? How does this compare with gymnosperms? Are pollen grains microspores or are they microgametophytes?

B. *Anther in sectional view.* Study prepared slides with stained cross sections of anthers in different stages of maturation. If your slides are of *Lilium*, note that the anther is four lobed and that each lobe is a microsporangium (pollen sac). In the center is a vascular bundle. In young anthers find the microsporangium wall, tapetum (a nutritive layer), and microsporocytes (microspore mother cells). More mature anthers show stages in meiosis, diads, and tetrads of microspores. Note that a microspore has a single nucleus and that the tapetum becomes disorganized during microspore formation. In a slide having anthers with mature pollen grains (young microgametophytes), identify the wall (outer rough exine layer and inner smooth intine), the tube cell and nucleus, and generative cell and nucleus.

C. *Germinating pollen* (Refer to Project 7, p. 44)

1. Culture. Put several drops of 10 per cent sucrose on a microscope slide. Sprinkle pollen grains (e.g., *Impatiens*, touch-me-not) on the surface of the sugar solution. Examine at 20-minute intervals. When not observing the slide, keep it in a slide humidity chamber (see Project 3: VI.C.2.a, p. 29).
2. Prepared slides. Examine the provided slides. Where do pollen tubes occur in nature? What is the mode of nutrition of microgametophytes?

IV. Megaspore, megagametophyte, and seed development

Study prepared slides with stained sections in various stages of development as follows:

A. *Ovule form.* Observe the form of the ovule and its relation to its stalk (funiculus) and the tissue (placenta) to which the funiculus is attached. Can you tell whether the ovule is orthotropous (ovule upright with the micropyle 180° away from the placenta and funiculus), anatropous (ovule inverted, with the micropyle facing the placenta and close to the funiculus), or otherwise?

B. *Megaspore and megagametophyte (embryo sac) development*
   1. Megaspore mother cell (megasporocyte) stage. Find the megasporocyte and other diploid sporophytic parts: nucellus (megasporangium), integuments, funiculus, micropyle, locule, placenta, and ovary wall.
   2. Megaspore stage. Identify megaspore or megaspores.
   3. Megagametophyte development. Look for stages in megagametophyte development. In a mature megagametophyte find an egg, synergid cells, polar nuclei (which may have fused), and antipodal cells.
      Note: If your slides are of *Lilium*, you should be aware that megasporogenesis and megagametophyte development proceed differently than in most angiosperms. How does *Lilium* differ?

C. *Embryo and seed development*
   1. Zygote stage. Find a zygote and also a primary endosperm nucleus. What is meant by "double fertilization"?
   2. Proembryo stage. Find a proembryo with its basal cell, suspensor, and embryonic initial cells, all surrounded by endosperm. Is the endosperm of this angiosperm triploid or is it pentaploid?
   3. Mature embryo stage. Find a mature or nearly mature embryo with its epicotyl, cotyledon(s), hypocotyl, and radicle. Endosperm may surround the embryo. Outside of this may be the remains of the nucellus. The seed coat may be seen to be composed of two or more distinct layers.

V. Fruit

A. *Sectional view.* Study stained sections on prepared slides and study sections that you have made of a variey of fruits. Identify pericarp (fruit coat) and seed. Look for embryo and endosperm surrounded by the seed coat. If endosperm is not present, where is food stored? Does the embryo have one or two cotyledons? From what parts of the flower did the following structures develop: entire fruit, pericarp, seed, seed coat, endosperm, and embryo?

B. *Variation.* Examine and classify the fruits on demonstration, using another book as a guide. What is the structure of the flower from which each type of fruit develops?

VI. Seeds and their germination (refer to Project 8, p. 47)

A. *External features of seeds.* Study the external features of dry and water-soaked seeds of common bean, castor bean, corn, and/or others.

B. *Internal features of seeds.* Dissect water-soaked seeds and examine them comparatively with respect to seed coats, presence or absence of endosperm, form and number of cotyledons, and size of embryo.

C. *Germination.* Plant some of each kind of seed in a mixture of peat moss and sand (1:1). Examine them from time to time for germination and the development of juvenile sporophytes (seedlings). Which of them show epigean and which hypogean germination? Identify the coleoptile and coleorhiza of corn or other grain.

VII. Comparison of the vegetative and reproductive structure of dicotyledons and monocotyledons

Certain characteristic differences in structure between dicots and monocots may be summarized as follows. Explore these differences as extensively as you can with the material and time available. Make freehand sections of stems and roots and employ differential staining (refer to Project 10: II.B, p. 59).

A. *Flower.* The parts of a dicotyledonous flower are commonly in four or fives or in multiples of four or five. In monocotyledons the floral parts commonly occur in threes or in multiples of three.

B. *Embryo.* An embryo of a dicotyledon usually has a terminal epicotyl and two lateral cotyledons, as well as a hypocotyl and radicle. The embryo of a monocotyledon usually has a lateral epicotyl (covered by a coleoptile), a single cotyledon, and a hypocotyl and radicle (covered by a coleorhiza).

C. *Leaf.* The leaves of dicots are generally net-veined. Those of monocots are usually parallel veined.

D. *Stele.*

1. The protostele of a dicot root usually has but few protoxylem poles, and there are only a few ridges radiating from the central mass of primary xylem. A monocot root has numerous protoxylem poles.
2. Many dicot roots develop a cambium. A monocot root rarely forms one.
3. Most dicot stems have a single cylinder of vascular bundles, most monocot stems do not. The vascular bundles appear to be scattered but their arrangement is precise.
4. Many dicot stems develop a cambium. A monocot stem rarely forms one.

VIII. Fossil angiosperms

Study the demonstration materials.

Index

Note: *Italic* page numbers indicate references to figures.

Index

405